THE FALCON'S MALTESER

"Anthony Horowitz is the
lion of children's literature."
Michael Morpurgo

"Horowitz has become a writer who
converts boys to reading."
The Times

"A first-class children's novelist."
TES

THE FALCON'S MALTESER

ANTHONY HOROWITZ

WALKER
BOOKS

For Dursley McLinden
29.5.65 – 7.8.95
who played Tim Diamond in the film
and in the TV series

First published 1995 by Walker Books Ltd
87 Vauxhall Walk, London SE11 5HJ

This edition published 2011

2 4 6 8 10 9 7 5 3 1

Text © 1986, 1995 Anthony Horowitz
Introduction © 2007 Anthony Horowitz
Cover illustration © 2007 Martin Chatterton

This book has been typeset in Sabon

Printed in Great Britain by Clays Ltd, St Ives plc

British Library Cataloguing in Publication Data:
a catalogue record for this book is available from the British Library

ISBN 978-1-4063-4038-9
www.walker.co.uk

*This book refers to a famous product, "MALTESERS" chocolates
manufactured by Mars, Incorporated. Mr Horowitz wishes to make it
clear that this book is solely his invention and that Mars, Incorporated
in no way initiated, sponsored or approved the work.*

CONTENTS

TIM DIAMOND INC.
23 THE CUTTING, CAMDEN TOWN, NW1

Dear Reader,

My name is Tim Diamond, but I don't know why I'm telling you that because the one thing I don't need right now is an introduction. The last time I introduced myself, I took two bullets in the chest. It's lucky I was hiding behind the chest at the time or I could have got hurt. Getting shot at is all in a day's work for me and I'm glad I don't do overtime. The streets where I live are pretty mean. And I mean <u>mean</u>. And not at all pretty. You'd be surprised how many people knock on my door, come into my office and try to kill me. Some of them don't even knock. But that's the sort of business I'm in. I'm a private eye and a lot of the people I meet like to keep their finger on the trigger – even the ones who can't afford the whole gun.

My guess is that you'll have heard of me. At the very least, you'll have seen my advertisement in the Yellow Pages. TIM DIAMOND, PRIVATE DETECTIVE: THE BEST IN THE   . I'd have liked to say more but they were charging by the word. Anyway, this book will tell you just about everything you need to know about me except my shoe size – and in case you're wondering, it's ten and a half. Eleven in wet weather.

So why am I writing this?

Well, the publishers – Walker Books – are re-launching "The Falcon's Malteser" with a new cover and, of course, a new price-tag. You see that picture on the front? It took their team of designers sixteen weeks working night and day to come up with it. Maybe it would have been easier if they'd read the book first. But that's the thing about publishers. I've met livelier people in a cemetery. They're paid almost nothing and they're worth every penny of it.

In case you're wondering (and I can't imagine why you would be), Walker Books is based in south London, right next to the River Thames ... and if something goes splash in the night, it's probably the managing director. He never used to be suicidal – not until he looked at his sales figures.

They work in a building which is old and crumbling and desperately in need of a face-lift ... a bit like my editor. Actually, she's had so much plastic surgery they've run out of plastic, and the last time she sneezed she turned into someone else. It's scary what people will do to keep themselves looking good – and she wasn't great when she started. Anyway, Walker Books needs your pocket money. They're so desperate, they'll even take your pocket. Remember that book token you got for Christmas that's been in your bottom drawer ever since? They want it. To you it may be another crummy paperback but to them it's lunch.

And that's why they asked me to write this introduction. I got a call from my editor at the start of the month. Her name is Jane Winterton and on top of all the cosmetic surgery she has a voice that sounds like fingers being scratched down a blackboard, or maybe an animal in pain.

Talk to her for too long and you want to throw yourself onto the nearest train. Or under it.

"Tim," she said. "We need your help."

"Who's been killed?" I asked. "And it had better not be the accountant."

"Oh, no," she simpered. "Mr Lloyd is fit and bouncing."

"Yeah. Like his cheques."

"What we need is one thousand, five hundred words for the new edition of "The Falcon's Malteser". We'll pay you fifty pounds."

"Fifty pounds?" I tried to work out the rate per word but I quickly gave up. I didn't have a pocket calculator small enough. "What's the idea?" I demanded.

"Well, obviously your brother Nick is the one who actually writes the books. But we thought it might be fun to hear something from you. Straight from the horse's mouth, so to speak."

She was the one calling me the horse. What a laugh! You should have seen her teeth.

"What if I'm busy?" I growled.

"Are you?"

I glanced around the empty office. It was true that right now I was between cases. My last client had asked me to find out who was stealing supplies from his glue factory, but he'd disappeared and I was beginning to think he must have come to a sticky end.

"OK," I said. "I'll think about it."

"We'd like something by the end of the week."

"I'm not sure about that. How about Friday?"

"See what you can do..." She rang off.

So that's the introduction to the introduction.

Here's the introduction. If you keep reading you might even get to the book.

I never dreamed when I set up as a private detective that I'd end up living with my kid brother, Nick – and if I'd thought I was going to dream it, I wouldn't have bothered going to sleep. Look at it from my point of view. I was twenty-five. He was thirteen. The day he walked through the door, his voice hadn't even broken – which is more than you could say for the door. The whole office was falling apart. The trouble was that business had been a bit slow ... in fact it could have been overtaken by a one-legged tortoise with a twenty-a-day cigarette habit. I had no money. No clients. And suddenly there was an extra mouth to feed. Worse still, that mouth was connected to an extra stomach.

The thing is, Nick was meant to have moved to Australia with our parents. I thought I'd seen the last of him when I waved goodbye at Heathrow Airport, but it turned out he had other ideas because by the time I got back to the flat he was already there.

The strange thing is that in a way I'm glad he never did make it to Australia. "The Falcon's Malteser" was our first case together and there were moments now and then when it was good to have someone around. I mean, from the moment Johnny Naples walked into my office, I knew this was no ordinary case. What was he doing with a box of Maltesers? Why did he need me to look after it? And why was the Fat Man so desperate to get his hands on it? The fact of the matter was that I needed someone to talk to.

"Two brains are better than one," I said to Nick.

"Sure, Tim," he replied. "But I guess we'll just have to manage with one between us."

I'm not sure what he meant by that. Nick has a strange sense of humour.

You might like to know that there are other books written about me: "Public Enemy Number Two", "South by South East", "The French Confection", "I Know What You Did Last Wednesday" and "The Blurred Man". Personally I haven't read them, because I was too busy being in them. Oh – and you may be wondering, who's this guy Anthony Horowitz whose name appears on the covers? He also works for Walker Books: they pay him to knock the books into shape after Nick has finished. I've never met him and they tell me I haven't missed much. Apparently he writes his own stuff too, and a lot of people have compared him to JK Rowling – but without the money or the good looks. What that man doesn't know about writing would fill a book … and nobody would read that one either.

So here it is. "The Falcon's Malteser." Teachers say that reading books is good for you, so get stuck into this one and prove them wrong.

Tim Diamond

13 February 2007

THE PACKAGE

There's not much call for private detectives in Fulham.

The day it all started was a bad one. Business was so slack it was falling down all around us. The gas had been disconnected that morning, one of the coldest mornings for twenty years, and it could only be a matter of time before the electricity followed. We'd run out of food and the people in the supermarket downstairs had all fallen about laughing when I suggested credit. We had just £2.37 and about three teaspoons of instant coffee to last us the weekend. The wallpaper was peeling, the carpets were fraying and the curtains ... well, whichever way you looked at it, it was curtains for us. Even the cockroaches were walking out.

I was just wondering whether the time hadn't finally come to do something constructive – like packing my bags and going back to Mum – when the door opened and the dwarf walked in.

OK – maybe you're not supposed to call them dwarves these days. Vertically challenged … that's what it says in the book. But not this book. The truth is, this guy was as challenged as they come. I was only thirteen but already I had six inches on him and the way he looked at me with cold, unforgiving eyes – he knew it and wasn't going to forget it.

He was in his mid forties, I guessed. It was hard to say with someone that size. A short, dark stranger with brown eyes and a snub nose. He was wearing a three-piece suit, only the pieces all belonged to different suits like he'd got dressed in a hurry. His socks didn't match either. A neat moustache crowned his upper lip and his black hair was slicked back with enough oil to interest an Arab. A spotted bow tie and a flashy gold ring completed the picture. It was a weird picture.

"Do come in, Mr…" my brother began.

"Naples," the dwarf, who already was in, said. His name might have come out of Italy but he spoke with a South American accent. "Johnny Naples. You are Tim Diamond?"

"That's me," my brother lied. His real name was Herbert Timothy Simple, but he called himself Tim Diamond. He thought it suited

12

his image. "And what can I do for you, Mr Venice?"

"Naples," the dwarf corrected him. He climbed on to a chair and sat down opposite my brother. His nose just reached the level of the desk. Herbert slid a paper-weight out of the way to give his new client a clear view. The dwarf was about to speak but then he paused. The nose was turned on me. "Who is he?" he demanded, the two h's scratching at the back of his throat.

"Him?" Tim smiled. "He's just my kid brother. Don't worry about him, Mr Navels. Just tell me how I can help you."

Naples laid a carefully manicured hand on the desk. His initials – JN – were cut into the ring. There was so much gold around that third finger he could have added his name and address too. "I want to deposit something with you," he said.

"Deposit?" Herbert repeated quite unneces-sarily. The dwarf might have had a thick accent, but it certainly wasn't as thick as my brother. "You mean ... like in a bank?" he continued, brilliantly.

The dwarf raised his eyes to the ceiling, took in the crack in the plaster and then, with a sigh, lowered them on to Herbert. "I want to leave a package with you," he said, briskly. "It's much important you look after it. But you must not open it. Just keep it here and

13

keep it safe."

"For how long?"

Now the dwarf's eyes darted across to the window. He swallowed hard and loosened his bow tie. I could see that he was scared of something or somebody in the street outside. Either that or he had a thing about double glazing.

"I don't know," he replied. "About a week maybe. I'll come back and collect it ... when I can. You give it to nobody else except for me. You understand?"

Naples pulled out a packet of Turkish cigarettes and lit one. The smoke curled upwards, a lurid blue in the chill morning air. My brother flicked a piece of chewing-gum towards his mouth. It missed and disappeared over his shoulder.

"What's in the package?" he asked.

"That's my business," the dwarf said.

"OK. Let's talk about my business then." Herbert treated his client to one of his "Don't mess with me" smiles. It made him look about as menacing as a cow with stomachache. "I'm not cheap," he went on. "If you want a cheap private dick, try looking in the cemetery. You want me to look after your package? It'll cost you."

The dwarf reached into his jacket pocket and pulled out the first good thing I'd seen that week: twenty portraits of Her Majesty the Queen, each one printed in brown. In other

14

words, a bundle of ten-pound notes, brand new and crisp. "There's two hundred pounds here," he said.

"Two hundred?" Herbert squeaked.

"There will be another hundred when I return and pick up the package. I take it that is sufficient?"

My brother nodded his head, an insane grin on his face. Put him in the back of a car and who'd need a plastic dog?

"Good." The dwarf stubbed out his half-smoked cigarette and slid off the chair. Then he removed a plain brown envelope from another pocket. It was quite thick with something vaguely rectangular bulging in the centre. It rattled faintly as he put it on the desk. "Here is the package," he said. "Once again, look after it, Mr Diamond. With your life. And whatever you do, don't open it."

"You can trust me, Mr Nipples," my brother muttered. "Your package is in safe hands." He waved one of the safe hands to illustrate the point, sending a mug of coffee flying. "What happens if I need to get in touch with you?" he asked as an afterthought.

"You don't," Naples snapped. "I get in touch with you."

"Well there's no need to be touchy," Herbert said.

It was then that a car in the street backfired. The dwarf seemed to evaporate. One moment he was standing beside the desk. The next he was crouching beneath it, one hand inside his jacket. And somehow I knew that his finger wasn't wrapped round another bundle of money. For about thirty seconds nobody moved. Then Naples slid across to the window, standing to one side so that he could look out without being seen. He had to stand on tip-toe to do it, his hands perched on the sill, the side of his face pressed against the glass. When he turned round, he left a damp circle on the window. Hair oil and sweat.

"I'll see you again in a week," he said. He made for the door as fast as his legs could carry him. With his legs, that wasn't too fast. "Look after that package with your life, Mr Diamond," he repeated. "And I mean … your life."

And then he was gone.

My brother was jubilant. "Two hundred pounds just for looking after an envelope," he crowed. "This is my lucky day. This is the best thing that's happened to me this year." He glanced at the package. "I wonder what's in it?" he murmured. "Still, that needn't worry us. As far as we're concerned, there's no problem."

That's what Herbert thought. But right from the start I wasn't so sure. I mean, two hundred pounds is two hundred pounds, and when you're throwing that sort of money around there's got to be a good reason. And I remembered the dwarf's face when the car backfired. He may have been a small guy, but he seemed to be expecting big trouble.

Just how big I was to find out soon enough.

TIM DIAMOND INC

The two hundred pounds lasted about half a day. But it was a good half-day.

It began with a blow-out at a café round the corner. Double eggs, double sausage, double chips and fried bread but no beans. We'd been living on beans for the best part of a week. It had got so bad I'd been having nightmares about them with giant Heinz cans chasing me down the High Street.

After that, Herbert put an ad in the local newsagent for a cleaning lady. That was crazy, really. There was no way we could afford a cleaner – but on the other hand, if you'd seen the state of our place, maybe you'd have understood. Dust everywhere, dirty plates piled high in the sink and old socks sprawled across the carpet from the bedroom to the front door as if they were trying to get to the launderette under their own steam. Then we took a bus into the West End. Herbert bought me a new jacket for the next term at school and bought himself some new thermal under-wear and a hot-water bottle. That left just about enough money to get two tickets for a film. We went to see *101 Dalmations*. Herbert cried all the way through. He even cried in the commercials. That's what sort of guy he is.

I suppose it was pretty strange, the two of us living together the way we did. It had all happened about two years back when my parents suddenly decided to emigrate to Australia. Herbert was twenty-eight then. I'd just turned eleven.

We were living in a comfortable house in a nice part of London. I still remember the address: 1, Wiernotta Mews. My dad worked as a door-to-door salesman. Doors was what he sold; fancy French sliding doors and tradi-tional English doors, pure mahogany, made in Korea. He really loved doors. Ours was the only house in the street with seventeen ways in. As for my mum, she had a part-time job in a pet shop. It was after she got bitten by a rabid parrot that they decided to emigrate. I wasn't exactly wild about the idea but of course nobody asked me. You know how some par-ents think they own their kids? Well, I couldn't even sneeze without written permission signed in duplicate.

Neither Herbert nor I really got on with our

parents. That was one thing we had in common. Oh yeah ... and we didn't get on with each other. That was the second thing. He'd just joined the police force (this was one week before the Hendon Police Training Centre burnt down) and could more or less look after himself, but of course I had as much independence as the coffee table.

"You'll love Australia," my dad said. "It's got kangaroos."

"And boomerangs," my mum added.

"And wonderful, maple-wood doors..."

"And koalas."

"I'm not coming!" I said.

"You are!" they screamed.

So much for reasoned argument.

I got as far as Heathrow. But just as the plane to Sydney was about to take off, I slipped out the back door and managed to find my way out of the airport. Then I high-tailed it back to Fulham. I'm told my mum had hysterics about 35,000 feet above Bangkok. But by then it was too late.

Now, by this time, Herbert had finished with the police force or to put it more accurately, the police force had finished with Herbert. He'd finally got the sack for giving someone directions to the bank. I suppose it wasn't his fault that the someone had robbed it, but he really shouldn't have held the door for the guy as he came out. But in the meantime, he'd managed to save up some money and had rented this run-down flat in the Fulham Road, above a supermarket, planning to set himself up as a private detective. That's what it said on the door:

TIM DIAMOND INC
PRIVATE DETECTIVE

Inside, you went up a staircase to a glass-fronted door which in turn led into his office, a long, narrow room with four windows looking out into the street. A second door led off from here into the kitchen. The staircase continued up to a second floor where we both had a bedroom and shared a bathroom. The flat had been made available to Herbert at a bargain basement price, probably because the whole place was so rickety it was threatening to collapse into the basement at any time. The stairs wobbled when you went up and the bath wobbled when you turned on the taps. We never saw the landlord. I think he was afraid to come near the place.

Dark-haired and blue-eyed, Herbert was quite handsome – at least from the opposite side of the street on a foggy day. But what God had given him in looks, He had taken away in brains. There may have been worse private detectives than Tim Diamond (the only inc in the building was the stuff he put in his pen). But somehow I doubt it.

I'll give you an example. His first job was to find some rich lady's pedigree Siamese cat. He managed to run it over on the way to see her. The second job was a divorce case – which you may think is run-of-the-mill until I tell you that the clients were perfectly happily married until he came along.

There hadn't been a third case.

Anyway, Herbert was not overjoyed to see me that day when I turned up from Heathrow carrying a hold-all that held exactly nothing, but where else could I go? We argued. I told him it was a *fait accompli*. We argued some more. I told him what a *fait accompli* was. In the end he let me stay.

Mind you, I often wondered if I'd made the right decision. For a start, when I say I like a square meal a day I don't mean a sawn-off Weetabix, and it's no fun starting the winter term in clothes you grew out of the summer before, with more holes in your socks than a Swiss cheese. We could never afford anything. Her Majesty's Government helped Herbert out a little, which is a fancy way of saying that he got the dole, and my parents sent the occasional cheque for my upkeep, but even so Herbert never managed to make ends meet. I tried to persuade him to get himself a sensible job – anything other than private detection – but it was hopeless. As hopeless as Herbert himself.

Anyway, we got back to the flat around

eleven and were making our way up the stairs past the office when Herbert stopped. "Wait a minute, Nick," he said. "Did you leave the door open?"

"No," I said.

"That's strange…"

He was right. The door of the office was open, the moonlight pouring out of the crack like someone had spilt a can of silver paint. We made our way back downstairs and went in. I turned on the light.

"Oh dear," my brother said. "I think we've had visitors."

That was the understatement of the year. A stampede of wild bulls would have left the place in better order. The desk had been torn open, the carpets torn up, the bookshelves torn apart and the curtains torn down. The old filing cabinet would have fitted into so many matchboxes. Even the telephone had been demolished, its various parts scattered around the room. Whoever had been there, they'd done a thorough job. If we'd been invited to a wedding, we could have taken the office along for confetti.

"Oh dear," Herbert repeated. He stepped into the rubble and picked up what was now a very dead cactus. A moment later, he dropped it, his lower jaw falling at about the same speed. "My God!" he shrieked. "The envelope!"

He stumbled over to the remains of his desk and searched in the remains of the top drawer. "I put it here," he said. He fumbled about on the floor. "It's gone!" he moaned at last. He got back to his feet, clenching and unclenching his fists. "The first job I've had in six months and now I've gone and lost it. You know what this means, don't you? It means we won't get the other hundred pounds. I'll probably have to pay back the two hundred we've already spent. What a disaster! What a catastrophe! I don't know why I bother, really I don't. It's just not fair!" He gave the desk a great thump with his boot. It groaned and collapsed in a small heap.

Then he looked at me. "Well, don't just stand there," he snapped.

"What am I meant to do?" I asked.

"Well … say something."

"All right," I said. "I didn't think it was a very good idea to leave the package in your desk…"

"It's a fat lot of use telling me now," Herbert whined. It looked as though he was going to cry.

"I didn't think it was a good idea," I continued, "so I took it with me." I pulled the envelope out of my jacket pocket where it had been resting all evening.

My brother seized it and gave it a big, wet kiss. He didn't even thank me.

THE FAT MAN

We didn't get much sleep that night. First we had to make our beds – and I'm not just talking sheets and blankets. Whoever had wrecked our office had done the same for the rest of the flat. It took about forty nails and two tubes of superglue before the beds were even recognizable, and then I found that Herbert had managed to stick himself to the door handle and had to spend another hour prising him free with a kitchen-knife. By then it was morning and I was too tired to sleep. Herbert sent me out for a loaf of bread while he put on the kettle. At least they hadn't dismantled the kettle.

There were three letters on the doormat and I brought them up with the bread. One was a bill. One was postmarked Sydney, Australia. And the third had been delivered by hand. Herbert filed the bill under "W" for waste-paper basket while I opened the Australian letter.

Darling Herbert and Nicky (it read),
Just a quick note as Daddy and me are about to go to a barbecue. They have lots of barbecues in Australia. The weather's lovely. The sun never stops shining – even when it's raining. You really ought to come out here.

I hope you are well. We miss you both very, very much. Have you solved any crimes yet? It must be very cold in England so make sure you wrap up well with a vest. I know they tickle, but pneumonia is no laughing matter. I'm enclosing a little cheque so you can go to Marks & Spencer.

Must go now. Daddy's at the door. He's just bought a new one.

I'll write again soon.

Love, Mumsy

It was written on the back of a postcard showing a picture of Sydney Opera House. There was a cheque attached with a paper-clip: seventy-five pounds. It wasn't a fortune, but at least it would pay for a few more tubes of superglue. Herbert pocketed the cheque. I kept the card.

The third letter was the most interesting. It was typed on a single sheet of paper with no

26

address at the top. It was a big sheet of paper, but it was a short letter.

DIAMOND –

TRAFALGAR SQUARE. 1.00 P.M. BE THERE.

The Fat Man.

"Who the hell is the Fat Man," I asked.

"The Fat Man..." Herbert muttered. His face had gone a sort of cheesey white and his mouth was hanging open. The last time I had seen him look like that had been when he found a spider in the bath.

"Who is he?"

Herbert was tugging at the letter. It tore in half. "The Fat Man is about the biggest criminal there is in England," he croaked.

"You mean ... the fattest?"

"No. The biggest. He's involved in everything. Burglary, armed robbery, fraud, arson, armed burglary... You name it, he's behind it."

"How do you know?" I asked.

"From when I was a policeman," Herbert explained. "Every crook has a file at New Scotland Yard. But the Fat Man has a whole library. He's clever. Nobody's ever been able to arrest him. Not once. A traffic warden once

27

gave him a parking ticket. They found her a week later, embedded in concrete, part of the M6 motorway. Nobody tangles with the Fat Man. He's death."

Herbert pressed the two halves of the letter together as if he could magically restore them. Personally, I was more puzzled than afraid. OK – so there was this master-criminal called the Fat Man. But what could he want with a no-hoper like Herbert? Obviously it had to be something to do with the dwarf's mysterious package. Had the Fat Man been responsible for the destruction of the flat? It seemed likely and yet at the same time I doubted it. You don't tear someone's place apart and then casually invite them to meet you in Trafalgar Square. One or the other – but not both. On the other hand, if he hadn't done it, who had?

"What are we going to do?" I asked.

"Do?" Herbert looked at me as though I were mad. "We're going! When the Fat Man invites you to jump in front of a tube train, you don't argue. You just do it. And you're grateful he wasn't in a bad mood!"

So later that morning we took the number 14 bus into the West End. This time I left the package – carefully hidden – back at the flat. It had been ransacked once and I figured that nobody would think of looking for it there a second time.

"How will we recognize the Fat Man?" I asked.

"I've seen mugshots," Herbert said.

"You mean – you even had pictures of him on your mugs?"

Herbert didn't laugh. You could have tickled the soles of his feet with an ostrich feather and he wouldn't have laughed. He was so scared, he could barely talk. *And* he ate the bus tickets.

The bus dropped us in Piccadilly Circus and we walked across to Trafalgar Square. It was another cold day with a bite in the air that bit all the way through. The tourist season had ended weeks before but there were still a few of them around, taking photographs of each other against the grey December sky. The Christmas decorations had gone up in Regent Street – it seemed that they'd been up since July – and the stores were wrapped in tinsel and holly. Somewhere, a Salvation Army band was playing "Away in a Manger". I felt a funeral march would have been more appropriate.

Trafalgar Square is a big place and the Fat Man hadn't been too specific about the meeting-point so we positioned ourselves right in the middle, under Nelson's Column. There were a few tourists feeding the pigeons. I felt sorry for them. Who'd be a pigeon in London ... or for that matter a tourist? I had a Picnic bar so I pulled out a couple of peanuts and fed them myself. I ate the rest of it. It was ten to one and in all the excitement I'd missed out on breakfast. Taxis, buses, cars and lorries rumbled all around us, streaming down to the Houses of Parliament and across to Buckingham Palace. I leant against a lion, looking out for anyone with a hundred centimetre waist. A pigeon landed on my shoulder and I gave it another peanut.

Big Ben struck one. According to my watch, it was five minutes fast.

"There he is," Herbert said.

I didn't see him at first. At least, I saw him but I didn't see him. A pink Rolls Royce had pulled up at the kerb, ignoring the blasts of the cars trapped behind it. A chauffeur got out, strolled round to the back and opened the door for one of the thinnest men I had ever seen. He was so thin that, as he moved towards us, he was like a living skeleton. His clothes – an expensive Italian suit and fur-lined coat – hung off him like they were trying to get away. Even his rings were too big for his pencil fingers. As he walked, he kept adjusting them to stop them sliding off.

I looked from him to Herbert and back again. "That's the Fat Man?" I asked.

Herbert nodded. "He's lost weight."

He reached us and stopped, swaying slightly as if the wind was going to blow him away. Close to, he was even more peculiar than far away. Hollow cheeks, hollow eyes, hollow gut. The man was a drum with the skin stretched tight over bones that you could probably see when the light was behind him.

"Mr Diamond?" he said.

"Yes," Herbert admitted.

"I'm the Fat Man."

There was a long silence. Herbert was too afraid to talk, but I don't like long silences. They make me nervous. "You don't look fat to me," I said.

The Fat Man chuckled unpleasantly. Even his laughter was hollow. "Who are you?" he demanded.

"Nick Diamond," I told him, adopting my brother's name. "I'm his kid brother."

"Well, my dear boy, might I suggest that you keep your young mouth closed? I have business with your brother."

I kept my young mouth closed. The Fat Man didn't bother me, but I was interested to know what his business was. Meanwhile, the chauffeur had followed him from the Rolls, carrying a folding chair and a tub of corn. The chauffeur was wearing glasses that were so dark they didn't show his eyes but two reflections of yourself. He unfolded the chair and handed his master the corn.

"Thank you, Lawrence," the Fat Man said. "You can wait in the car."

The chauffeur grunted and walked away.

31

The Fat Man sat down, then dug a hand into the tub and threw a spray of pods across the concrete. The pigeons came at us in a rush. He smiled briefly.

"You look well," Herbert muttered.

"Thank you … Timothy, if I may so call you." The Fat Man was genuinely pleased. "My doctor advised me to lose weight." He shrugged. "One must bow to the voice of reason – although some might say I have taken it a touch far. For the past year I have eaten nothing but yogurt and have shed a hundred and thirty-five kilograms. I have, however, retained my old nickname for professional purposes." The hand dug again, scattering more corn for the pigeons. "On the subject of which," the Fat Man continued, "I will be brief. You were visited yesterday by an old friend of mine. A small friend. I am led to understand that he might have entrusted you with something, something that I want. Something that I'm willing to pay for."

Herbert said nothing so I chipped in. "How much?"

The Fat Man smiled at me a second time. He had dreadful teeth. In fact he was pretty dreadful all over.

"You seem a bright lad," he said. "I'm sure the nurses will just adore you in the casualty ward."

I shrugged. "We don't have it," I said.

"You don't?" His eyebrows lifted themselves towards his bald head. At the same time, he fed the pigeons.

"Our place was turned over last night," I explained. "Perhaps you know about that already. Whoever did it, took what you're looking for."

"That's right!" Herbert agreed. "That's what happened."

The Fat Man looked at us suspiciously. He was pretty sure that we were lying. But he couldn't be certain. A pigeon landed on his head with a flutter of grey feathers. He punched it off, then threw corn at it. At last he spoke. "Taken?" he murmured.

"Absolutely," Herbert said. "When we got back from the cinema, it wasn't there. Otherwise we'd love to give it to you. Really we would."

I groaned silently. We'd have been all right if only Herbert had kept his mouth shut. But he couldn't have convinced a six-year-old and I could tell that the Fat Man had seen right through him. I glanced nervously at the chauffeur, who was watching us from the front seat of the Rolls. Was he armed? Almost certainly. But would he try anything in the middle of Trafalgar Square?

"Very well," the Fat Man said, and suddenly his voice was colder than the winter wind. "We shall play the game your way, my

33

friends. If you want to find out what the bottom of the Thames looks like on a December night, that's your affair." He stood up and now his face was ugly. Actually, it had been ugly before he had even started but now it was even worse. "I want the key," he growled. "Perhaps, soon, you will find it again. Should such a happy event take place, I'm confident you won't be foolish enough to keep it from me." He dipped two fingers into his top pocket. When he pulled them out again, he was holding a card which he gave to Herbert.

"My number," he went on. "I am a patient man, Timothy. I can wait all of forty-eight hours. But if I haven't heard from you in two days, I think you may wake up to find that something very unpleasant has happened to you. Like you no longer have any feet."

"Why do you want this … key so badly?" I demanded.

The Fat Man didn't answer me. We'd hit it off – him and me. The way he was looking at my head, I figured he'd like to hit that off too. But then his eyes wandered. He jerked his hand, sending the rest of the corn flying. The pigeons were all around him, bowing their heads at his feet.

"I hate pigeons," he said in a faraway voice. "Flying rats! London is infested with them. I hate the noise they make, day and night, the filth that they leave behind them. The government ought to make them illegal. And yet they're encouraged! It makes me sick to think of them scuttling across the pavements, infesting the trees, carrying their germs and diseases..."

"So why do you feed them?" I shouldn't have asked, but I had to know.

The Fat Man laughed briefly, mirthlessly. Then he spun the empty carton in my direction. "Poisoned corn," he said.

He walked back to the car and got in. A few feet away, a pigeon suddenly gurgled and keeled over on its side. A moment later, two more joined it, their feet sticking up in the air. By the time the Rolls Royce had reached the corner of Trafalgar Square and turned off towards Hyde Park, we were surrounded by corpses.

"Do you think he's trying to tell us something?" I said.

Herbert didn't answer. He wasn't looking much better than the pigeons.

OPENING TIME

Before the bus had even arrived to take us back to Fulham, we both knew that we were going to have to open the dwarf's package. We hadn't had it twenty-four hours but already our flat had been ransacked and we'd attracted the poisonous attention of the biggest crook in the country. OK – so Johnny Naples had paid us two hundred pounds. He made us promise not to open the envelope. But promises are easily broken. So are necks. I knew which I wanted to see get broken first.

There was a woman waiting at the door when the bus dropped us off. What with the dwarf and the Fat Man, I figured I'd already seen enough weird people for one day, but it seemed that today, like buses and musketeers, they were coming in threes.

She was an old woman with grey, curling hair that stuck out like someone had just electrocuted her. Her lipstick, a vivid shade of crimson, was pretty electrifying too. Her skin was a mass of wrinkles, hanging on her like an old coat. An old coat hung on her too, a sort of seaweed green with artificial fur trimmings. She had a hat like a tea cosy on her head and a bulging carpetbag in her hand. Although this was a high street in the middle of Fulham, her feet were lost in blue fluffy slippers.

We assumed that she had drifted out of the local lunatic asylum and let ourselves into the flat, ignoring her. It was only when we got into the office and found her still behind us that we realized that she had been waiting to see us. Now she took one look at the wreckage and whistled, smacking her lips together afterwards as if she'd just swallowed a toffee.

"Cor blimey!" she exclaimed. "Luv-a-duck! What a blooming mess!"

"Who are you?" Herbert demanded.

"Charlady," she replied. She gave us a big, crimson smile. "I saw your ad in the newsagent."

With everything that had happened, we'd quite forgotten about our advertisement for a cleaner. But here a cleaner was.

"Oh yes," Herbert muttered. "What's your name?"

"Charlady."

"Yes. I know." He frowned. I shrugged. Maybe she didn't understand English. Maybe somebody had dropped her when she was a baby. Herbert tried again, more slowly. "What – is – your – name?"

"Charlady!" she said for a third time. "Betty Charlady. That's my name. But you can call me Betty."

Without waiting for an invitation, she stepped further into the room, waving a feather duster which she had produced out of nowhere like a demented magician. Herbert and I looked at each other as she brushed it lightly across the remains of a shelf. The shelf fell off the wall. The cleaning lady scowled. "Crikey!" she said. "Wot a disaster. You don't need a blooming cleaner 'ere, luv. You need a master carpenter!"

"Wait a minute..." Herbert began.

"Don't you worry!" she interrupted. The duster had vanished and now she was holding a hammer. "It won't take me a minute. I'll soon 'ave this place looking like new."

I didn't doubt her. The carpetbag was so bulky it could have had a box of nails, a screwdriver and even a stepladder concealed in it too. But Herbert had managed to hold her down long enough to get her attention.

"I ... we ... well..." He'd got her attention, but he didn't know what to do with it.

"How much do you charge?" I asked.

"Twenny a day," she chirped, then, seeing the look of dismay on our faces, "Well ... a tenner for you. You look nice enough lads to me. And a private detective too! I love detective stories. Ten quid a day and I'll bring me own tea bags. What do you say?"

I could see Herbert was about to send her on her way so I moved quickly. We'd spent the two hundred pounds but we still had the cheque that Mum had sent us that morning. If Betty Charlady could re-build the flat and then clean it too – and all for ten pounds a day – it seemed too good a bargain to miss.

"You can start on Monday," I said.

"Nick..." Herbert protested.

"Do you really want to live in this?" I asked, pointing at the room.

"E's right," Betty chipped in. "E's a lovely boy, ineee! Wot is 'e? Your bruvver?" Herbert nodded. "E's a real knock-out." She curtsied at me. "A proper little gentleman. Monday, you say? Well, I'd still like to start now if it's all the same with you. Strike while the iron is 'ot, as I always say."

"The iron's in about a hundred pieces," I said. "Along with the ironing-board."

It wasn't that funny, but she threw back her head and laughed like a drain. You know the sort of gurgling sound that water makes when you take the plug out of the bath? Well, that was the sort of drain she laughed like.

"We're rather busy now," Herbert said. I could see he was itching to get at that package.

"Can you come back on Monday?"

"I'll be 'ere," Betty promised. "Nine o'clock on the dot."

"Make it ten."

"Ten o'clock then." She curtsied again. "Wot a little darling – eh?" She winked. "Ten o'clock. Blimey!" Then she went.

We waited until we heard the outer door close before we retrieved the package. There was a loose floorboard in the office – in fact there were more loose floorboards than sound ones – and I'd hidden it underneath, covering it with a layer of dust. Herbert took the envelope and I shook it. Once again it rattled. He was about to open it, but then he froze.

"It could be a bomb," he whispered.

"A bomb?" I repeated. "Why should Naples have left us a bomb?"

"Well..."

"And who would search the place for a bomb?"

Herbert nodded. "That's right," he said. "You're right, Nick. Of course it isn't a bomb. I mean, there's no way it could be a bomb." He laughed. "I mean, who could possibly think..." He thrust it into my hands. "You open it."

With a little smile, he retreated into the far corner of the room, leaving the package with me. I shook it again. The Fat Man had said he wanted "the key". Whatever the package contained, it certainly wasn't a key. It sounded more like marbles – a lot of marbles in a cardboard container. I could feel the lid bending under my fingers. Herbert was watching me like a hawk. No. He was more like a rabbit. I tossed the package into the air and caught it. He blinked and shivered.

A bomb? Of course not.

But it could still be booby-trapped.

I stuck my thumb under the flap and slid it slowly sideways, trying to feel for a concealed wire or thread. Johnny Naples hadn't used a lot of spit when he stuck it down. Perhaps his tongue had been as dry as mine was now. The flap came loose without tearing. I caught a flash of red inside. There was a box of some sort. I tilted the package.

The box slid out on to the floor. Herbert dived for cover. But there was no bang.

And then we were both looking down, wondering if we'd gone crazy. Or perhaps we were about to go crazy. Certainly someone, somewhere had to be crazy.

There was only one thing in the dwarf's package.

It was a box of Maltesers.

D FOR DWARF

I don't know if you're into sweets. Personally, I can do without them. With the sort of pocket money I get, I have to do without them. I mean, with my pocket money, I can't even afford pockets. Anyway, Maltesers are those chocolate balls that crunch when you eat them. In America they have something similar called Malted Milk-balls. I expect you can buy them just about anywhere in the world.

The question was, Why had Johnny Naples paid out two hundred pounds to have us look after a box of sweets? Why had someone gone to so much trouble – wrecking the flat – to get their hands on them? And how had the Fat Man got mixed up in all this? Chocolates were the last things he needed – he was on a diet. It just didn't make sense.

We'd opened the box up. In for a penny, in for a pound (or 146g, to be exact). The contents certainly looked like ordinary Maltesers. They smelled ordinary. And they tasted ordinary. Herbert had some sort of idea that they might be chocolate-covered diamonds or something. It was only after I'd eaten half a dozen of them that he changed his mind and suggested that they might contain some sort of new-fangled poison. If looks could kill, I'd bury my brother.

"What we've got to do," Herbert said, "is find Naples."

For Herbert that was a pretty brilliant piece of deduction. The Fat Man had given us two days to get back to him. Johnny Naples had said he'd return in about a week. That left five days in which all sorts of unpleasant things could happen. The only trouble was, Naples hadn't told us where we could reach him. We had no address, no telephone number.

Herbert echoed my thoughts. "I wonder how we could get hold of him?" he asked.

"We could try Yellow Pages," I suggested. "V for vertically challenged?"

"Yes!"

I groaned as he reached for the telephone book. "I was only joking," I said.

"Were you? Of course you were!" Herbert dropped the book and gazed out of the window.

Meanwhile, I was fingering the envelope. The Maltesers hadn't told us anything, but looking underneath the flap I found a small, white label. The dwarf, in a hurry to seal the package, must have missed it. "Look at this," I said.

Herbert took the envelope. "It's an envelope," he said.

"Yes. But look at the label."

Herbert found it and held it up to the light. "Hammett's," he read. "18p." He frowned. "That's cheap for a box of Maltesers."

I shook my head. "That's the price of the envelope, not the sweets," I explained. "Look – the price is handwritten, but the name is printed. Hammett's ... that must be the stationer's or newsagent where he bought the envelope to put the Maltesers in."

"That's terrific!" Herbert exclaimed. "That's great, Nick." He paused. "But how does it help us?"

"If the dwarf wanted to buy an envelope, he probably bought it fairly near wherever he's staying," I said. "So all we have to do is find out how many Hammett's shops there are in London, visit them all and ask them if they remember selling an envelope to Naples."

Herbert sighed. "They probably sell hundreds of envelopes," he said. "And they must have thousands of customers."

"Yeah. But how many of their customers are dwarfs?"

"That's true." He considered. "So how do

we find Hammett's?"

"We look in the Yellow Pages."

Herbert snatched up the book again. Then he turned and looked at me disdainfully. "That was my idea in the first place," he said.

I didn't argue. Arguing with someone like Herbert is a bit like hitting yourself with a brick.

As it turned out there were six Hammett's in London.

We found them under the section headed "Newsagents and news vendors." There were three south of the river, one in Notting Hill Gate, one in Kensington and one in Hammersmith. By now it was too late to visit them all, so we decided to take the three in the south first and pick up some second-hand furniture from a friend with a shop near Clapham Common at the same time. It took us a couple of hours and a lot of wasted shoe leather but at least that evening we were able to sit down again.

The next day was a Saturday. We left the flat for a second time but struck out in Kensington and Hammersmith. That just left Notting Hill Gate. The last Hammett's was a run-down place on the Portobello Road in the middle of the famous antiques and bric-a-brac market. The sun was shining and the market was busy with young couples splashing out on Victorian brass towel-holders and Edwardian stripped

45

pine blanket boxes. The air was thick with the smell of chips and over-cooked kebabs. Outside the shop there was an old boy selling genuine antique number plates. Doubtless they had fallen off a genuine antique lorry.

The shop was small and dark. That seemed to be the trademark of the entire Hammett chain. You probably know the sort of place: sweets and chocolates on one side, newspapers and magazines on the other with the dirty stuff on the top shelf. Herbert made straight for it, thumbing through a copy of *Playboy*, "looking for clues" as he put it. Meanwhile, I took a quick look at the stationery and odds-and sods section. This was the first branch we'd visited that actually stocked the right-sized envelopes. I examined a price label. The handwriting was the same.

There was only one man behind the counter. He was about forty, a cigarette dangling out of the corner of his mouth, his skin the unhealthy shade of white that comes from sitting in a dingy newsagent's all day smoking. While Herbert continued his own private investigation, I took the envelope and went over to him.

"Excuse me," I said. "I know this is going to sound crazy, but do you remember selling one of these envelopes to a dwarf?"

The man looked past me at Herbert. "Are you going to buy that?" he barked. Herbert pushed the magazine away from him and blushed. Then he came over and joined us. "Now, what do you want, son?" the newsagent asked.

"My brother's a private detective," I explained. "We're trying to find a dwarf ... greasy hair, suntan. We think he bought an envelope here a couple of days ago."

"Yeah ... I remember that." The newsagent nodded. "A short guy... "

"Most dwarfs are," I muttered.

"Came in here ... last Thursday."

It had been Thursday when Johnny Naples came to see us. I was beginning to get excited, but then Herbert had to pipe up. "Diamond's the name," he said. "Tim Diamond."

"He didn't tell me his name," the newsagent said.

"No. I'm telling you my name."

The newsagent frowned at me. "Is he all right?" he asked.

"Sure." I scowled at Herbert. "Look – this is important. Did the dwarf buy anything else here? Like some Maltesers, for example."

I could see that the man was beginning to have second thoughts about the state of my own sanity, but he knew I was serious. He considered for a minute. "He didn't buy any sweets," he said. "But ... now I remember. He had a box of Maltesers with him when he came in. I saw him put them in the envelope. What else did he buy? There was something..." He

snapped his fingers. "It was a pair of scissors."
Now it all came back. "He was in a hurry.
Nervous sort. Kept on looking out into the
street. Like he was being followed or something. He bought an envelope and a pair of
scissors. Then he went."

"We need to find him," I said.

"Is he in some sort of trouble?" the
newsagent asked.

"He might be if we don't find him," I
replied.

"But he won't necessarily be if we do," Herbert added unnecessarily.

The newsagent hesitated. He didn't trust us.
If I had been him, I wouldn't have trusted us
either. Just then the door opened and somebody else came in – to buy a packet of
cigarettes or something. "Look, I don't have
time to waste with you two jokers," the
newsagent said. "You want to speak to the
dwarf, you'll find him at the Hotel Splendide
at the bottom of the Portobello Road."

"How do you know?" I said.

"I know the owner. He told me he had a
dwarf staying there."

"And what's the owner's name?" Herbert
asked.

"Jack Splendide."

The further you go down the Portobello Road,
the crummier it gets. It's just about OK until

you reach the Electric Cinema, but after that it's downhill all the way. You come to a flyover at the bottom by which time you're in a different world. You've left the antique shops and the bustling stalls behind you. Now you're in a flat wasteland, up to your ankles in litter. It's amazing how quickly a short walk can take you from one side of London to the other.

The Hotel Splendide was the sort of place that would be hard to find unless you knew it was there – perhaps the sort of place you might choose if you didn't want to be found. It was right at the far end of the Portobello Road, halfway down a narrow cul-de-sac, nestling in the armpit of the flyover which swept round the building as if holding it in a clammy, concrete embrace. You wouldn't get much sleep at the Hotel Splendide, not with the traffic roaring past only a couple of metres from your bedroom window. For the top floor of the building, beneath the flat roof, was level with the raised highway. Roll over in bed and you risked being run over by a lorry. That is, if the bedbugs and cockroaches hadn't got you first.

It was a square, ugly building, the colour of mouldy cheese. A red neon sign with the name glowed behind a first-floor window, only the glass was so dirty you could hardly read it. A row of dustbins stood outside the entrance, their overflowing garbage adding to the delightful atmosphere. You know how some

49

guides award knives and forks to hotels in recognition of their quality? Well, the Hotel Splendide wouldn't even have merited a tooth-pick.

There was a drunk lying half-asleep next to the dustbins, the top of a wine bottle poking out of the brown paper bag that he clutched in one hand. A dog – an Alsatian – lay sprawled beside him. It was drunk too. We stepped past them and went into the hotel. The door was hanging off its hinges. The interior smelt of sweat and disinfectant.

We found ourselves in what passed for a reception area. Some hotels advertize theatres and restaurants. In this one the posters adver-tized soup kitchens and delousing clinics. There was a counter opposite the door and behind it an unshaven man reading a cheap paperback

The paperback was even cheaper than this one and it didn't have as many pages which was just as well because the guy who was read-ing it didn't look as if he was up to *War and Peace*. He was wearing a grimy shirt and jeans with one of those stomachs that have managed to force their way over the top of the belt and sag down to the thighs. He was sucking a cigar that had gone out perhaps a week ago. He didn't look up as we approached. He flicked a page in his book, grunted and went on reading.

"You Jack Splendide?" Herbert asked.

"Who wants to know?" He talked without moving his lips. But the cigar waggled between his teeth.

"The name's Diamond," Herbert said. "I'm a private eye."

"Ya don't say!" Splendide yawned and went back to the book.

"We're looking for someone who's staying here," I explained. "A dwarf. His name's Johnny Naples. He owes a client of ours a lot of bread."

"That's right," Herbert said. "And if we find him, we'll cut you in for a slice."

We were making it all up, of course, but it was the only way to get past the hotel manager. He jerked a thumb in the direction of the stairs. "Room 39," he said.

We climbed five flights of stairs, trying to stop them creaking beneath our feet. The carpet was threadbare, the walls damp and discoloured. We could hear TV sets blaring away in the distance and a baby crying. I reckon I'd have cried if I'd had to stay there. Room 39 was at the back of the hotel, at the bottom of a corridor. We guessed it was 39 because it came after 37 and 38. But the number had fallen off. The door was closed.

"Do you think this is a good idea?" Herbert whispered.

"Have you got a better one?" I asked.

"We could go home…"

"Come on, Tim," I said. "We've found him now. It can't hurt to—"

That was as far as I got. The gunshot wasn't loud, but it was close enough to make me jump the way you do when a car backfires or somebody drops a plate. It had come from the other side of the door. Herbert froze, then tried to lurch away, but fortunately I managed to grab hold of his jacket. I didn't want to go into the room by myself. I didn't want to go into the room at all. But if I'd run away then, I'd never have forgiven myself.

Still clutching Herbert, I opened the door. It wasn't locked. In the Hotel Splendide, the rooms didn't have locks. Some of them didn't even have doors.

The first thing I saw was a flapping curtain and a shadowy figure disappearing outside. I couldn't even tell if it was a man or a woman. There was just the flash of a leg hanging over the edge of the sill and then it was gone.

It was a small room, just big enough for a bed, a table, a chest of drawers and a corpse. I closed the door behind me. Johnny Naples was lying on the bed. He wasn't dead yet but the big red splodge on his shirt told me that his time was running out about as quickly as his blood. I went over to the window and looked outside. But I was too late. Whoever had climbed out had jumped the short distance to the flyover and run for it. Maybe they'd had a car waiting for them. Anyway, they were gone.

The dwarf groaned and I looked back again. The room was probably in a mess to begin with but I guessed there had been a fight. There was a chair upturned on the floor and a lamp had been knocked over on the table. My eyes fell on a packet of book-matches. I don't know why I picked them up and put them in my pocket. I knew we didn't have a lot of time and that any clue – no matter how small – might help. Maybe it was just that I didn't want to look at the dwarf. Anyway, that's what I did.

Johnny Naples opened his mouth and tried to speak.

"The falcon…" he said. Then a nasty, bubbling sound.

Then… "The sun…" That was it. His eyes closed. The mouth stayed open.

D for Dwarf. D for dead.

Herbert had picked something up off the carpet.

"Nick…" he began.

It was a gun. And it was still smoking.

And he was still standing there, holding it, when the door crashed open again. The man who had been drunk outside the Hotel Splendide was standing there and he had a gun too. The Alsatian was with him, growling softly.

There were two more people behind him.

"Police!" he shouted.

Herbert fainted.

The man swung round to cover him. "You're under arrest," he said.

THE FALCON

Johnny Naples was taken to the morgue. We were taken to the Ladbroke Grove police station. I don't know which of us got the better treatment. While he was carried out on his back, covered with a nice clean sheet, we were dragged out, handcuffed together and thrown into the back of a van. It had turned out, of course, that the drunk in the street had been a plain-clothes policeman. The Alsatian was a plain-clothes police dog. The Hotel Splendide had been the subject of a major police stake-out and we'd more or less had our chips the moment we'd walked in.

We were left to stew in a bare-bricked interrogation room. Or to freeze, rather. That place couldn't have been much warmer than the morgue. There was one metal table, three metal chairs and five metal bars on a window that would have been too small to climb out of anyway. A blackboard lined one wall and there was a poster on the other reading "Crime doesn't pay", underneath which somebody had scrawled "nor does policework". The room smelt of stale cigarette smoke. I wondered how many hardened criminals had grown harder waiting there.

Herbert had said little since he woke up. But after about twenty minutes he suddenly looked around as if he had only just realized where he was. "Nick..." he said.

"Yes?"

"Do you think ... you don't think the police think I had anything to do with what happened to the dwarf, do you?" he asked.

"No," I replied soothingly. "You went up to see him. There was a gunshot. You were found holding a smoking gun. The dwarf was dead. I'm sure the police won't think you're involved."

At that moment there was a rattle as a key was turned in the lock and the door swung open. Herbert groaned. The man who had just come in didn't look too happy either.

"Herbert Simple," he said.

"Inspector Snape," Herbert muttered in a strangled voice.

"Chief Inspector Snape," the man growled. "No thanks to you."

The Chief Inspector was blond-haired and built like a rugby player, with those slightly squashed shoulders that come from too many scrums. His skin was the colour of raw bacon and he spoke with a northern accent. He was wearing an off-white shirt that had probably been pure white when he put it on and a tie that had slipped over his collar in its struggle to get away from his bulging neck. He was followed by a smaller, squatter version of himself with black, permed hair, an open-neck shirt and a gold medallion glittering in the forest of his chest. The assistant – if that's what he was – stood there, pounding one fist into the palm of his hand, looking at us with unfriendly, muddy-brown eyes. Well, if these are the cops, I thought, hate to meet the robbers.

"Herbert Simple," Snape repeated, drawing up a chair.

"Can I hit him?" the other policeman asked.

"No, Boyle." The Chief Inspector smiled unpleasantly. "Herbert Simple." He said the name a third time, chewing on the words like they were stuck in his teeth. "The worst police constable that ever served in my station. In two months you did more damage than the Kray brothers managed in twenty years. The day you left, I cried like a baby. Tears of pleasure. I never thought … I hoped, I prayed that I would never see you again." His pig-like eyes were turned on me. "And who are you, laddy?" he asked.

"His brother," I said.

"Bad luck, son. Bad luck."

"Can I hit *him*?" Boyle asked.

"Relax, Boyle." The Chief Inspector took out a cigarette and lit it. "Now, the question I'm asking myself is, Why should a luckless, hopeless, brainless ex-policeman like Herbert Simple be mixed up with a man like Johnny Naples?"

"I didn't shoot him!" Herbert cried.

"I believe you." Snape's nostrils quivered as they blew out two streams of smoke. "If you'd wanted to shoot the dwarf, you'd have probably missed and shot yourself in the foot. After all, when we sent you for weapons training, you managed to shoot the instructor. But the fact still remains that your fingerprints are on the gun – and nobody else's. So perhaps you'd better tell me what you were doing there."

"Naples was my client," Herbert squeaked.

"Your client?"

"He's a private detective," I explained.

"A private detective?" Chief Inspector Snape began to laugh. He laughed until the tears trickled down his cheeks. At last he managed to calm himself down, wiping his eyes with the back of his hand. Boyle handed him a handkerchief and he blew his nose noisily. "Now I've heard everything!" he said. "A private detective. And your client's dead. That makes sense. The moment he came to you he was a marked man. But what private detection

58

did Naples want?"

"It's private," I said.

That wiped the smile off Snape's face. At the same time, Boyle grunted and lumbered towards me. I'd seen prettier sights in London Zoo. Fortunately for me, Snape held up a hand. "Forget it, Boyle," he snapped.

"But Chief..."

"He's under-age."

Boyle grunted again and punched the air. But he hung back.

"You should watch yourself, son," Snape said. "Boyle here is very into police brutality. He watches too much TV. The last suspect we had in here ended up in intensive care and he was just in for double parking."

"It's still private," I said.

"All right," Snape grumbled. "If you want to see your big brother arrested for murder..."

"Nick...!" Herbert whimpered.

"Wait a minute," I said. "We don't have to break a client's confidence."

"He's dead," Snape said.

"I noticed. But he's still our client." I gave him my friendliest smile. "Look, Chief Inspector," I said. "You tell us what you know and we'll tell you what we know. That seems fair to me."

Snape looked at me thoughtfully. "How old are you?" he asked.

"Thirteen."

"You're smart for your age. If you go on as smart as this, maybe you won't reach fourteen."

"Just tell us."

"Why should I? How do I know you know anything at all."

"We know about the key," I said. "And about the falcon."

I admit that was two shots in the dark. The Fat Man had mentioned a key and with his dying breath Johnny Naples had muttered something about a falcon. Neither of them made any sense to me, but I had gambled that they would mean something to this Snape character. And I was right. He had raised an eyebrow at the mention of the key. The other one joined it when I followed with the falcon.

He finished the cigarette, dropped the butt and ground it out with his heel. "OK," he said. "But you'd better be on the level, Nick. Otherwise I'll let Boyle spend a little time alone with you."

Boyle looked at me like he was trying to work out a new pattern for my face.

"Johnny Naples flew in here from South America a month ago," Snape began. "We picked him up when he came through passport control, then we lost him, then – just a few days ago – we found him again at the Hotel Splendide. We've had him under observation ever since. You and your brother were the first

60

people to see him as far as we know. He never went out – not while we were watching."

"Why were you watching him?" Herbert asked.

"That's what I'm trying to tell you," Snape snapped. He lit himself another cigarette. He didn't look like a chain-smoker, but that's the sort of effect my big brother has on people. "Johnny Naples was a nobody," Snape went on. "A quack doctor with a run-down practice in the back streets of La Paz, Bolivia. But with his last patient he struck lucky. You already know about the Falcon, but I wonder how much you know? His full name, for example – Henry von Falkenberg. I reckon he was out of your league. To be fair, von Falkenberg was in a league of his own.

"Look – every country has its big crooks. In England the Fat Man is probably number one. America has the godfathers. In Italy there are the Fettucine brothers. But the Falcon was an internationalist. He was half-English, half-German, loyal to neither country and living, when we last heard of him, in Bolivia. There wasn't a single criminal organization in the world that he wasn't doing business with. You steal a lorry-load of mink coats in Moscow? You sell it to the Falcon. You want to buy a kilo of cocaine in Canada? Just have a word with the Falcon. He was the number one, the top man, the king of crime. If there was a country in the world where the police didn't want him, he'd have taken it as a personal insult.

"Now, like any big businessman, the Falcon needed funds – a financial platform on which to build his deals. But unlike most businessmen, he couldn't just open an account at your local building society. He didn't trust the Swiss banks. He didn't trust his own mother – which is probably why he had her rubbed out back in 1965. The only currency the Falcon would deal in was diamonds: uncut diamonds. The franc might fall, the rouble might rise – but diamonds held their own. In every major city he had his own little stash of diamonds: in Paris, Amsterdam, New York ... and London. In fact, London was the centre of his operations, so that's where he had the biggest stash. We can't be sure, but we believe that perhaps only a mile from here, he'd managed to conceal diamonds to the value of three and a half million pounds."

He paused for effect and he got it. I licked my lips. Herbert shook his head and whistled.

"The Falcon was a great criminal," Snape continued. "But a month ago his luck ran out. He could have been arrested. He could have been machine-gunned by a rival gang. But in the end he was run over by a bus. It was a crazy end to a crazy life. It happened just outside La Paz airport as he crossed the road to catch a plane to England. We believe he was carrying the key to the diamonds with him. And the man who just happened to be on the scene, who travelled with him in the ambulance on the way to the hospital, was Johnny Naples.

"So the Falcon is lying on his back with the life running out of him and he – and only he – knows where a fortune in diamonds is hidden. Now, we can't be certain, but people who are dying tend to blurt out secrets that they would otherwise keep to themselves and we believe the Falcon told Johnny Naples where he could find those diamonds. Look at it this way. A few days later, Naples junks in his job and takes a first-class flight to London. There's no reason why he should have come here unless you put two and two together and make..."

"Three and a half million," I said.

"Right." Snape stood up and walked over to the blackboard. He had produced a piece of chalk from his pocket. "So Johnny Naples flies to the end of the rainbow; in this case, England. But he's not alone. Because all sorts of people are interested in the diamonds now that the Falcon is dead." He turned round and scrawled a name on the blackboard.

The Fat Man

"He's number one. The Fat Man had often done business with the Falcon. If anybody knew about the secret stash it would be him. And he could use the money. Give the Fat Man three and a half million pounds and maybe he could go international himself. He could become the next Falcon. He probably knew where the dwarf was staying before we did. Did he kill Johnny Naples? If so, he'll be on his way to the diamonds ... and that's bad news for all of us."

Snape wrote a second name beneath it.

Beatrice von Falkenberg

"She's the dark horse," Snape continued. "The Falcon's wife – his widow – once Holland's greatest actress. He fell in love with her when he saw her in *Othello*. She played the title role. From all accounts it wasn't a happy marriage. She spent six months of the year in London and six months in La Paz. Did he ever tell her where the diamonds were hidden? If he didn't, she'll want to know..."

Two more names followed.

William Gott
and Eric Himmell

"They were the Falcon's right-hand men, his two lieutenants. If they could get their hands on the diamonds, they'd have enough money and enough power to take over the Falcon's empire. Gott and Himmell are killers. Although they were born in Germany, they were both educated at Eton. During that time, the vicar and the PE instructor went missing and the assistant headmaster was found hanged with his own old school tie. They arrived in London the day after Johnny Naples. They're here now, and they're deadly."

The Professor

"He's another mystery. But if anybody knows where the diamonds are, it's likely to be him. He was the Falcon's technical adviser, his tame egg-head. He was brilliant but crooked. For example, he invented computer fraud five years before someone invented the computer. If the diamonds are in some sort of safe, he'll have probably built it. But about a year ago he went missing. He could be dead. Nobody's heard of him since then."

Snape turned to the blackboard and wrote a final name.

Herbert Simp

That was as far as he got. The chalk broke in his hand.

"And at last we come to you," he said.

65

"Hopeless, horrible Herbert Simple. You say Johnny Naples was your client. I want to know why. I want to know what he wanted. I want to know what he said. I want to know what you two are doing mixed up in all this and I want to know now!"

He paused.

Things were beginning to make some sort of sense. Not a lot of sense, mind you, but at least we knew what stakes we were playing for. Johnny Naples had come to London in search of three and a half million pounds and he had left us a box of Maltesers. It wasn't a lot to go on, but it was all we had. The trouble was, if we told Snape what Naples had given us, we'd lose that too. The way I saw it was like this. A lot of people were interested in what had taken place in our office that Thursday morning. The Fat Man was one of them. And perhaps it had been Gott and Himmell who had ransacked the place that same night. Sooner or later they'd come gunning for us and if the worst came to the worst, we'd have to give them the Maltesers. Which meant we had to keep them from Snape.

And – OK – I'll be honest. If we were really sitting on the key to a fortune, I wanted to be the one to turn it. There were plenty of things I could do with three million pounds. I reckoned I'd let Herbert keep the other half.

"Come on," Snape growled. "It's your turn.

What did Naples want?"

There was another long silence. Boyle shuffled forward and I noticed that this time Snape made no move to stop him.

"Naples came here looking for the money," I said. "You were right there. But he was followed. He was afraid. That's why he came to see us. He thought we'd be able to give him some sort of protection."

"Nick!" Herbert muttered.

"He didn't tell us anything more than that…"

Boyle's hand clamped down on the back of my neck. He half-dragged me to my feet. Now I knew how a piece of scrap iron feels when it's picked up by a mechanical grabber. I waited for him to crush me. "You're lying," he hissed.

"Scouts honour!" I pleaded.

"You knew about the key," Snape reminded me.

"Only because Naples mentioned it. But we haven't got it. You can search the office if you like."

"We already have," Boyle said.

"Then you'll know that somebody tore it apart. Look – if we knew anything, why do you think we went to the Hotel Splendide? The place was searched and we got scared. We went to see Naples to ask him what was going on, but by the time we got there, he was dead. Honest!"

For a moment the only sound in the room was a vague creaking as my neck splintered in Boyle's grip. But then he must have got some sort of signal from Snape. He released me and I collapsed in my chair. My legs had turned to jelly. I could hardly move my head.

"OK. We'll play it your way, son," Snape said humourlessly. "We'll let you go. I don't believe you and nor will the Fat Man or any of the other nasties waiting for you out there. It'll be interesting to see which one of them gets to you first."

"And I suppose you'll stand by and watch," I muttered, rubbing my neck.

"Don't worry," Snape said. "We'll be round to pick up the pieces."

GRANNIES

It's funny how the smell of police stations sticks on you long after you've gone. Snape was decent enough to get a police car to take us home and we carried the smell with us, down past the Albert Hall and through Earl's Court. They say that good detectives have a "nose" for crime. They "sniff" out clues and when things are going well, they're on the right "scent". After a couple of hours in the Ladbroke Grove interrogation room, I could see what they mean. The strong arm of the law could do with a strong under-arm deodorant.

We had a bath when we got in and changed into fresh clothes. Then Herbert suggested we should go out and get something to eat. I didn't argue. He'd been very quiet since we'd walked in on the dead dwarf and I could tell something was brewing. Perhaps he was finally going to pack in the private detective business and send me packing too. All the same, I dug the Maltesers up from beneath the floorboard and took them with me. That was funny too. Before, when I hadn't known what they were worth, I'd slung them about like you would any packet of sweets. Now that I knew they carried a three and a half million pound pricetag, I could feel them burning a hole in my pocket.

We walked down the Fulham Road towards Kensington Station. Herbert was still quiet. And he was jumpy. When a guy stopped us to ask us the time, he jumped, disappearing behind a parked car. I found him there a minute later, crouching down, pretending to tie up his shoes. It would have been a bit more convincing if his shoes had had laces. The truth was, Herbert was afraid, certain we were being watched. The taxi-driver on the other side of the road, the old man walking his dog, the couple kissing at the bus stop ... as far as Herbert was concerned, any one of them could have been working for the Fat Man, for Beatrice von Falkenberg, for the police ... whoever.

We stopped at a fast-food restaurant called Grannies. It got the name because all the hamburgers were served in granary bread buns. As a sort of publicity stunt, someone had also had the bright idea of only employing grannies – little old ladies with grey hair and glasses. The only trouble with all this was that for a fast-food restaurant, it was actually pretty slow. The chef must have been about a hundred and two. One of the waitresses used a walking-frame. But the food's OK and we were in no hurry. We took a table by the window. Herbert chose the chair that looked out. There was no way he was going to sit with his back to the street.

We ordered Grannyburgers and chips with chocolate milkshakes on the side and hardly said anything until it arrived. I picked up the tomato ketchup holder and squeezed it. The stuff spat out, missing the plate and splattering on to the white table. It looked like blood.

Herbert put his knife and fork down. "Nick ..." he began.

"Herbert?" I said expectantly. Actually, I knew what to expect now. I should have seen it coming.

"This case is getting out of hand," he said. "I mean ... it's getting dangerous. The way things are going, I reckon somebody could soon get hurt."

"You mean – like Johnny Naples?" I reminded him.

"Right." Herbert stared at the tomato sauce, his lip curling. "And he wasn't just hurt," he went on. "I mean, he probably was hurt. But he was also killed."

"You can't get more hurt than that," I agreed.

71

He nodded. "So what I'm saying is, maybe it's time you split. You're a good kid, Nick. But you're only thirteen. This is a case for Tim Diamond."

It was incredible. Maybe it was the shock of what had happened that day or maybe it was the milkshake, but Herbert was trying to get rid of me. "This is a case for Tim Diamond" – it was a line out of a bad movie, but Herbert really believed it. I could see him switching into his private detective role even as he sat there, shoulders slumped, eyes hard. He'd have had a cigarette dangling out of the corner of his mouth if cigarettes didn't make him throw up.

"I figured I'd send you to Aunty Maureen in Slough," he went on. I shuddered. Aunty Maureen, my mother's sister, had a semi-detached house and a semi-detached false hip. She was only fifty-years-old but in need of round-the-clock nursing. Whenever I stayed with her, I ended up as her round-the-clock nurse. "Or you could always go to Australia," Herbert added.

I took a deep breath and pronged a forkful of french fries. Whenever Herbert got into these moods, I had to tread carefully. If I ever suggested that the great Tim Diamond needed any help from his thirteen-year-old brother, I'd have been on the next plane to Sydney faster than you could whistle

"Waltzing Malteser".

"It's nice of you to think of me, Tim," I said. "And I don't want to get in your way. But I reckon I'd be safer with you."

"Safer?" He took a bite out of his burger.

"Sure. I mean, the Fat Man could come for me in Slough. I might get kidnapped, or brutally beaten with Aunty Maureen's false hip."

"That's true."

"But I feel safe with you," I continued. "Back in the Hotel Splendide, for example. I don't know what I'd have done without you."

Herbert smiled modestly.

"The way you fainted. It was ... heroic."

Now he scowled. "You're not taking the mickey, are you?"

"Me? No way."

I felt it was time to bring the conversation to a close so I took out the box of Maltesers and put them on the table.

"That's what we should be worrying about," I said. "Three and a half million pounds, Herbert. And it's our only clue."

"I don't get it," Herbert said. Herbert never did.

"Look..." I spoke slowly, trying to make it easy for him. "Johnny Naples comes to England with the key to a fortune. That's what the Fat Man asked us for – remember? A key. Now, all he's got is this box of Maltesers, but maybe he doesn't know what it means either."

73

"How do you know that?" Herbert asked.

"Because Snape told us that the dwarf had been in England for a whole month before he was killed. Maybe the Falcon didn't have time to tell him everything before he died. Naples had a rough idea and came over here to look."

"Go on."

"All right. So Naples comes to England. He checks into the Hotel Splendide. And he starts looking. But unfortunately for him, there are lots of people interested in him. The same people who are now interested in us. But Johnny Naples still manages to find out what the Maltesers mean. He takes them with him – like you'd take a treasure map. So that nobody will see what he's carrying, he buys an envelope to put them in. He goes from the hotel to Fulham. But then he sees that he's followed. So what does he do?"

"I don't know," Herbert said, breathlessly. "What does he do?"

"He comes to us. He's in the street and he happens to see your name on the door. You're a private detective. That's perfect. And maybe your name rings a bell."

"No, Nick," Herbert interrupted. "It's the little button by the door that rings the bell..."

"No," I groaned. "I mean Tim *Diamond*. Diamonds are what this is all about."

"Oh – I see."

"Johnny Naples comes in and gives us the

envelope. You remember how scared he was? He knew that he was being followed. So he gives us the package – which is what everybody wants – and promises to come back when the heat is off."

"But he didn't come back," Herbert said.

"No. Because he got killed."

"Oh yes!"

"And now we've got the Maltesers. And if we can work out where he was going and what he was going to do with them when he got there, we'll be rich."

"That's terrific!" Herbert exclaimed. As I had hoped, all thoughts of Slough and Aunty Maureen had left his head. Quickly, he finished his meal. Then he picked up the box. "Perhaps the diamonds are inside," he suggested. "Covered in chocolate."

"No," I said. "I doubt if you could fit three and a half million's worth inside and anyway, I've already eaten six of them and they certainly didn't taste like diamonds."

"Then what...?"

It was a good question. You can go and buy a box of Maltesers in any sweetshop, but to save you the money, let me just describe the box we had. It had the name written in white letters on a red background, surrounded by pictures of the chocolate balls themselves. This was on the top and on all four sides. On one side it also carried the inspiring message –

"The lighter way to enjoy chocolates" and on the other, the weight: 146g 5.15 oz.

There was more on the bottom. It read "Chocolates with crisp, light honeycombed centres" and then there was the usual blurb about the milk solids and the vegetable fat that had achieved this miracle. In addition there was a guarantee: "This confectionary should reach you in perfect condition..." and a line asking you to keep your country tidy.

After that, there was a red code number: MLB 493 and, in a red panel, "Best before 28-12-96". In the left-hand corner, painted in blue, was the bar-code, the series of thick and thin lines that you get on all products these days. There was a number beneath that too: 3521 201 000000. And that is about as complete a description of a box of Maltesers as you are ever going to find in a library or bookshop.

It was not very helpful.

The waitress hobbled over and we ordered two Grannypies. We sat in silence, waiting for them to arrive. The question was, how could you hide the location of a fortune in diamonds on a box of sweets – and for that matter, why choose a box of sweets in the first place? The answer was in our hands and even then I might have been able to guess, for the truth is, I had forgotten one important detail. One thing that Johnny Naples had done had slipped my mind. I was still trying to work it out when Herbert spoke.

"Any luck?" he asked.

"No."

We finished our puddings and ordered the bill.

"How about the little dots?" Herbert asked.

"Little dots?"

"Under the letters." He pointed at the Maltesers. "They could spell out another message."

"But there aren't any little dots," I said.

"They could be written in invisible ink."

"I can't see it."

"That's because it's invisible." He smiled triumphantly.

"Listen," I said. "If Johnny Naples didn't know what the Maltesers meant, he'd have had to find out – right?"

"Right," Herbert agreed.

"So if we can work out where he went while he was in England, maybe we'll find out, too."

"Right." Herbert frowned. "But he's dead. So where do we start?"

"Maybe here," I said.

I took out the book of matches that I had found in the hotel and gave it to him. They belonged to a place called the Casablanca Club with an address in the West End. There was a map on the inside of the cover and three matches left.

"Where did you get this?" Herbert asked.

"I picked it up in the dwarf's room at the hotel," I said. "I thought it might be useful."

"Yes." Herbert considered. "We'll go there tomorrow," he said. "If we can work out where Johnny Naples went while he was in England, maybe we can find out what the Maltesers mean."

I nearly choked on my milkshake. "That's brilliant!" I exclaimed.

"Sure thing, kid," Herbert said.

I didn't remind him that I'd said exactly the same thing only a few moments before. But nor did he remind me about Slough. This might be a case for Tim Diamond, but so long as I played my cards right, it seemed there was still room for his little brother Nick.

THE CASABLANCA CLUB

We were woken up at nine the next morning by the engineer who'd come to mend the phone and we just had time to fall asleep again before we were woken up by Betty Charlady who'd come to mend the flat. She had brought with her a sack of tools and was soon assembling Herbert's desk, hammering away at the wood with a mouth full of nails. It seemed incredible that she should do all this for a lousy ten pounds a day, but I assumed I brought out the motherly instinct in her. Strange how I could never do the same for my mother.

While Herbert got dressed and shaved, I nipped out for eggs, milk and bread. We hadn't had time to cash the cheque and money was running low so I had to squeeze more credit out of the supermarket owner. The owner – Mr Patel – is a decent old stick. He also owns a decent old stick which he tried to hit me with as I ran out without paying, but at least I was able to rustle up a decent breakfast for Herbert and me, and a cup of tea for Mrs Charlady.

After breakfast, Herbert rang the Casablanca Club and I discovered that it would be open that night – although to members only. Betty Charlady was screwing a chair back together in the office at the time and she must have overheard the call for when she came into the kitchen she was scowling

"Wassis Casablanca Club?" she asked.

"It's in Charing Cross," I said. "We're going there tonight."

"You shouldn't do it, Master Nicholas," Betty muttered. "At your age."

I handed her a cup of tea. She took it and sat down, her eyes searching across the table for a biscuit. "It's part of our investigation," I explained. "A client of ours may have gone there so we have to go there, too."

But Mrs Charlady wasn't impressed. "These London clubs," she said. "They're just dens of innik-witty." She shook her head and the grey curls of her hair tumbled like lemmings off a cliff. "You go if you have to. But I'm sure no good will come of it…"

Nonetheless, Herbert and I made our way to the Casablanca Club that same night, arriving just after twelve. There's a corner of Charing

Cross, just behind the station, that comes straight out of the nineteenth century. As the road slopes down towards the river, you leave the traffic and the bright lights behind you and suddenly the night seems to creep up on you and grab you by the collar. Listen carefully and you'll hear the Thames water gurgling in the distance and as you squint into the shadows you'll see figures shuffling slowly past like zombies. For this is down-and-out territory. Old tramps and winos wander down and pass out underneath the arches at the bottom, wrapped in filthy raincoats and the day's headlines.

The Casablanca Club was in the middle of all this. A flight of steps led down underneath a dimmed green bulb and if you didn't know what you were looking for, there was no way you'd find it. There was no name, no fancy sign. Only the tinkle of piano music that seemed to seep out of the cracks in the pavement hinted that in the dirt and the dust and the darkness of Charing Cross, somebody might be having a good time.

We climbed down to a plain wooden door about five metres below the level of the pavement. Somebody must have been watching through the spyhole for it opened before we had time to knock.

"Yes?" a voice said.

Friendly place, I thought.

"Can we come in?" Herbert asked.

"You members?"

"No."

"Then beat it!"

The door swung shut. At the last moment, Herbert managed to get his foot in the crack. There was a nasty crunching sound as his shoe, and possibly his foot too, got chewed up in the woodwork, but then the door swung open again and I managed to push my way through and into the hall. A bald man in a dinner jacket gave me an ugly look. If he ever wanted to give anyone a pretty look, he'd need major plastic surgery.

"We're friends of Johnny Naples," I said.

The man shrugged. "Why didn't you say so before?" he asked.

"You didn't ask," I said.

He opened the door again. Herbert was writhing on the concrete outside, clutching his mangled foot. "Instant membership – ten quid," the bald man said. He glanced at me. "You're under-age," he muttered.

"You don't look too good yourself," I replied.

"How old are you?" he asked.

"Twenty-five."

"Twenty-five?" He sneered. "You got a driving licence?"

"No. I got a chauffeur."

I walked on, leaving Herbert to find the

money and pay. In the dim light I could have been any age. Anyway, I was taller than Johnny Naples had ever been and they'd allowed him in.

Funnily enough, the first waiter who saw me mistook me for the dwarf in the half-light. "Mr Naples!" The words were two drops of oil squeezed into my ear and I was led to a table at the front of a large room. There was so much smoke in the air that my eyes had more water in them than the house whisky. I loosened my tie and sat down. It felt like there was more smoke in the air than there was air in the smoke. Another waiter passed. "Good evening, Mr Naples."

He put a silver bucket and two glasses on the table. I leant forward. There was a bottle of champagne in the bucket, surrounded by ice-cubes, already uncorked. "With the compliments of the house," the waiter said. I scratched my head. The dwarf must have been quite a regular here. Came regular, drank regular... I wondered what else he did regular at the Casablanca Club.

I looked around me. There were perhaps a hundred people there, sitting at tables or crowding round the bar where three black-tied waiters shook cocktails behind a curving marble counter. The air was filled with the hubbub of conversation, as thick and as indistinct as the cigarette smoke. There was a dance floor at one end but tonight there was no band, just a black pianist stroking the ivories with fingers that looked too stubby to sound so good. Right in front of my table there was a stage about the size you'd expect a stage to be in a run-down drinking club. The place had no windows and no ventilation. The smoke had smothered the light, strangled the plants and it wasn't doing a lot for me either.

I drank some champagne. I'd never drunk the stuff before and I can't say I really liked it. But I was thirsty and it was free. Herbert joined me, muttering about the ten pounds and a moment later a spotlight cut through the clouds and the crowd fell silent. A figure moved on to the stage, a woman in her fifties, who dressed like she was in her thirties, with jewellery flashing here and there to keep your eyes off the wrinkles. She was attractive if you didn't look too closely. At one time she might even have been beautiful. But the years hadn't been good to her. They'd taken the colour out of her hair, put a husk in her voice, hollowed out her throat and slapped her around a bit for good measure.

I drank some more champagne. The bubbles were going right up my nose and dancing behind my eyes. The pianist had come to the end of a tune but as the woman moved forward he began another and she sang almost as if she didn't care what she was doing. She sang two or three songs. When she finished, she got a scattering of applause and as the talk started up again, she moved down to our table and sat opposite me. Only when she was close enough to see the pinks of my eyes (the whites had gone that colour in all the smoke) did she see who I was.

"You're not Johnny," she said.

"We're friends of his…" I said. I let the sentence hang in the air. I needed her name to complete it.

"Lauren Bacardi," she said. "Where's Johnny?"

I looked at Herbert. From the way she was talking, the little guy had obviously meant something to her and I didn't know how she would take the news. I hoped he'd think of a gentle way to tell her. You know, with a bit of tact.

"He's dead," Herbert said.

"Dead?"

"Yup." He nodded. "Dead."

She took out a cigarette and lit it. I guessed she needed something to do with her hands. After all, to smoke in the unique atmosphere of the Casablanca Club, you didn't actually need to light another cigarette. "Was he … killed?" she asked.

"Yeah," I said. I drank some more champagne. The more I drank, the better I liked it. "You knew him?"

She smiled sadly. "We were friends." Her eyes were far away. They seemed further away than her nose. Maybe it was the champagne. I thought she was going to get up and walk out of our lives. The way things turned out, it would have been better if she had. But the pianist had slid into a bluesy number and she needed to talk. "Johnny and I knew each other for ten years," she said. "But we never met. Not until a month ago.

"We were pen-pals. He was in South America. I was over here. Maybe you'll laugh at me, but we kind of fell in love by post." She flicked ash on to the carpet. "We wrote letters to each other for ten years and he never even mentioned that he was a dwarf. I only found out a month ago when he came over and by then I'd more or less agreed to marry him. The little rat…"

She puffed at her cigarette. I knocked back the champagne. Herbert was watching both of us anxiously.

"He came over," she went on. "He just turned up one day on my doormat. No. He was standing on a chair on the doormat – to reach the bell. He had these plans. We were going to be rich. We'd buy this little house in the South of France with low ceilings. Johnny didn't like high ceilings. He told me that he knew where he could lay his hands on three and a half million pounds – enough money to take me away from all this…"

She raised her hands, taking in the whole of the Casablanca Club with ten chipped and nicotine-stained fingernails.

"Did he have anything with him?" I asked. "A box, for example?"

"You mean the Maltesers?" Lauren Bacardi smiled. "Sure. He never went anywhere without them. He seemed to think they were important, but he didn't know why. It nearly drove him mad … if he wasn't mad already. I mean, how could a box of sweets be worth all that dough?"

I poured myself some more champagne. Herbert whisked it away before I could drink it. I wanted to argue but suddenly there were two of him and I wasn't feeling so good.

"But maybe he was on the level," Lauren went on. "Why else would anyone want to wipe him out? I mean, Johnny never hurt anyone in his life. He was too small.

"And he was afraid all the time he was in England. He wouldn't stay at my place. He hid himself away in some flea-pit hotel and whenever we went out together he always made like he was being followed. I thought he was imagining things." A single tear trickled down her cheek, turning a muddy brown as it picked up her make-up. "Just my luck," she whispered. "Johnny getting himself killed just one day after he'd found the answer."

"He found the diamonds?" Herbert cried.

"No." She shook her head. "Just the answer. We were out together one day and he saw something; something that made everything make sense."

"What was it?" Herbert and I asked more or less together.

"Miss Bacardi?" the waiter interrupted. "There's someone at the door with some flowers for you."

"For me?" She got to her feet, swaying slightly in front of us. "Just give me one minute."

She moved away in the direction of the front entrance, followed by the waiter. I reached for the bottle but Herbert stopped me. "Do you know how much that stuff costs?" he hissed.

"It was free," I told him.

"Well … you're only thirteen. What would Mum say?"

"Mum…" I muttered and for a fraction of a second actually missed her. That was when I knew that I'd had more than enough to drink.

Neither of us said anything for a while, and in that silence I became aware of a little voice whispering in my ear. It was my common sense. It was trying to tell me something that I'd have known at once if I hadn't had so much to drink. Something was wrong. I played back what had just happened and suddenly I knew what it was. The flowers. Why had the waiter made Lauren Bacardi walk all the way to the entrance instead of bringing them to her? And there was something else. Maybe it was just a coincidence. Maybe it didn't mean anything. But now I remembered. The waiter had spoken with a German accent. I was on my feet making for the door before I knew what I was doing. Herbert ran after me, calling my name. But I wasn't going to stop and explain what was going on. I pushed my way through the crowd, ignoring the shouts of protest and the crash of breaking glass. That was one time I was glad I wasn't fully grown. Before anyone could see me to grab hold of me I was gone.

I reached the door and the cold night hit me like an angry woman, slapping my face and tearing at my hair. The first thing I saw was the remains of what had been a bouquet of flowers. But now the cellophane was torn and the flowers were scattered over the steps, the stalks broken. At the same time, I heard someone calling out. It was Lauren Bacardi. I took the steps three at a time and as I reached the street, I just had time to catch sight of her being bundled into the back of a dark blue van. A shadowy figure slammed the door and ran round to the front. The engine was already running. A moment later, so was I.

I ran across to the van, meaning ... I don't know. I guess I thought I'd be able to pull the door open and get Lauren out, but of course it was locked. So instead I jumped on to it, slamming into the metal like a hamburger hitting a griddle and hung on for dear life as the van roared away. I'd managed to get a foothold of sorts on the licence plate and I had one hand on the door handle, one hand curled round the rim at the edge. I was half spread-eagled and travelling at about thirty miles an hour when the van turned a corner. Whoever was driving put their foot down then. Perhaps they'd heard they had an unwelcome passenger. I reckon the van was doing sixty when I was thrown off. It was hard to tell. After all, I was sort of somersaulting through the air and if I'm going to be honest I might as well add my eyes were tightly closed like I was praying – which, in fact, I was.

All I knew was that me and the van had parted company. It roared off to the left, its tyres screaming. I flew off to the right. I should have been killed. I could have been killed. But if you go down that part of London at night, you'll find that the offices put a lot of junk out on the pavements, to be cleared up by the refuse trucks the next day. My fall was broken by a mountain of cardboard boxes and plastic bags. Better still, the bags were full of paper that had been put through the shredder; computer print-outs and that sort of thing. It was like hitting a pile of cushions. I was bruised. But nothing broke.

A minute later Herbert reached me. He must have been convinced that I was finished because when I got to my feet and walked towards him, brushing paper cuttings off my sleeves, he almost fainted with surprise.

"Did you get the van's number?" I asked.

He opened and closed his mouth again without speaking. It was a brilliant impersonation of a goldfish. But I wasn't in the mood to be entertained.

"The licence plate..." I said.

"No."

"Why not?"

"You were standing on it..." He still couldn't believe what he'd just seen.

I looked back down the empty road. Lauren Bacardi had been about to tell us something important and now she was gone. Our only chance of finding the secret of the Maltesers might have gone with her.

"Let's get a taxi home," I said.

"NICE DAY FOR A FUNERAL"

I wasn't feeling too good the next day. I woke up wishing I hadn't, tried to close my eyes and groaned into the pillow. There was something unpleasant in my mouth. I tried to spit it out but I couldn't. It was my tongue. Outside, it was raining. I could hear the water pitter-pattering against the windows and dripping through the leak in the bathroom ceiling. I looked out. It was another grey London day with little yellow spots dancing in the air. I figured a couple of Alka-Seltzer would see to the spots but it looked like we were going to be stuck with the weather.

It took me about twenty minutes to get out of bed. The tumble I had taken the night before must have been harder than I had thought. My right shoulder had gone an interesting shade of black and blue and it hurt when I moved my fingers. Actually it hurt when I moved anything. Somehow I managed to wiggle out of my quilt and, bit by bit, I forced the life back into my battered frame. But it was an hour before I'd made my way downstairs and into the kitchen. It was still raining.

Herbert was sitting there reading a newspaper. When he saw me, he flicked on the kettle and smiled brightly.

"Nice day for a funeral," he said.

"Very funny," I groaned, reaching for the medicine chest.

"I'm being serious." Herbert slid the newspaper in front of me.

I opened the medicine chest – a red plastic box with a white cross on it. It contained two plasters and a tin of cough sweets. Clearly Herbert wasn't expecting an outbreak of bubonic plague. I groaned for a second time and pulled the newspaper before me. With an effort, I managed to get the print to unblur itself.

Herbert was right. There was going to be a funeral later in the day – just a few minutes down the road as luck would have it. Or was it luck? I wasn't thinking straight, that was my trouble. The guy being buried was one Henry von Falkenberg. It appeared that the Falcon had flown home.

There was nothing about the Falcon's three and a half million pounds in the paper. They didn't even mention he'd been a crook. In fact it was just one of those fill-in stories, the sort of thing they print between the crossword and the gardening report when they haven't got enough news. This was a story about a wealthy businessman living in Bolivia who had once lived in England and had decided that he wanted to be buried there. The only trouble was, the week he'd died, there'd been a baggage handler's strike in La Paz and – now that he was dead – "baggage", included him. He'd spent the last four weeks sharing an airport deep-freeze with a load of corned beef from Argentina.

But now the strike was over and von Falkenberg could be buried in his family plot just down the road from our flat. It was too good an opportunity to miss, hungover or not. How many of the names on Snape's blackboard would turn up to pay their last respects to the Falcon?

We had to be there.

Herbert reached for the telephone book. "3521201," he said.

"What's that?" I asked.

"Brompton Cemetery."

I'd written the number down for him and he rang them. He spoke briefly before he put the phone down.

"The funeral's at twelve," he said. "Recommended dress: black tie and wellington boots."

Perhaps you know Brompton Cemetery – a

stretch of ground between Fulham Road and the Brompton Road – a stone's throw away from the football ground. I sometimes walked there on Sundays which isn't as creepy as it sounds. After all, there's not much grass in Fulham and with the sun shining it isn't such a bad place to be. Anyway, the best thing about walking in a cemetery is walking out again. Don't forget, not everyone can.

From the Fulham Road you pass between a pair of tall, black iron gates and follow the path. You don't even know you're in a cemetery until you're a short way up and pass the first graves. It's pretty at first. This is the old part of the cemetery, the romantic bit with the grass waist high and the stones poking out at odd angles like they've grown there too. Then you turn a corner and there's a cluster of buildings curving round an open space like some sort of weird Victorian summer house. Now everything is flat and you can see all the way up to the Brompton Road, a green stretch with the crosses sticking up like the masts of a frozen armada.

We got there at five to twelve, squelching through the rain and the mud, our raincoats pulled up tight around the neck. About a dozen people had braved the weather to make their farewells to the Falcon ... and the Argentinian Corned Beef Company had sent a wreath, which was a nice gesture. The first person we met was a less pleasant surprise: Chief Inspector Snape looking about as cheerful as the cemetery's residents. Boyle was behind him, dressed in a crumpled black suit with a mourning band on his arm.

"Simple and Simple," Snape cried, seeing us. "I was planning to visit you as soon as this little shindig was over."

"Why?" Herbert asked.

"We've been receiving reports of an incident in Charing Cross. I thought you might be able to help us with our enquiries into the disappearance of a certain singer. One Lauren Bacardi. It looks like a kidnap. And guess which kid is our prime suspect?"

"Search me," I said.

"I probably will one of these days," Snape assured me. He smiled at his little joke and I have to admit that jokes don't come much more little than that. "I've got you for murder, for kidnap, for under-age drinking, failing to pay for one bottle of champagne and causing a disturbance," he went on. "I could lock you up right now."

"You're dead," Boyle whispered.

Snape sighed. "Thank you, Boyle."

"Why don't you arrest us?" I asked.

"Because you're more useful to me outside. I mean, you'd be nice and safe in a cosy police cell, wouldn't you?" He gestured at the other mourners now grouping themselves around

96

the grave. "I'm still waiting to see what happens to you. Come on, Boyle!"

Snape and Boyle went over to the grave. We followed them. It turned out that the Falcon was to be buried in the old part of the cemetery where the grass was at its highest, the gravestones half buried themselves. There was a vicar standing in the rain beside what looked like some sort of antique telephone box. It was a stone memorial, about two metres high, mounted by a stone falcon, its beak slightly open, its wings raised. There was a stone tablet set in the memorial below, with a quotation from the Bible cut into it.

THE PATH OF THE JUST IS AS SHINING LIGHT,
THAT SHINETH MORE AND MORE
UNTO THE PERFECT DAY.

Proverbs iv 18

The names of the dead von Falkenbergs were written beneath it: a mother, a father, two grandparents, a cousin ... there were seven of them in all. A rectangular hole had been cut into the earth to make room for an eighth. As we approached, the coffin was being lowered. Henry von Falkenberg had come to join his ancestors.

It was raining harder than ever. The vicar had begun the funeral service, but you could hardly hear him for all the splashing. I took the opportunity to examine the other mourners. It was a pity about the weather. What with the umbrellas, the turned up collars and the hunched shoulders it was impossible to see half of them. If the sun had been shining I'd have got a better look.

But I did recognize Beatrice von Falkenberg. It had to be her – a tall, elegant woman in black mink with a servant holding an umbrella over her from behind. Her eyes and nose were hidden by a widow's veil but I could see a pair of thin lips set in an expression of profound boredom. She was dabbing at her eyes with a tiny white handkerchief but she didn't look too grieved to me. Snape had said that she had been Holland's greatest actress. She wouldn't have won any Oscar for this particular performance.

There was a man standing a short way from her and he caught my attention because he alone carried neither raincoat nor umbrella. He was short and pudgy with silver hair, round glasses in a steel frame and a face like an owl. As the vicar droned on, he shuffled about on his feet, occasionally steadying himself against a gravestone. Like the widow, he didn't look exactly heartbroken. His eyes were fixed on the von Falkenberg memorial but it was easy to see that his mind was miles away.

Who else was there? I recognized a journalist who worked on the local newspaper and who had done a piece on Herbert and me when we'd set up the business. But apart from Snape, Boyle and the widow, the rest of the crowd were strangers to me. The vicar was hurrying through the service now, tripping over the words to get to the end and out of the rain. His surplice was splashed with mud and pages of his Bible were straggling out of the spine. When he scooped holy dirt into the grave, the wind caught it and threw it back in his eyes. He blinked, spat out an amen and ran. Beatrice von Falkenberg turned and went after him. Snape and Boyle hung back. Owl-face jammed his hands into his pockets and sauntered off in the other direction, towards the Brompton Road.

"Very moving. Very touching."

It was a familiar voice and it came from beneath a multicoloured golfing umbrella held by a man who had crept up to stand beside me. I looked round. It was the Fat Man. I should have known that he would be there. "How nice to see you again," he said in a voice that said exactly the opposite.

"Come on," I said to Herbert. I wanted to get back to the flat, out of the rain.

But the Fat Man blocked my way. "Do you like funerals?" he asked. "I'm thinking of arranging one. Yours."

"I'm too young to die," I said. "What brings you here, Fat Man?"

"Von Falkenberg and I were old friends ... very dear friends," he explained. "There was something about him that I very much admired... "

"Yeah – his money," I said. "Well, we still haven't found your key. Perhaps you ought to ask Gott or Himmell."

He obviously knew the names. His eyes narrowed and his mouth twitched as if he had just swallowed one of his poisoned corn pellets.

"We are looking for it, Mr Fat Man," Herbert said.

"And we'll let you know as soon as we've found it."

"I gave you two days." The Fat Man plucked the carnation out of his button-hole and threw it into the grave. "You've run out of time." Then he turned his back on us and walked away.

I'd had enough. Coming to the funeral had been a mistake – a dead end in every sense of the word. We hadn't picked up anything apart, perhaps, from double pneumonia. And if it had been a chance to meet a few old friends, they were all old friends I'd have preferred to avoid. Herbert sneezed. "I need a shot of Scotch," he said for the benefit of the undertaker or anyone else who might be listening. I knew that once we got back to the flat, he'd actually fix himself with a shot of cod-liver oil.

But I was wrong there. Things didn't turn out quite the way I expected.

We made a couple of stops on the way back. Herbert had cashed the cheque and we had enough money to lash out on a packet of Alka Seltzer and another box of Maltesers.

"What do you want them for?" Herbert asked.

"I've got a headache," I said.

"No ... the Maltesers."

So I explained. Whoever had snatched Lauren Bacardi might know by now that Johnny Naples had spent the last month of his life traipsing around London with a box of Maltesers. And they might come looking for them. The dwarf's box was still safely hidden underneath the floor. I'd bought the second box as a sort of insurance. I'd leave it somewhere nice and easy to find, just in case anyone else broke in.

We got back to the flat and let ourselves in, dripping on the doormat. Maybe I noticed that the street door was unlocked when it wasn't supposed to be. Maybe I didn't. I don't remember. What with the rain, I was just glad to be in. We went upstairs. Herbert sneezed again. The office door was open and this time I did notice.

"Herbert," I said.

We went into the office. Herbert's eyes must have gone straight to the desk because he went and picked something up. "What's this doing here?" I heard him say.

But I didn't look at him. My eyes were on the corpse stretched out beside the window. It took me a minute before I remembered where I'd seen him before, but I should have known from the moment I saw the chauffeur's uniform. It was Lawrence, the Fat Man's driver. He was still wearing his one-way glasses, but one of the lenses had become a spider's web of cracks, shattered by the bullet that had gone one-way through it.

"Nick..." Herbert whimpered in a voice of pure jelly.

I looked up. And I saw it all.

"What's this doing here?" Herbert had asked. I replayed the words in my head. "This" was a gun. It had been lying on the carpet beside the desk. Now he was holding it. At that moment, the door opened. Snape and Boyle had followed us in. And there was me kneeling beside another dead man. There was Herbert, again, holding the gun that had just killed him. And there were the two policemen looking at us in open-mouthed astonishment.

"You're..." Snape began.

"No..." Herbert moaned.

"I don't believe it," I said.

CROCODILE TEARS

Herbert and I spent the night back at the Ladbroke Grove police station. I'd never slept behind bars before – not that I got a lot of sleep that night either. There was a double bunk in our cell and I took the top level, with Herbert underneath. He'd caught a nasty cold in the cemetery and every time I was about to drift away he'd let loose with a deafening sneeze and I'd be awake again. The bunk wasn't too comfortable either: just a narrow board with an inch-thick mattress, a sheet and two blankets you could have struck a match on. I dropped off around midnight. Then I climbed back on and tried to get some sleep.

"Nick..." It could have been any time when Herbert's disembodied voice floated up out of the darkness.

"Yes?" I said.

"Are you awake?"

"No. I'm sleeptalking."

"Nick, I've been thinking." Herbert paused, sneezed, continued. "Maybe I'm not cut out to be a private detective after all."

"Whatever makes you think that, Herbert?" I asked.

"Well ... I'm wanted for two murders, kidnap and disturbing the peace. The Fat Man wants to kill me. My flat has been torn apart. And I haven't actually been able to detect anything."

"You may have a point," I agreed.

He sighed. "In the morning I'll tell Snape everything. He can have the Maltesers. I wish I'd given them to him in the first place."

That woke me up like a bucket of iced water. Three and a half million pounds in diamonds and he wanted to give them away! I leant over the side of the bunk. It was so dark that I couldn't see a thing but I hoped that I was addressing Herbert's ear rather than his feet. "Herbert," I said. "If you whisper one word about those Maltesers, I will personally kill you."

"But Nick..."

"No, Herbert. Those Maltesers are the only hope you've got."

"But ... uh ... uh..." He sneezed again. "But I might get sent to prison!" he protested.

"Don't worry," I said. "I'll visit you every Friday."

They woke us up at seven in the morning. We were allowed to wash and then a guard brought us each a mug of tea. I asked for a bacon sandwich but all I got was a nasty look. Then it was back into the interrogation room – for Herbert but not for me. Snape stopped me at the door. Boyle was with him, growling softly. That was one guy I wanted to steer clear of. I wouldn't even have trusted Boyle to take my fingerprints. Not if I wanted to keep my fingers.

"You can go, laddy," Snape said. "It's only big brother we want."

"How long are you going to keep him for?" I asked. "It's only five days to Christmas."

"So?"

"He hasn't had time to buy my present yet."

Snape was unimpressed. "We'll keep him as long as it takes," he said. "I'll tell a social worker to visit you – to make sure you're all right."

"I'll visit him!" Boyle grunted.

"No you won't, Boyle!" Snape hissed.

I jerked a thumb at the police assistant. "He needs a social worker more than me," I said.

Boyle lumbered a few steps towards me but then Snape grabbed hold of him. For a minute it was as if I wasn't there.

"You're being ridiculous, Boyle." Snape muttered. "I've told you about those violent videos…"

"I just want to..." Boyle began.

"No! No! No! How many times do I have to tell you. This isn't the right sort of image for a modern metropolitan police force."

"It used to be," Boyle growled.

"In Transylvania," Snape replied. He turned back to me. "Go on, son. Out of here." he said. I glanced at Herbert who sneezed miserably. The door slammed. And suddenly I was alone.

I didn't do much that morning. There wasn't much I could do. As I sat in Herbert's office with my feet up on his desk I tried to work out who might have pulled the plug on the Fat Man's chauffeur and why. By mid-morning I had it more or less figured. It went like this: The Fat Man has given us two days to come up with the goods and we've run out of time so he decides to have a rummage round our flat for himself. He sees us arriving at the Falcon's funeral and that gives him the chance he wants. While he holds us up in the cemetery – there was no other reason for the little chat we had – his faithful chauffeur and house-breaker, Lawrence, is turning the place over. At least, that's what he thinks.

But whoever kidnapped Lauren Bacardi (and my money's still on Gott and Himmell) has been asking her questions. She tells them about the box of Maltesers. So they nip back to pick them up and that's when they find

Lawrence. Maybe there's a fight. Maybe they just didn't like him. Either way, they shoot him just before Herbert and I get back from the funeral. They make a hasty exit through the bathroom window and over the roof. We get left with the body.

Simple as that.

I opened the drawer of Herbert's desk. The box of Maltesers was still there – the fake box that I'd bought myself. The real box was still under the floorboard, covered in dust. I was just about to pull it out and have another look at it when the telephone rang.

"Hello?" It was a woman's voice. Soft, hesitant, perhaps foreign. I figured she must have a wrong number. I didn't know any soft, hesitant, perhaps foreign women. But then she asked, "Tim Diamond?"

"He's not here," I told her. "I'm his partner."

"His partner?"

"Yeah – but right now I'm working solo. How can I help you?"

There was a pause at the other end of the line. Then the lady made up her mind. "Can you come out ... to Hampstead? I need to see you."

"Who is this?"

"Beatrice von Falkenberg."

That made me think. So the black widow had finally come crawling out of the woodwork – or to be more accurate, the telephone exchange. What did she want me for? "Suppose I'm busy..." I said.

"I'll make it worth your while."

"You'll pay for the tube fare?"

"Take a taxi."

I agreed so she gave me an address on the West Heath Road and told me to be there by twelve. I wondered if this was another decoy – if the moment I was gone somebody else would be elbowing their way into the flat. But so long as the fake Maltesers were in the desk, I reckoned I was covered. I changed my shirt and ran a comb through my hair. When I left, I was still a wreck, but at least I was a slightly tidier wreck. Once the widow discovered I was only thirteen-years-old, I didn't think she'd really care how I dressed.

I'd charge her for a taxi but I took the tube to Hampstead and then walked. Hampstead, in case you don't know it, is in the north of London in the green belt. For "green", read "money". You don't have to be rich to live in Hampstead. You have to be loaded. It seemed to me that every other car I passed was a Rolls Royce and even the dustbins had burglar alarms. I got directions from a traffic warden and walked round the back of the village. A quarter of an hour later I arrived at the Falcon's lair.

It was a huge place, standing on a hill overlooking the Heath. Whoever said crime doesn't pay should have dropped by for an eyeful. It was the sort of house I'd have dreamed about – only I'd have had to take a mortgage out just to pay for the dream. Ten bedrooms? Eleven? It could have slept fifteen or more under those gabled roofs and with the price of property in that part of town I reckoned forty winks would probably cost you ten quid a wink. And that was just the top floor. Through the windows on the ground floor I could glimpse a kitchen as big as a dining-room and a dining-room as big as a swimming-pool. There was a swimming-pool too, running along four windows to the right of the front door. Mind you, the way things were around here, that could have just been the bath.

I reached out and pressed the front door bell. It went *bing-bong*, which was a bit of an anti-climax. After all that had gone before, I'd been expecting a massed choir. The door opened and there was another anti-climax. Beatrice von Falkenberg opened it herself. So what had happened to the butler? She looked at me with disinterest and mild distaste. I could see we were going to get along fine.

"Yes?" she asked.

"I'm Nick," I said. "Nick Diamond. You asked me to come here."

"Did I?" She shrugged. "I was expecting

someone older."

"Well... I can come back in twenty years, if you like."

"No, no ... come in."

I followed her in, suddenly feeling like a scruffy kid in bob-a-job week. She was young for a widow; maybe about forty with black hair clinging to her head like a bathing cap. Her skin was pale, her lips a kiss of dark red. She was wearing some sort of houserobe with a slit all the way up to her waist and she moved like she had never left the stage – not walking but flowing. Everything about her spelt class. The slim, crystal champagne glass in one hand. Even the tin plate with the lumps of raw meat in the other.

"I was about to feed my pet," she explained.

"Dog?" I asked.

She glanced at the plate. "No. I think it's beef."

We'd gone into the room with the swimming-pool. It had been designed so that you could sit around it in bamboo chairs sipping cocktails from the bar at the far end, watching the guests swim. Only there were no bamboo chairs, the bar was empty and I was the only guest. I looked around and suddenly realized that although I was in a millionaire's house, the millions had long gone. There was no furniture. Faded patches on the walls showed where the pictures had once been. The curtain-rails had lost their curtains. Even the potted plants were dead. The house was a shell. All it contained was a widow in a house-robe with a glass of champagne and a tin of raw meat.

"Fido!" she called out. "Come on, darling!"

Something splashed in the water. I swallowed. Apart from the widow in the house-robe with the champagne and the tin of raw meat it seemed that the house also contained an alligator. The last time I saw an alligator it was hanging on some rich woman's arm with lipsticks and purses inside. But this one was no handbag. It was very alive, waddling out of the pool, its ugly black eyes fixed on the plate of meat.

"Don't worry," the widow said. "He's very fond of strangers."

"Yeah – cooked or raw?" I asked.

She smiled and tossed Fido a piece of meat. Its great jaws snapped shut and it made a horrid gulping sound as its throat bulged, sucking the meat down. She held up a second piece. "I want the Maltesers," she said.

"Maltesers?"

She threw the piece of meat but this time she made sure that it fell short so the creature had to stalk forward to get it. It stalked forward towards me. "They belonged to my husband," she went on. "The dwarf stole them, I want them back."

111

I pointed at the alligator. It was getting too close for comfort. As far as I was concerned, a hundred miles would have been too close for comfort. "Do you have a licence for that thing?" I asked.

"I don't know," she said. "It was a present from my late husband."

"Have you ever thought about pussy cats?"

"Fido ate the pussy cats."

I thought of turning and running but I couldn't be sure I'd make it to the door. The alligator had short, wrinkled legs but at the moment I can't say mine felt much better. It was only a metre or so away. Its black eyes were fixed on me, almost daring me to make a move. The whole thing was crazy. I'd never been threatened with an alligator before.

"I don't have the Maltesers," I said. "Tim has them."

"And where is he?"

"In prison ... Ladbroke Grove police station."

She paused for a long minute and looked at me with cold eyes. The eyes burrowed into me, trying to work out if I was telling the truth. In the end they must have believed me because she laughed and threw the rest of the meat into the swimming-pool. The alligator corkscrewed round and dived after it.

"I like you," she said. "You're not afraid." She walked over to me and put an arm round my shoulders. She hadn't managed to frighten me so now she was trying to charm me. She wouldn't manage that either. Given a choice, I'd have preferred to go out with the alligator.

"When Henry von Falkenberg died," she said, "all his money went with him. This house isn't mine, Nick. I've had to sell the contents just to pay the rent. Even Fido is going to the zoo. It breaks my heart but I can't afford to keep him. And now I don't have a friend in the world." There were tears in her eyes. Crocodile tears, I thought. Or alligator. "There is only one hope for me, Nicholas. The Maltesers. Henry wanted me to have them. They belong to me."

"What's so special about them?" I asked.

"To you – nothing," she replied. "But to me... They're worth five hundred pounds if you'll get them back for me. That's how much I'll pay you."

"I thought you had no money."

"I'll find it. Maybe Fido will end up as suit-cases after all."

She walked me back to the door and opened it.

"Talk to Herbert," she said. "When the police release him, bring the Maltesers here. I will have the money, I swear it. And to you they are useless. You must see that."

"What about my taxi fare home?" I asked.

"When you come with the Maltesers..." She

113

shut the door.

"See you later, alligator," I muttered.

So that was Beatrice von Falkenberg! A strange, lonely woman, sharing her memories with a strange, lonely pet. I walked back down the road towards Hampstead and as I went I turned over two questions in my mind. If the Falcon had been so secretive, how come she had found out about the Maltesers? It seemed unlikely that he had told her. So who had?

The second thing was even stranger. She had telephoned me and asked to speak to Tim Diamond. I hadn't said anything on the subject of my brother. So how had she known that his real name was Herbert?

KILLER IN THE RAIN

I didn't go back to the flat that afternoon. It wouldn't have been the same without Herbert. Quieter, tidier, less dangerous and generally nicer ... but not the same. Also I was worried about him. I wouldn't want to spend half an hour with Snape and Boyle, let alone a whole day. Boyle could have killed him by now. On the other hand, if he told them about the Maltesers, I'd kill him myself. Either way he was in big trouble and the sooner I found out just what was going on, the better it would be for him.

Things might have been different if Lauren Bacardi had been able to tell me where the dwarf had been when he worked out what the Maltesers meant. If I could see what he had seen, maybe I'd be able to work it out too. But I had a nasty feeling that the only way I'd be able to talk to Lauren again would be with a

Ouija board. The people who had snatched her were playing for keeps. By now she probably had more lead in her than a church roof.

That just left the dwarf. Johnny Naples might be pushing up the daisies himself, but if I could pick up his trail I might still learn something. His book matches had led me to Lauren Bacardi. I wondered what else I might find in his room. So that afternoon I took the tube to Notting Hill and walked back down the Portobello Road to the Hotel Splendide.

I passed Hammett's newsagent on the way. The old guy who owned it was standing in the window and he saw me pass. I'm only guessing now but I reckon he must have picked up the telephone and called the hotel a moment later. And at the hotel, Jack Splendide must have made a phone call of his own. Like I say, I'm only guessing. But it took me ten minutes to walk from the newsagent to the hotel and that was just about all the time they needed to arrange my death.

The hotel was just like I remembered it, leaning carelessly against the flyover. The plain-clothes policeman and the dog had gone, of course, but the dustbins were still there, spitting their leftovers into the gutter. It was after three and already it was getting dark, the sun sliding behind the horizon like a drunk behind a bar. An old man carrying two plastic bags full of junk stumbled past, on his way from one nowhere to another. A cold wind scattered the litter across the street. Depressing? Well, it was five days to Christmas and I was pretty depressed myself.

I went into the hotel. Jack Splendide was sitting behind the counter where I'd found him on my first visit. He was reading a dirty paperback. It was so dirty, you couldn't read half the words. It looked like somebody had spilt their breakfast all over it. He was still sucking a cigar – probably the same cigar, and he hadn't changed his shirt either. The last time he'd changed that shirt I probably hadn't been born.

"Hello," I said.

"Yeah?" He really knew how to make a guy feel welcome.

"I want a room."

"How long for?"

"One hour."

He frowned. "We only rent by the night. Fifteen pounds. Sixteen pounds with a bed."

I'd managed to grab all Herbert's cash before we parted company and now I counted out the money on to the counter. Splendide took it, then stood up, reaching for the key.

"I want Room 39," I said.

"Suppose it's taken?"

I gestured at the hooks. "The key's there," I said. "Anyway – who needs it? The room doesn't have a lock."

"This is a class hotel, kid." He was offended. The cigar waggled between his teeth like a finger ticking me off. "You don't like it, you can book in someplace else."

I didn't like it. But I had to go through with it. "Just give me the key," I said.

He argued a bit more after that. I thought he was holding out for more money, but of course he was keeping me waiting on purpose. That was what he had been told to do. In the end he let me have the key – like he'd been intending to all the time. I should have been smart enough to see right through his little act, but it had been a long day and I was tired and ... OK, maybe I wasn't as smart as I thought.

Anyway, he gave me the key and I climbed up the stairs to the fifth floor, then along the corridor to Room 39. It was only when I'd opened the door and gone in that I began to think that maybe this wasn't such a good idea after all. It was unlikely that the room had been cleaned since the dwarf's death – it was unlikely that the rooms at the Hotel Splendide were ever cleaned – but the police would have been through it with a fine-tooth comb. But now that I was here, it wouldn't hurt to have a look. And I had paid.

I began with the drawers. There was a big, asthmatic chest of them. They groaned when I pulled them open and the brass rings rattled. But apart from a bent safety-pin, a mothball and a moth it had killed, they were empty. Next I tried the table. That should have had two more drawers but somebody had stolen them. That just left the bed. I went and sat on it, remembering how Johnny Naples had lain there with that red carnation blossoming in the button-hole of his shirt. He had sat in this room. He had lived in it. He had worked out the location of a three and a half million pound fortune in it. And he had died in it.

The traffic thundered past about two metres away from the window. It was still a mystery how he had ever managed to sleep in it.

My eye was drawn to a dustbin in one corner. It was a green plastic thing, so broken and battered that it should have been in a dustbin itself. I leant across and flicked a hand through the rubbish that lay in the bottom. There wasn't much: two crisp packets, the wrapper from a bar of chocolate, a couple of dud batteries and an empty packet of cigarettes. I was about to leave it when I remembered. It wouldn't have meant anything to the police – that was why they'd overlooked it – but it meant something to me. Back in the office, the day it had all started, the dwarf had smoked Turkish cigarettes. And this was a Turkish cigarette packet. It had belonged to Naples.

I plucked it out of the dustbin and opened it, hoping ... I don't know ... for a telephone number scrawled on the inside or something like that. What I got was even better. It was a shower of paper: little white squares that had been neatly torn up. I knelt down and examined the scraps. Some of them had writing on them, parts of words written in blue ink. I slid them across the carpet with a pointed finger, putting the jigsaw back together again. It didn't take me long before I had it: five words in English with what I guessed were the Spanish translations written beside them.

DIGITAL
PHOTODETECTOR
LIGHT EMITTING DIODE

Frankly, they were a disappointment. Why had Johnny Naples written them down? I was certain they had to be connected with the Maltesers. That would explain why, after he'd torn the paper up, he'd taken the extra precaution of hiding them in the cigarette packet. He'd have flushed them down the toilet if the hotel had toilets. It was the Spanish translations that helped me figure it out. Suppose Johnny Naples had come across the five words in his search for the diamonds. His English was good, but it wasn't that good. He might not have understood them. So he'd have written them down to look up later.

The only snag was, I didn't understand them

either. Obviously, they were something to do with science, but science had never been my strong point. If you met my science teacher, I think you'd know why. I don't think science was his strong point either.

I scooped the pieces up and put them in my pocket. I'd searched the drawers, the table and the bin. That just left the bed. I tried to look underneath it but a wooden rim running down to the carpet made that impossible. It was one of the oldest beds I had ever seen, a monster of thick wood and rusty springs with a mattress half a metre thick and about as comfortable as a damp sponge cake. It took all my strength to heave the thing up on its side but I was determined to look underneath. Not that there was much to discover: a yellowed copy of the *Daily Mirror*, one slipper and about ten years' worth of accumulated dust.

But it was the bed that saved my life.

I was just about to pull it down when I heard the window shatter and at the same time a car roared away.

Something dark green and about the size of a cricket ball flew into the room. It took me about one second to work out that it wasn't a dark green cricket ball and another second to throw myself to the ground. The grenade hit the bed and bounced back towards the window. Then it exploded.

I should have been killed but I was already

hugging the floor and there was this great wall of springs and mattress between me and it. Even so it was like being inside a Rainbow Screecher on Guy Fawkes' Night. Suddenly it seemed that the whole room was on fire – not just the room, the very air in the room. The floor buckled upwards like a huge fist, pounding me in the stomach. The explosion was so loud I thought it would crack open my skull. All this happened at once and at the same time I was seized by the shock wave and hurled back, twisting in the air, and finally thrown out of the room, my shoulders slamming into the door and carrying it with me. I was unconscious by the time I hit the floor. I don't know how long I stayed like that. Maybe ten minutes. It could have been ten days.

I woke up with a mouth full of splinters and two hysterical opera singers screaming in my ears. Actually, there weren't any opera singers, but that's what it sounded like. My clothes were torn to ribbons and I could feel the blood running from a cut above one eye. Other than that, I seemed to be in remarkably good health for someone who had just been blown up. There would be plenty of bruises, but there were no broken bones. I stood up – one bone at a time – and leant against a wall for support. The wall slid away. There was too much dust and smoke in the air to see. I stood where I was, waiting for things to settle down a bit before I made any sudden move.

Which was just as well. The Hotel Splendide had been waiting for an excuse to fall down for twenty years or more. The grenade had been all it needed. The whole of the back wall, the one that faced the flyover, had simply collapsed and I was now standing on a piece of floor that stretched into thin air. I shivered as the breeze whipped the smoke up around me. The traffic roared past, a blur of brightly-coloured metal whirling endlessly into the night. I was surprised that nobody had stopped ... but how could they? It was a flyover. Doubtless the police would shut it down soon enough but anyone stopping right now would only add a multiple pile-up to the evening's entertainment.

I stepped back, looking for the staircase or whatever might be left of it. This looked like being the hotel's last night. It was on fire, the flames spreading rapidly, the wood snapping, water hissing out of broken pipes. My hearing still wasn't back to normal but I could just about make out the sound of people shouting. In the distance, police cars or fire engines or something with sirens were drawing nearer. A naked man ran past, his face half-covered in shaving foam. I followed him. We'd both had a close shave that day.

My guardian angel must have been working overtime just then. Lucky it didn't belong to a trade union. The iron bar narrowly missed my head and I didn't even notice it until it smashed into the wall, spraying me with plaster. I wheeled round and there was Jack Splendide, lifting the bar to try his luck again. His shirt was in shreds and his stomach wasn't a whole lot better. Both his trouser legs had been blown off at the knee. I realized he must have been close to the dwarf's room when the explosion happened – perhaps in the room next door. And he didn't seem too happy that I'd survived.

He swung the bar again and this time I dodged. He was about twenty kilograms overweight and that made him slow. On the other hand, he didn't need to be too fast. He was between me and the staircase. I had the flames on one side of me and a five-storey fall right behind me. I wondered if I could jump across on to the flyover. It was only about two metres, but the way I was feeling right now it was about a metre too far. I leapt back, avoiding a fourth blow. Now I was in the ruins of what had been Room 39. The flames were getting nearer. So was Jack Splendide.

He was shouting at me. What with all the din and the screaming in my ears, it was difficult to make out what he was saying but I gathered that he blamed me for the destruction of his hotel. He must have really liked that place. There were tears running down his cheeks and he was holding that iron bar (part of a towel-rail) with genuine affection. I wanted to explain that it wasn't my fault that a passing motorist had decided to hurl a bomb at me, but he wouldn't listen to reason. Jack Splendide had flipped. And he wanted me dead.

The iron bar came curving up over his shoulder as he swung it with both hands, but then the top got snarled up in a loop of wire. As it came down, it tore the wire out of the wall and for a few seconds electric sparks danced in the air. That distracted him just long enough for me to grab hold of a piece of table and bring it crashing into his stomach. He howled and dropped the bar. I hit him again, this time propelling him forward right to the edge of the floor.

He flailed at the air with his hands. There was a fall of at least fifteen metres to the cold, hard concrete below and I thought that was just where he was heading. Unable to regain his balance, he yelled and plunged forward, his body lunging out into the night. But at the last moment he managed to grab hold of the very edge of the fly-over. And that was how he finished up: a human bridge. His feet were on the floor in what was left of Room 39. His hands were desperately clutching a piece of metal jutting out of the side of the flyover. His body sagged between the two.

I looked behind me. The flames were closing in. I wouldn't even make it through the shattered doorway now. But I didn't fancy jumping across to the flyover. Jack Splendide was the only answer. A human bridge. I took two big steps. One foot in the small of his back and I was across – safely standing on the edge of the road.

"Kid ... hey kid!" I heard him and walked back over to him. He was a big, strong man but he couldn't stay like that much longer. "Help me!" he hissed, the sweat dripping off his forehead. The wind jerked at my shirt. The cars roared by, only inches away now. Some of the drivers hooted at me but they couldn't see Jack Splendide. I crouched down close to him. By now I'd been able to put a few things together.

"Who was it, Splendide?" I asked. "Who threw the grenade?"

"Please!" His hands tightened their hold as his body swayed.

"You must have told them I was here. Who was it?"

There was no way he could stall me. He was getting weaker by the minute and across the gap the flames were creeping up on him. He could probably feel them with the soles of his feet. "It was the Fat Man," he gasped. "He guessed you might go back to the hotel. He paid me ... to call if you did."

"Why?"

"You insulted him, kid. Nobody insults the Fat Man. But I didn't know he was going to try and kill you. I mean ... the grenade. Honest, kid. I thought he was just going to take a shot at you – to scare you."

Yeah, I thought. And you came up to the fifth floor to watch.

"Help me!" he whimpered. "Give me a hand up, kid. I can't hold on much longer."

"That's true," I said, straightening up.

"You can't leave me here, kid. You can't!"

"Wanna bet?"

I walked away, leaving him stretched out between the flames and the flyover with a long, long way to fall if he let go. Maybe the police or firemen reached him in the end. To be honest, I don't really care. Jack Splendide had set me up to be killed. He might not have been expecting a grenade, but he'd known the Fat Man didn't play games.

It had begun to rain. Pulling the remains of my shirt closer to my shivering skin, I walked down the flyover and forgot about him.

THE PROFESSOR

I was woken by the smell of lavender. Lavender? Yes – perfume. You've smelt it before, Nick. Where? I can't remember but maybe it was mixed with the raw meat and ... I swallowed, stretched, opened my eyes.

"Blimey, you're a sight!" Betty Charlady exclaimed.

I was half stretched out on Herbert's desk in his office. I'd had to walk home the night before and by the time I'd got in I'd been too tired to go upstairs. I'd looked at the second flight of steps. They led to a bed with a crumpled sheet and a screwed up quilt. I'll never make it, I'd thought and so I'd gone into the office and collapsed there. And now Betty Charlady was standing in front of me, looking at me like I'd dropped in from another planet.

"What happened to you?" she demanded, shaking her head and sending the artificial daisies on her hat into convulsions.

"I had a bad night," I said. "How did you get in?"

"Through the door."

"It was open?"

She nodded. "You ought to lock it at night, Master Nicholas. You never know who might visit…"

I needed a hot bath, a hot meal, two Disprin and a warm bed – not necessarily in that order. Instead I went up and washed my face in the sink while Betty made breakfast: boiled eggs, toast and coffee. I looked at myself in the mirror. Somebody else looked back. His hair was a mess, there were bags under his eyes and he had a nasty cut on his forehead. I felt sorry for the guy. If he felt as bad as he looked he must be in pretty rotten shape. I wondered if he felt as rotten as me.

Ten minutes later, I was sitting down in the kitchen, eating. Betty had insisted on cutting my toast into soldiers which was pretty embarrassing. I'd been threatened, blown up, attacked – and here I was being treated like a kid again. But I suppose she meant well.

"Where's Mr Timothy?" she asked.

"Herbert?" I said. "He's in jail. Accused of murder."

"Murder!" she shrieked. "That's a crime!"

"Well … yes."

"No. I mean accusing Mr Herbert of doing

anything like that." She sniffed. "Anybody could see he wouldn't hurt a fly."

She was right there. Herbert ran away from them. He was probably the only private detective in the country who was even scared of goldfish.

"So you're doing all the detective work for him," she said. I nodded. "Have you found out anything yet?"

Had I found anything out? Well, I'd found out that Beatrice von Falkenberg had a strange taste in pets. I'd found out that if you stood too close to an exploding grenade it made your ears hurt. I'd found out that the Fat Man still wanted to lose weight and that I was the weight he wanted to lose. But when you added up everything I'd found out, it would just about fit on the back of a postage stamp and you wouldn't even need to write in small letters.

"No, Betty," I said. "I haven't found out anything. Not unless you know what a digital detector or a photo lighter is."

"A wot?" she asked.

The scraps of paper that I had found in the dwarf's room were still safely in my shirt pocket. The trouble was, my shirt pocket was still in the hotel. It had been blown off the shirt by the blast and for the life of me I couldn't remember exactly what the words had been.

"I'm going to have a bath," I said.

"I'll run it for you," Betty volunteered.

I shook my head. Any more encouragement and she'd be offering to scrub my back. "No, thanks ... you go home. I can manage."

"But what about the cleaning?"

I reached into my pocket and pulled out one of Herbert's ten-pound notes. It hurt me to see it go, but there was no denying that Betty had done a good job. When she'd come, the flat had looked like a junk-yard. Now it was more like an industrial slum. "Here you are," I said. "Come back next week, after Christmas."

"Ooh! Ta!" She took it. "Happy Christmas, Master Nicholas," she burbled.

"Happy Christmas, Betty," I said.

Some time later, the doorbell dragged me out of a beautiful sleep. I looked at my watch. It said five to ten. It had said five to ten when I'd gone to bed. Either it had been a short sleep or I needed a new watch. I held it up to my ear and shook it. There was a dull *ping* and the second hand fell off. Well, that's what comes of buying a second hand watch.

I pulled on a pair of jeans and a sweater and made my way downstairs. The bell was still ringing. Whoever was down there was leaning on the button. I pressed the intercom to let him in, hoping he wouldn't do the same to me. I don't like being leaned on and in the last few days I'd had more than enough of it. I went into the office and had just sat down when my client walked in.

Correction – he didn't walk, he staggered. And I smelt him before I saw him. It must have been around lunchtime but he'd been drinking since breakfast and he'd brought the stale reek of whisky as his visiting-card.

I recognized him from somewhere. He was around sixty, small, fat, unshaven, owlish, with round glasses, dressed in a crumpled grey raincoat with bottle-sized pockets.

He fumbled his way towards one of the chairs that Betty Charlady had repaired for us and sat down heavily, stretching out his legs. He was wearing green socks. I could see them through the holes in the soles of his shoes. I waited for him to say something but he wasn't in a hurry. He pulled a single cigarette out of his pocket, straightened it between his thumb and forefinger and twisted it into his mouth. He lit it with a trembling hand. The match had almost burned itself out before he found the end of the cigarette. He wasn't just a drunk. He was a short-sighted drunk. Suddenly I remembered where I'd seen him. He'd been at the Falcon's funeral, standing – swaying – next to Beatrice von Falkenberg.

"It's good to sit down," he said.

"You tired?" I asked.

"No. It's just that I keep falling over when I stand up. Or bumping into things." He sucked in smoke. "You see, sir, I got this problem… "

"Drink?" I muttered sympathetically.

"Thanks. I'll have a large Scotch."

I shook my head and slid an ash-tray towards him. He flicked the cigarette and scattered ash across the top of the desk. "Who are you?" I asked.

"The name's Quisling," he said. "Quentin Quisling."

"Your parents liked q's," I said.

"Yeah – bus queues, shopping queues … but that's not why I'm here. You may have heard of me, sir. I used to be called the Professor."

Sure I'd heard of the Professor. That had been another of the names on Snape's blackboard. What had Snape told me? The Professor had been the Falcon's tame scientist, something of a whizz-kid. But a year ago he'd gone missing. Looking at him now, I could see where he'd been. On the skids. Professor Quisling might have been smart once but now he looked like Billy Bunter grown old and sick. He had the skin of a five-year-old cheese and he spoke with a wheezy, grating voice. He puffed smoke into the air and coughed. Cigarettes were killing him while booze was arranging the funeral.

"I wanted to see your brother," he said.

"He's not here."

"I can see that, sir. I don't see much. But I can see that." He pulled a half-bottle of whisky out of his pocket, unscrewed it, squinted and tilted it towards his throat. The liquid ran down the side of his neck. He groped for the cigarette and found it. "All right," he said. "I'll split it with you. Fifty-fifty."

"The cigarette?" I asked.

"That's very funny, sir. I can see you have a sense of humour." He screwed the cigarette between his lips and coughed. It was a horrible cough. I could hear the marbles rattling in his lungs. "You know who I am?" he asked.

"You just told me."

"I used to be the Falcon's brains." He stabbed at his chest with a bent thumb. "He wanted something fixed, I fixed it."

"Light bulbs?" I asked.

"Oh no, sir. I invented things for him. Things you wouldn't understand."

"So what happened to you?" I asked.

"This happened to me." He waved the bottle. "But I know what you've got, sir. Indeed I do. I saw you at the funeral and I figured it out. A packet of Maltesers, would it be? Well … I know what to do with them. Together we could make money."

"What are you suggesting, Professor?" I said.

"You give them to me and you wait here." He smiled at me with crooked, sly eyes. "I'll come back tomorrow with half the money."

I nodded, pretending to consider the offer. In fact I was amazed. Here was a guy who was killing himself as sure as if he had a noose around his neck. He couldn't afford a decent pair of shoes and he was dressed like a dummy in an Oxfam shop. But he thought he could pull a fast one on me just because I was a kid and he was a so-called adult. For a moment he reminded me of my maths teacher. You know the sort. Just because they can work out the angles in an isosceles triangle, they think they rule the world. I decided to play him along.

"I give you the Maltesers," I said. "And you come back with half the loot?"

"That's right, sir," Quisling said. He finished the half-bottle and lobbed it towards the dustbin. It missed and smashed against the wall. He didn't seem to notice.

"But what do the Maltesers do?" I asked.

"They open the…" He stopped himself just in time. "I'll tell you when I bring the money," he said.

I knew that once I'd given him the Maltesers I'd never see him again. But I'd had an idea. I pulled open the drawer of the desk and took out the box that I'd hidden there a few days before. "This is what you want," I said. He reached forward hungrily but I didn't let go. "You will come back?" I queried.

"Sure, sir. I'll come back. On my mother's grave."

135

The old girl probably wasn't even dead. "When?" I asked.

"Tomorrow morning," he said.

I lifted my hand and he snatched the box away.

"In the morning," he repeated.

The door slammed shut behind him.

I waited thirty seconds before I followed him. He wouldn't see me behind him. With his eyesight he wouldn't see me if I stood next to him. And if Quentin Quisling really did know where the Falcon's diamonds were hidden, he would lead me to them. The box of Maltesers I'd given him would, of course, be useless. But perhaps I'd let him keep them – after he'd led me to the end of the rainbow. That was the way I'd planned it but of course that was far too easy, and when nothing can go wrong that's when everything always does. I'd reached the front door. I'd turned round to lock it behind me. I could hear an engine turning – a van parked close by. There was a movement in the street. I glanced up just in time to see something short and unpleasant come thudding down. It hit me behind the ear. I was out like a light.

FAIRY CAKES

I wish somebody had told me it was Knock Out Nick Diamond Week in London. It had happened to me twice in two days and I was getting a bit tired of it. Being knocked out isn't so bad. It's waking up that's the real problem. Your head hurts, your mouth is dry and you feel sick. And if it's pitch dark and you're locked up in the back of a van that could be going anywhere, it's pretty scary too.

I was still in London. I could tell from the sound of the traffic and from the number of times we stopped. Once – when we were at a traffic light or something – I heard vague voices outside and thought of hammering on the side of the van. But it probably wouldn't have done any good and anyway, by the time I'd made up my mind, the van had moved off. A few minutes later, we stopped. The door was pulled open. There wasn't a lot of light left in the day but what there was of it streamed in and punched me in the eyes.

"Get out," a voice said. It was a soft voice, the sort of voice you'd expect to float on the scent of violets. It had a slight German twang. I'd heard that voice once before.

I got out.

The first thing I saw was a road sign. It read: Bayly Street SE1 which put me somewhere on the south bank of the river, opposite the City. I looked around me. This was warehouse territory. The old brick buildings rose up five storeys high on both sides of the road, the narrow gap of sky in between criss-crossed by corrugated iron walkways, hooks and chains, pipes and loading platforms. A hundred years ago, Bayly Street would have been on its feet. Twisted coke cans, broken slates and yards of multicoloured cables spilled out of the deserted buildings like entrails. The street was pitted with puddles that seemed to be eating their way into the carcass.

Another sign caught my eye, bright red letters on white: McAlpine. It was a death warrant in one word for Bayly Street. There's nothing more destructive than a construction company. They'd gut the warehouses and build fancy apartments in the shell. Each one would have a river view, a quarry-tiled garage and a five-figure price tag. That's the trouble with London. The rich have got it all.

There was a man standing beside the van, holding a silenced gun which he was pointing in my direction. He might have been a gangster, but he went to a smart tailor. He was dressed in a pale grey suit with a pink tie. His shoes were as brightly polished as his smile. A moment later, the driver's door opened and a second man got out. He was dressed identically to the first, except that his tie was a powder blue. They were both short and thin and both wore their hair parted down the middle – one dark, one blond. They were both approaching fifty and had spent a lot of money trying to back away again. Their slightly plastic faces had to be the work of a slight plastic surgeon. Know what I mean? Cut out the fat, take up the wrinkles, re-tone the flesh, thank you sir, and make sure you don't sneeze too violently. I had a feeling the two men were fond of each other.

"This way," Blondie said, gesturing with the gun.

"After you," I replied.

"I don't think so."

There had to be men at work on a construction site nearby. I could hear them now, their hydraulic drills jabbering away in the distance, the mechanical grabbers churning up the mud. I thought of making a break for it. But there was no chance. There was nobody in sight and they'd have shot me down before I'd gone five metres. The driver had walked across to a heavy wooden door and unlocked a padlock the size of a soupplate. It led into a room like an abandoned garage: bare concrete floor, burnt-out walls, junk everywhere. For a nasty minute I thought that this was it and that I was about to reach the last full-stop, but there was a staircase in one corner and Blondie steered me towards it. We went up five flights. Each floor was the same – derelict and decaying. But then we came to another door and another padlock. The fifth floor was different.

It was open-plan and about as big as a tennis-court, only it would be difficult to have a game – not with a grand piano parked in the middle. It had a large, wide window – more like a French door really – reaching from floor to ceiling, but being five storeys up it didn't lead anywhere. The room was furnished with a grey carpet, grey silk curtains and a silvery three-piece suite arranged around a white marble table. There was an open-plan kitchen with a tray loaded with cups and plates for tea.

The dark-haired man went into the kitchen while Blondie waved me over to the sofa.

"And who are you?" I asked, although I already had a good idea.

"I'm William," Blondie said. "And that's Eric." He gestured.

"Gott and Himmell," I muttered. The two German schoolboys from Eton. That gave me

140

a complete score on Snape's blackboard.

"We thought it was time we invited you to tea," Gott went on. "I do hope you like fairy cakes."

The kettle boiled. Himmell filled the pot and brought the tray over to the table. "Who's going to be mother?" I asked. They both raised their eyebrows at that. I couldn't believe it. These were meant to be the Falcon's two right-hand men but they looked about as dangerous as my two maiden aunts. But then I remembered the way they'd brought me here and the fact that there were two dead bodies to be accounted for. They might look like a joke. But they could still make you die laughing.

Himmell poured the tea into china cups decorated with roses interlaced with swastikas, and then handed round the fairy cakes. I didn't feel like eating but it looked like he'd made them himself and I didn't want to hurt his feelings.

"Who plays the piano?" I asked. Polite conversation seemed like a good idea.

"We both do," Gott said. "But now, my friend, it's your turn to sing." Himmell laughed at that. I didn't. I've found funnier lines in a Latin dictionary. "You have something we want," Gott went on. "Let me explain, Nicholas … if I may call you Nicholas? A charming name."

I bit into the fairy cake. It tasted like Fairy Liquid.

"We were following the dwarf the day he visited you and your brother. We didn't know then what he was carrying. We searched your apartment that evening but we found nothing. Then we ran into Miss Bacardi."

"Is she here?" I asked.

"You'll see her soon enough. She told us about the Maltesers. Most … unusual. So we went back to your flat for a second time. That was the day of the Falcon's funeral. We were certain that we would find the Maltesers then. But after we'd broken in, we were surprised. Who was the man waiting for us?"

"His name was Lawrence," I said. "He was the chauffeur of the Fat Man. He was after the Maltesers too."

"It was unfortunate for him." Gott sighed. "He said some very hurtful things. So Eric hurt him. In fact, he killed him. I have to tell you, Nicholas. Eric is a lovely person. Lovely. But he gets moody sometimes. And when he's moody, he shoots people."

I smiled at Himmell. "Nice fairy cakes," I said.

"We still want the Maltesers," Gott said. "We know your brother is in prison. And we know you know where they are. So either you tell us now or…"

"Or what, Gott?" I asked.

142

"It would be a terrible shame," he replied. "You're a very nice boy. Really very sweet. How old are you?"

"Thirteen."

"Yes – far too young to end up in a plastic bag with six bullets in your chest. Would you like some more tea?"

Himmell filled my cup. He didn't seem to have quite such a good grasp of the English language as his friend. They were still both smiling at me with their plastic smiles and I wondered if, after the face-lifts, they were capable of anything else. Gott finished his tea and smacked his lips.

"Thank you," he said. "You do make a lovely cup, Eric."

"Anudder cup?"

"*Nein danke.*" He turned to me. "So where are they?"

I'd been thinking. I'd have been happy to tell them if I thought it would get me out of there. But somehow I didn't believe it. Once they'd got what they wanted, they wouldn't need me and I'd be in that plastic bag like a shot. And I mean shot. I had to buy time. Given a bit of time, maybe I could find my way out of this jam.

I coughed. "Well, it's a bit tricky..." Himmell's face fell. He was still smiling, but I reckon his nose and chin must have sunk a good centimetre or two. "I mean, I do have them. They're at Victoria Station. In a left-luggage locker. But Herbert has the key."

"The number?"

"Um … one hundred and eighty!" I'd been making it up as I went along and I sang out that number like a darts commentator on finals night.

"At Victoria Station?"

"Yes. But you can't open it."

He lifted the gun. "I think we can."

Gott got to his feet and strolled over to the piano. Then he sat down on the stool and rubbed his hands over the keys. I stood up. "Thanks for the tea," I said. "If that's all you wanted to know…"

"You're not going anywhere." Gott played a chord. "Eric!"

Himmell had a few cords of his own. I don't know where he'd got the rope from but there was nothing I could do. While Gott played a tune on the piano, Himmell tied me up. He did it very professionally. My hands went behind my back where they were introduced to my feet. By the time he'd finished, I couldn't even twitch in time to the music and I could feel my fingers and toes going blue as the blood was cut off. Gott finished his little recital and stood up.

"Well, Nicholas ," he said. "We're going to Victoria Station." He looked at his watch. "We'll be back around five. And if you've been

144

lying, we'll bury you around five thirty."

I tried to shrug. I couldn't even manage that with all the ropes. "If this is what they teach you at public school," I said, "I'm glad I went comprehensive."

"Take him into the back room," Gott snapped. "It's time he met our other guest."

Himmell picked me up and carried me across the room. I'm not heavy but he was still stronger than I thought. There was a door at the far end, beyond the piano. He drew back a metal bolt with one hand and opened it.

"When are you going to let me out of here?" a voice demanded. A voice I knew.

Himmell threw me down on the floor. I found myself sitting opposite Lauren Bacardi. She was tied up just like me.

"Company for you," Gott said.

He closed the door and locked it behind him. A minute later I heard the two Germans leave for Victoria Station. I wondered what they'd find in Locker 180. I wondered if there even was a Locker 180. I just knew that I had until five to get out of here. I'd bought myself time OK. But I didn't fancy paying the price.

With an effort, I tried to put them out of my mind. I looked round at Lauren. "Hi," I said.

"I know you," she said.

"Yeah. Nick Diamond. We met at the Casablanca Club – the night they came for you."

She nodded. "I remember. Thanks a bunch, Nick. I was enjoying my life until you came along."

She was still dressed in the glitzy clothes she had worn for her singing act but the fake jewellery was gone and she had washed off some of the make-up. She looked better without it. She was sitting in the corner with her knees drawn up, a plate and a mug on the floor beside her. There was no furniture in the room, which was about as big as a large store cupboard. It was lit by a single small window which would have been too high up to reach even if we hadn't been tied up. I gave a cautious tug at the ropes. In the movies, there would have been a piece of broken glass or something for me to cut them with. But it looked like I was in the wrong movie.

I gave up. "I'm sorry about this," I said. "But I didn't lead them to you."

"No? Then who did?"

It was a good question. How had they found out about her? "You told them about the Maltesers?" I said.

She sniffed. "Why else do you think I'm still alive?"

"Enjoy it while you can," I said. "They're going to be back at five and they're not going to be very happy. I strung them a line out there. When they get back, I reckon they're going to want to string me up with one."

146

"Then we'd better move."

"Sure. If I can just get across to you, maybe you can get at my ropes with your teeth and..."

I stopped. Lauren Bacardi had wriggled. That was all she had done but now the ropes were falling away from her like over-cooked spaghetti. It was incredible. I tried it myself. But while she got to her feet, unhooking the last loop from her wrist, I stayed exactly where I was.

"That's a real trick," I said. "How did you do it?"

"Before I became a singer I worked in cabaret," she told me. "I was the assistant to an escapologist ... Harry Blondini. I spent two and a half years being tied up. Harry loved ropes. He used to wear handcuffs in bed and he was the only guy I ever knew who took his showers hanging upside-down in a strait-jacket. He taught me everything he knew."

By now she was kneeling beside me, pulling the knots undone. "Why didn't you escape before?" I asked.

"There was no point. The door's barred from the outside. There's nothing I can do about that. And even if I could reach the window, it's too small for me to get through."

Too small for her, but when she gave me a leg-up about fifteen minutes later, I found I could just squeeze through. Gott and Himmell hadn't bothered to lock it. Why should they have? They'd left me tied up and anyway, it didn't lead anywhere. It was five storeys up and just too far below the roof for me to be able to scramble up there. I paused for a moment on the window ledge, my legs dangling inside, my head and shoulders in the cold evening air. I could see men working on a construction site in the distance and I shouted, trying to attract their attention. But they were too far away and anyway, there was too much noise.

I looked down. It made my stomach heave a little. The pavement was a long, long way below. I could see the French windows that led back into the main living-room about three metres away. If I could break in through them, I could open the door and let Lauren out and at least we'd be on the way to safety. But the windows were too far away and although they had a narrow ledge of their own, there was no way I could reach it. Unless...

This was a warehouse and like all the other warehouses it had a hook on a metal arm jutting out of the wall – in this case exactly halfway between the two windows and about a metre above them. In the old days it would have been used to hoist goods up from the street on a rope. The rope was gone, of course. But rope was at least one thing we had in plenty.

I squeezed myself back into the room.

"No way out – eh?" Lauren muttered.

"There might be." I explained what I had in mind.

"You're crazy," she said. "You can't do it."

"I've got to do it," I said. "Better crazy than dead."

Ten minutes later I was half-in and half-out again, but this time with a length of rope around my waist. We'd taken the rope that Himmell had used to tie us up and knotted it into a single length. There was a good four metres of it. I held the slack in my hand and now I began to swing it a bit like a lasso. Then I threw it, holding on to the end. The loop flew out towards the hook, missed and fell. I pulled it in and tried again. I hooked it on the fourth attempt.

So there I am, five storeys up, leaning out of a window. There's a rope leading from me to a hook and then back again and I tie the end around my waist too. Remember that isosceles triangle I mentioned? Well, it's a bit like that. The two windows are the lower corners. The hook is the point at the top. All I have to do is jump and the rope will swing me across like a pendulum from one side to the other. At least that's the general idea.

I didn't much like it. In fact I hated it. But I was running out of time and there didn't seem to be any other way.

I jumped.

For a giddy second I swung in the air, one shoulder scraping across the brickwork. But then my scrabbling hands somehow managed to grab hold of the edge of the French windows. I pulled, dangling in mid-air, supported only by the rope, my legs kicking at nothing. I pulled with all my strength. And then I was crouching on the ledge, trying hard not to look down, my heart beating in my chest like it would rather be someplace else.

I stayed where I was until I'd got my breath back, afraid of falling back into space. The ledge could only have been twenty centimetres wide and my whole body was pressed against the window panes. Without looking back into the street, I reached down and pulled off my shoe. Slowly I lifted it up. It was cold out there, but the sweat was running down inside my shirt. My eyes were fixed on the grand piano on the other side of the window. Somehow looking at it made me forget where I was and what I was doing. I held the shoe firmly in one hand, then brought it swinging forward. The heel hit the window, smashing it. I dropped the shoe into the room then, avoiding the jagged edges of broken glass, slipped my hand through, found the lock, turned it. The window opened. With a sigh of relief I eased my way inside, then untied the rope and pulled it in after me.

I hadn't got very far, but at least I was still alive.

Gott and Himmell had left the tea things out. I put my shoe back on and took a swig of milk out of the jug. Then I went over to the door and drew back the bolt.

Lauren raised an eyebrow when she saw me. "So you made it?" she said.

"Yeah," I said. I would have said more but for some reason my teeth were chattering at about one hundred and fifty miles per hour. It must have been even colder out there than I'd thought.

Lauren tried the door that led to the staircase. It was locked. Then she strolled across to the broken window and looked out.

"That's great, Nick," she drawled. "We're out of the cupboard but we can't get out of the room. There's nobody near enough to hear us shouting for help. You've sent our German friends on a wild goose chase and when they get back they're going to string you up and use you for target practice. We don't have enough rope to climb down with and we don't have any guns."

"That's about it," I agreed.

"Then you'd better think up something fast, kid." She pointed out of the window. "Because here they're coming now."

THE LAST CHORD

I ran back over to the window. Lauren was right. The blue van was at the end of Bayly Street. It would have reached us already if a lorry hadn't backed out of the construction site, blocking its path. Now it was stuck there while some guy in a yellow hat tried to direct the driver. Fortunately it was a tricky manoeuvre. They'd be stuck there for maybe another couple of minutes. How had they got back from Victoria so quickly? I played back what had happened in my mind and realized that my great escape had probably taken about an hour. It's amazing how time flies when you're enjoying yourself.

Lauren was in the kitchen, rummaging through the drawers. "What are you doing?" I asked.

"I'm looking for a knife." She held up an egg-whisk.

"This is all I can find."

"They've got guns," I reminded her. "You're not going to get very far with an egg-whisk."

"I know. I know." She threw it over her shoulder. "So what are we going to do?"

What were we going to do? If we yelled for help, the only people who would hear us would be Gott and Himmell. The noise from the construction site would see to that. Even if we found a knife, it would be no defence against automatic pistols. There was no way out and any minute now they'd be coming in. I looked out of the window. The lorry seemed to be pinned at an angle across the road. The man in the yellow hat was frantically giving directions, swatting at invisible flies. I heard the lorry grind into gear. It began to edge backwards. Soon the road would clear and the blue van would come. It would come right underneath the window. I tried to remember where it had stopped when they brought me here. That time they'd parked in front of the door. Would they park there again? Perhaps.

"Lauren," I said.

"Yes?" She'd found a corkscrew and a dessert spoon.

"Quickly…"

The window that I'd broken in through was, like I said, a French window. It came all the way down to the floor. I looked out again. The lorry had almost completed its turn. The man in the yellow hat was walking away, his job done.

"The piano," I said.

"The piano?"

"Come on!"

"Nick – this is no time for a concert."

"That's not what I have in mind."

I got my shoulder down to the piano and began to push. It was on castors which helped, but even so it must have weighed a ton. It was a Bechstein, a great chunk of black wood with a gleaming white ivory smile. God knows how much it had cost but if this is what you needed to be a pianist, it made a good argument for taking up the triangle. Lauren had twigged what I was doing and now she stood there, staring.

"Honey," she said. "You can't be serious."

"Deadly serious," I said.

"Deadly," she agreed.

She came over and joined me. With the two of us pushing, the piano moved more easily. Inch by inch we drew closer to the open window. It was going to be a close fit but the piano would just about slide through the frame. It occurred to me that that was probably how they'd got it in here in the first place. How long had it taken them to hoist it up? The return journey was certainly going to be a hell of a lot faster.

"Are you ready?" I asked.

"Yes."

I gazed over the top of the piano. The lorry was in the clear now, rumbling quickly away. The blue van slid forward towards us. I flexed myself. There was a bust of Beethoven or someone on the piano. He was frowning as if he knew what was about to happen. The blue van drew closer, slowing down as it prepared to park.

We pushed with all our strength. The piano shot forward. Its back leg went over the ledge and with a hollow jangle it teetered on the brink, the pedals digging into the carpet. The van was almost level with us now. I pushed again. The piano resisted. Then, with a wave of relief, I felt it topple over backwards. I can tell you now, Bechstein grand pianos are not built with any consideration for aerodynamics. It must have been a bizarre sight as it plummetted through the air: a huge black beast with three rigid legs and no wings. It flew for all of two seconds. Then it crashed fair and square into the van.

It was the Bechstein's last chord, but it was a memorable one. If you imagine someone blowing up an orchestra in the middle of Beethoven's Fifth, you'll get the general idea. It was an explosion of music – or a musical explosion. A zing, a boom and a twang all rolled into one and amplified a hundred times.

They heard it at the construction site. I doubt if there was anywhere in London that they didn't hear it.

It was the Bechstein's last chord and I somehow doubted that the van would be doing much more travelling either. It hadn't been completely crushed but it must have been disappointed. Steam was hissing out of the radiator and two of the tyres were spinning away like giant coins. Black oil formed a sticky puddle around the wreckage. The exhaust pipe had shot away like a rocket and was lying about forty metres down the road. The whole twisted carcass of the van was covered in splinters of wood and wires. One of the piano's legs had shattered the front window. I didn't like to think what it had done to the driver.

"Quite a performance, honey," Lauren said.

"Concerto for piano and van," I muttered.

And now people did come running. Suddenly it was as if Bayly Street had become Piccadilly Circus. They came from the construction site, from left, from right, from just about everywhere. They looked at the carnage. Then they looked up. I leant out of the window and waved.

It was about twenty minutes later that one of the construction workers appeared in the Germans' living-room. He was carrying a pair of industrial pliers which he must have used to cut through the two padlocks. Lauren and I were sitting on the sofa waiting for him.

"The piano…" He gaped at us. "Was it yours?"

"Sure," I said. "But don't worry. I wasn't much good at it anyway."

We walked out of the room leaving him standing there. Well, what was he expecting? An encore?

We managed to slip away in the crowd, but not before I'd heard that – miraculously – nobody had been killed.

Apparently the driver of the van would have to be cut away from the steering wheel while the passenger had managed to impale himself on the gear-stick. A doctor had already arrived but Gott and Himmell were more in need of a mechanic. We got a taxi back to the office where I picked up the real Maltesers and then we went straight on to Lauren's place. There were too many people looking for me in Fulham. From now on I'd have to keep my head down and my raincoat collar up. She lived in a mansion block in Baron's Court – about a ten-minute drive away. It was one of those great brick piles with fifty doorbells beside the front door and fifty people who don't know each other inside. She had a basement flat which must have been all of ten centimetres above the main Piccadilly tube line. Every time a train went past the floor rumbled. Or maybe it was my stomach. I hadn't had a decent meal in twenty-four hours and I was hungry.

She left me in the living-room while she went into the kitchen to fix supper. It was a cosy room in a theatrical sort of way, with a gas fire hissing in the grate, a kettle on the floor and odd bits of clothes thrown just about everywhere. The furniture was old and tired, with a sofa that looked like it was waiting to swallow you up whole.

The walls were plastered with posters from theatres and music halls where Lauren had appeared, either as a singer or as an escapologist's assistant. It was a room with a past but no future. A room of rising damp and fading memories.

When she came back in she had changed into some sort of dressing-gown and had brushed her hair back. For a woman old enough to be my grandmother she looked good. But then you should see my grandmother. The food she was carrying looked even better. She had it on a tray: omelettes, salad, cheese, fruit, a bottle of red wine for her and Coke for me. We didn't say much while we ate. We were just glad to be there. Glad to be alive.

"Thanks," I said when I finished the omelette.

"I should thank you, Nick." Lauren poured

herself some more wine. Her hand was trembling a little. "If it hadn't been for you ... hell ... they were going to kill me."

"You were the one who got out of the ropes," I reminded her. I glanced at the poster above the gas fire. It showed her with a flashy guy in a sequinned straitjacket. He had greasy black hair, a moustache and a toothpaste advertisement smile. "Is that Harry Blondini?" I asked.

"Yes." She stood up and turned the record-player on. There was a click and a solo saxophone slithered through the room. She'd lit herself a cigarette and the smoke curled in time to the music. Her eyes told me everything I needed to know about the escapologist. But she told me anyway. "I loved him," she said. "For two years we worked together in the theatre and we lived together for five. We were going to get married. But then, at the last minute, he ran off with a snake-charmer. What did she have that I didn't – apart from two anacondas and a boa constrictor? That was the day before our wedding – the day before we were meant to tie the knot." She smiled a half-smile. "Well, what should I have expected from an escapologist? He escaped. And he broke my heart.

"That was when I took up singing. I've been singing for twenty years, Nick. The same old songs. And in all that time I've only met two decent people. Johnny Naples and you. You're a nice kid, Nick. If I'd ever had a son, I'd have liked him to be like you.

"All I've ever wanted is a place of my own – maybe somewhere in the sun, like the South of France. Look at this place! Ten metres underground – I never get to see the sun. And the Casablanca Club's the same. When they finally bury me, I'll actually be going up in the world. But it's a lousy world, Nick. Lousy…"

Maybe she'd had too much wine. I don't know. I'd asked her a simple question and she'd given me her life history. It was lucky I hadn't asked her anything tricky. We could have been there all night. I'd had enough. I was tired and I was dirty.

"I need a bath," I said.

She shook her head. "Of all the baths in all the towns in all the world, you have to walk into mine. There's no hot water."

"Then I'll just turn in."

"You can sleep on the sofa."

I took the tray back into the kitchen while she got me a couple of blankets. It was after she'd said goodnight and I was about to leave that I remembered the one question I'd meant to ask her. It was the whole reason I was there.

"Lauren," I said. "Back in the Casablanca Club … you were about to tell me something. You told me that you were out with Johnny when he saw something. It made the Maltesers

160

and everything else make sense."

"That's right."

"Well … where were you?"

She paused, silhouetted in the doorway. "We were buying sausages," she said. "In Oxford Street. In Selfridges. In the food department."

SELFRIDGES

I don't like Oxford Street on the best of days –
and let me tell you now, December 24th isn't
one of them. Bond Street Station had been
doing a good impersonation of the Black Hole
of Calcutta and Lauren and I were glad to get
out. But there was little relief outside. The
Christmas rush had turned into the Christmas
panic and the season seemed to have run
pretty short of good will. Taxi drivers blasted
their horns. Bus drivers leant out of their
windows and swore. You couldn't blame
them. The traffic probably hadn't moved since
December 22nd. There were so many people
clawing their way along the pavement that
you couldn't see the cracks. And everyone
was carrying bulging bags. Of food, of decorations, of last-minute presents. I sighed.
Herbert was still in prison.

He'd been there almost a week now. It

looked like Christmas for me was going to be the Queen's speech and two frozen turkey croquettes.

But there was Selfridges with its white pillars, gold clocks and flags fluttering across the roof. Somewhere inside the department store – in the food section – Johnny Naples had seen something that could have made him three and a half million pounds. The thought cheered me up. I clutched the Maltesers. Lauren had lent me a sort of shoulder-bag and I had brought them with me. I wouldn't have felt easy without them.

We crossed the road, weaving between the traffic, and went in the front entrance. We were greeted by a cloud of sweet, sickly scent. This was the perfume hall. They stocked all the perfumes in the world – and you could smell them all at once.

"Do you want to try this one?"

A pretty girl leant over a counter, holding out a bottle of aftershave towards me. I shook my head. She had a nice face. But she was a couple of years early.

It was hot in Selfridges. The air had been chewed up by air-conditioning machines and spat out again. That was how it smelt. Second-hand. We went into the menswear department, following the signs that read "food".

"Come along and meet Father Christmas on

163

the third floor in the magical grotto." The voice came out of invisible speakers, floating above the heat and the crowd.

"See all your favourite nursery rhymes. On the third floor. It's open now."

The food department was even worse than perfume and menswear. It was like nuclear war had just been announced. The shelves were being stripped, the shop assistants bullied. I felt Lauren put her hand round my arm.

"This way," she said.

"I'm with you." But it was an effort. Relax for a minute and I'd have been swept away on a river of rampant consumerism, drowned in a lake of last-minute shopping.

"If we get separated, we can meet outside Marks and Spencer," she said. "It's just across the road."

We made our way round the centre section of the food department, which was more or less like any supermarket. There were separate bars here and there – juice, sandwiches and cookies – but most people were ignoring them. The meat counter was at the back. There was a number in what looked like a car headlamp, hanging from the ceiling. Every few seconds there was a loud buzzing and the number changed. "Now serving 1108" it read when we got there. It buzzed again – 1109. A clutch of housewives stared up at it. They were all clutching tickets like they'd just gone in for some sort of raffle.

So Selfridges sold sausages. I could see them through the glass front of the cabinet. They looked very nice. I'm sure they tasted great. But I didn't see what that had meant to Johnny Naples. What did sausages have to do with the Falcon?

"Lauren..." I began.

"He was standing here," she said. "Then he suddenly turned round and went that way." She pointed.

"You mean he went straight on?"

"No. We'd come from that way. He retraced his steps."

I followed in the footsteps of the dead dwarf. They took me further round the central supermarket, past the nuts and into the fruits where some fancy items nestled amongst the plums and Granny Smiths. "Brazilian Loquats, £3.50 kg" a sign read. That was probably a bargain if you knew what to do with a loquat. After that it was chocolates and then cash-tills. There was a row of six of them – with six women in brown coats and white straw hats. Five of them were ringing up prices on their tills like they were typing a novel. The sixth was just passing the purchases over a little glass panel in the counter and the prices were coming up automatically.

But I still hadn't seen anything that made me any the wiser. As far as I could see, Selfridges didn't even sell Maltesers.

"It was here," Lauren said.

"Here – what?" I sounded tired and depressed. Maybe that was because I was. It had been a wild goose chase and I didn't even have enough money to go back to the meat counter and buy a wild goose.

"He knew," Lauren insisted. "He was standing where you were. And he suddenly smiled…"

I looked around and suddenly I wasn't smiling at all. There was a door opposite, leading into the street. Two men had just come in with the crowds. I think I saw them a few seconds before they saw me.

"Lauren," I hissed.

"What?"

I gestured. They'd changed since our first encounter but I'd have recognized Gott and Himmell anywhere. They were still wearing identical suits – pale green with embroidered waistcoats this time. But Himmell (with the blond hair) now had his left arm in plaster. Gott was walking with a stick. Both men had so many plasters on their face that I could hardly see any skin. But the skin I could see wasn't looking too healthy.

"You told them about the sausages," I said.

"Of course I told them," Lauren growled. "They were going to give me some more of their fairy cakes."

166

She'd told them. They'd come to look at the food department for themselves. And now they'd seen us.

"Let's move," I said.

We moved.

We ducked to the left – through an archway and down a flight of stairs past wines and spirits. Looking over my shoulder, I saw Gott giving Himmell some hurried instructions. A moment later I collided with a pair of little old ladies. With a little old screech they flew into a pile of crystallized fruit which collapsed all around them. I didn't stop to apologize. Manners maketh man, my father used to say. But Gott and Himmell weren't far behind. And they had every good reason to unmaketh me.

"Which way?" Lauren asked.

I stopped. There was a door leading out to Orchard Street but it was blocked with about a dozen people fighting their way in. That left us a choice of three or four directions.

"Wait a minute, Lauren..." I said.

I was about to say that this was ridiculous. Gott and Himmell might be crazy, but there was no way they were going to try anything. Not in the middle of Selfridges on Christmas Eve. I was going to say that they'd wait for us outside and that we'd have to give them the slip when we left. I was going to say...

But right then a cabinet of watches behind my head exploded. Just like that. Glass flew out in glittering fragments. A shop assistant screamed. I spun round. Gott was standing at the top of the stairs. He was holding a gun. It was silenced so there had been no bang. But it was smoking. And nobody had noticed. They hadn't heard anything and they were too busy with their shopping to stop anyway.

"That way!" I cried.

Lauren went one way. I went another.

She must have missed the way I was pointing. She ran down a corridor back into menswear while I made for the escalator. There was no time to hesitate. And perhaps it was for the best. We had more chance of getting away if we split up.

"The meeting place for customers who have lost their companions is on the lower ground floor..." The voice poured soothingly out of the speakers. Lauren had certainly lost me. But unless I lost the Germans, our only meeting-place would be the morgue.

The escalator was slow. Impossibly slow. And I couldn't run up it – I was hemmed in by shoppers on both sides. I squatted down and looked back, wondering if Gott and Himmell had missed me. They hadn't. There was no sign of Gott but Himmell was standing there, taking aim. This time I think I heard the *phutt* as the bullet came out. Just above my head, a white box with the figure "1" on it suddenly shattered and the light went out inside. I reached the top of the escalator and swung round past a collection of hats, then on to a second escalator with a third after that. On the third floor, not even knowing if Himmell was still behind me, I ran forward – through the children's clothes department and on.

I stopped to catch my breath at another of the archways. There were fewer people up here. After all, who buys children clothes for Christmas except relatives who should know better? I couldn't see Himmell and I thought I'd lost him, but then a plastic dummy about twelve centimetres away from me suddenly lurched over backwards with a hole in its forehead and fell with a clatter of broken plastic. Gott had gone after Lauren. But Himmell was still after me. I turned and ran.

And now there were more people. I didn't mind that. The more the merrier as far as I was concerned. It took me a few seconds to realize where I was heading and by then it was too late to go anywhere else. There was a sign:

To Santa's Grotto

Now I remembered the loudspeaker announcement. Father Christmas and my favourite nursery rhymes. I'd almost prefer to spend the afternoon with Himmell.

The straggle of people had become a queue. I ignored it. A few people protested as I ran past them but most of them had little children with them and they weren't going to start a fight. I ran on, past a red screen and down a brightly-lit corridor. It led into a pram park and there was a woman standing behind a desk, gently controlling the crowd. She called out to me but I ignored her, sliding down a ramp to crash into a brick wall. Fortunately, the brick wall was made out of cardboard. I glanced back, hoping that I'd at last shaken Himmell. But there he was, one arm in white plaster jutting out of his body as if he'd been caught in the middle of a karate chop. His other arm was jammed into his pocket. I knew what it was holding.

I dived into Santa's grotto. I didn't like it. But I had no choice.

It was packed inside with everyone talking in low voices while nursery rhymes played on the loudspeaker system. There were a lot of models – Elizabethan villages and that sort of thing, illustrating the rhymes. They'd fixed them up with those little dolls that do jerky movements. They didn't fool me. Jack and Jill looked slightly ill while Miss Muffet seemed to be having convulsions. The models were arranged so that the passage swerved round with dark sections and light sections. I moved as quickly as I could, pushing aside anyone who got in the way. Nobody complained. With their arms full of little kids asking inane questions, they had more than enough to worry about.

So had I. I felt trapped in Santa's grotto. I needed an exit. I saw one, but it was blocked by a security guard. I turned another corner past Little Jack Horner and stopped again next to Humpty Dumpty. There was no sign of Himmell. Perhaps he was waiting for me outside. Some of the children were more interested in me than in the models. I suppose I must have looked pretty strange, panting and sweating – the way you do when you're running for your life. I took a couple of steps further into the grotto. At the same moment, Humpty Dumpty exploded in all directions, his arms and legs soaring into the air. All the King's soldiers and all the King's men certainly won't be able to put that one together again, I thought as I forced my way through the crowd.

And still nobody knew anything was wrong. It was incredible. But it was also gloomy. And if you've got your eyes on a ship with thirty or so white mice, maybe you won't notice when a private detective's younger brother is being murdered behind you. I looked round. Himmell had been held up by a tough-looking gang of seven-year-olds. Still walking backwards, my eyes fixed on him, I turned a corner. Somebody seized me. I was jerked off my feet. I twisted round again. I couldn't believe it. I'd bumped into Santa Claus and he'd pulled me on to his lap.

Now he looked at me with cheerful eyes and a white-bearded smile. He really was the complete department store Santa: red hat, red trousers and tunic, bulging stomach and bad breath.

"You're a bit big for Santa, aren't you?" he asked in a jolly Santa voice.

"Let me go," I said, squirming on his lap.

But he clung on to me. I got the feeling he was enjoying himself. "And what do you want for Christmas?" he asked.

"I want to get away from a guy who wants to kill me."

He laughed at that. There were a whole lot of people in Santa's chamber and if I hadn't been so angry I'd have been red with embarrassment. A little girl – she can't have been more than six – pointed at me and laughed. Her parents took a photograph.

"Ho ho..." Santa boomed out.

He didn't make the third "ho".

There was another quiet *phutt* and he keeled over. I threw myself on to the floor. Himmell was on the other side of the chamber, reloading his gun. Nobody was looking at him. They were looking at Santa, at the body twitching on the chair, at the red stuff that was staining his beard. The little girl began to cry.

"Don't worry," I said. "Santa's OK."

172

Santa died. I fled.

I got out of the grotto just as the people began to scream in earnest. I could still hear them as I ran across a floor of women's clothes, searching for a way out.

"Security to third floor, please. Security to third floor." The calm, unruffled voice came over the loudspeakers as I spotted a fire exit, pulled it open and found myself in a quiet stairwell. I wanted to go back down to street level but even as I stood there, I could hear the tramp of feet coming up. They didn't sound like shoppers. They were too fast, too determined. It had to be the security guards. I looked up. The stairway was clear. I made for the fourth floor.

Through a door, along a corridor, through another door and suddenly I'd burst into the toy department. I was tired now. I couldn't run much more. And the noise and the colour of the toys somehow drained away the last of my strength. Robots buzzed and clicked. Electric organs played hideous tunes. Computer games bleeped and whined. Something whipped past my head. I thought it was another bullet and jerked back, sending a whole pile of robots flying. But it was only a sales assistant with a paper glider. The robots writhed on the floor. I shrugged and staggered off into the toys.

I was sure I'd lost Himmell now. From toys I went into sports – first the clothes, then snooker tables, weights, golf clubs and hockey sticks. I rested against a counter that had been set up for a special promotion. There was a sign reading:

Discover the delights of deep-sea diving

A young salesman was showing an American couple the latest equipment: masks, wetsuits, harpoons.

"The harpoon works on compressed air," I heard him say. "You just pull the lever here, load it like this and then—"

And then Himmell appeared. He'd come from nowhere. He was only about three metres away from me. I had nowhere else to run. He had his hand in his pocket and now he brought it up, the jacket coming with it. He smiled. He was going to shoot me through the pocket. Then he would just walk away. And no one would know.

I lunged to one side, grabbed the harpoon gun, then wheeled round. The salesman shouted. I pressed the trigger.

The gun shuddered in my hands. The harpoon shot out, snaking a silver rope behind it. For a moment I thought I'd missed. The harpoon seemed to sail over Himmell's shoulder. But then I saw that one prong had gone through his suit, pinning him to the wall. The American stared at me.

"Good gun!" I said. And dropped it. Himmell lunged forward but he wasn't going anywhere. He was stuck there like a German calendar.

"You little...!" he began.

I didn't want to hear him. I found another fire exit and this time I managed to get out of Selfridges without being stopped. I crossed the road and made my way around the front of Marks and Spencer. I was relieved to find Lauren waiting for me.

"What kept you?" she said.

"You got away OK?" I asked.

"Sure. Gott could hardly walk, let alone run. Himmell was in better shape."

"Yeah," I agreed. "He was."

Lauren sighed. "Well, that was a waste of time," she said. "We didn't learn anything."

I thought back to the food department, to the things I had seen. And suddenly I understood. It was as if I'd known all along, only someone had to sock me on the jaw to make me realize it. I smiled. Johnny Naples must have smiled that way. Lauren saw it. "Come on..." I said.

The same taxis and the same buses were jammed in the same place as we crossed Oxford Street again. We got back on the tube. It would take us to South Kensington where we'd get a bus.

I knew. But I had to be sure.

INFORMATION

"The bar-code," I said.

"The what?"

"Those little black and white lines you get on the things you buy."

"What about them?"

I pulled the Maltesers out of the shoulder-bag and showed them to Lauren. "Look," I said. "You see? It's got a bar-code."

"So what?"

"That's what they were using in Selfridges. The girl was passing her products over a scanner and the scanner was telling the cash-till how much the products cost." Lauren looked blank so I went on. "Maybe if you pass *this* bar-code over a scanner, it'll do something different."

"Like what?"

"I don't know. That's what we're going to find out."

I needed a science lesson in a hurry and for once in my life I was sorry school had shut for the holidays. But I had another idea. Journalists write about technology and things like that. They know a little bit about everything. And I knew a journalist: Clifford Taylor, the guy who'd interviewed Herbert and me. He'd been at the Falcon's funeral too, so I figured he must still work on the same newspaper, the *Fulham Express*. That was where we were heading now. I had to be sure that I was right.

Nobody reads the *Fulham Express* but everybody who lives in Fulham gets it. They don't have any choice. It's one of those free newspapers that come uninvited through the letterbox in a shower of plumber's business cards, minicab telephone numbers and special offers from the *Reader's Digest*. It's delivered every Wednesday in the morning. And you can see it every Wednesday, in the afternoon, stuffed into litter bins or drinking up the dirt in the gutter.

We took a bus all the way down the Fulham Road, past Herbert's flat, to the bottom – Fulham Broadway. This was the Fulham Road at its worst: dirty in the rain, dusty in the sun, always run-down and depressing. I'd occasionally walked past the office of the *Fulham Express* but I'd never been inside before. It was on the main road, next to a bank. Lauren and I climbed up a flight of stairs and found ourselves in a single, rectangular room with a printing press at one end and a photocopying machine at the other. In the middle there were two tables, piled high with newspaper clippings. The room must have been a dance studio at one time because it had mirrors all the way down one wall, making it seem twice as big as it was. Even so, it was small.

Clifford was there, feverishly working on a story that in a few days someone would use to wrap their fish and chips. I coughed and when he didn't respond, I walked up to him. He was the only person there.

"Clifford..." I said.

"Yes?" He looked up.

"You don't remember me?"

"If you're from the dance class, you're too early. The newspaper has the room until five—"

"I'm Nick Diamond."

He took his glasses off and wiped them. There were sweat patches under his arms and his acne had got worse. He was a mess. I doubted if he could even spell personal hygiene. "Nick who?" he asked.

"Diamond." I glanced at Lauren who shrugged. "You interviewed me," I reminded him. "My brother's a private detective."

Now he did remember. "Of course! Absolutely! How's it going? There's not much call for private detectives in Fulham—"

"I know," I interrupted. Clifford liked talking. When he'd interviewed us, he'd talked more than we had. "I wondered if you could help me," I said.

"Sure. Sure."

"It's a sort of scientific question. Do you know anything about shopping?"

"Shopping?" He frowned. "I don't think I know anyone called Shopping. There's Chopin ... but he's a composer, not a scientist."

"No." I sighed. "I'm talking about shops. And about bar-codes. I want to know how they work."

Clifford ran a hand through his hair. There wasn't that much left for him to run it through. In fact, he had more dandruff than actual hair. "OK." He leant back and put his feet up on the desk. "Technology is mainly about one thing: information. The electronic storage and transmission of information. Computers store information. Satellites send information. But all this information isn't written out like a book. No way. It's turned into what's known as digital information.

"What does digital information look like? Well, in the old days it would have been a hole punched into a computer tape. There are holes in the modern compact disc too – although they're too small to see. And a bar-code is another form of digital information. It's as simple as that.

"All products have a bar-code on them these days. If you look at them, you'll see that there's a number with thirteen digits underneath it. That's all a bar-code is. A number – a unique number that can tell the computer everything it needs to know."

I'd taken out the box of Maltesers again while he talked. Clifford's eyes lit up when he saw it. He leant forward and took it.

"Take this box," he said. "Here's the bar-code on the bottom." He pointed to the strip of blue and white lines in the left-hand corner. "Part of it would tell the computer that this is a product made by Mars. Another part of it would tell the computer that it's a box of Maltesers, that it weighs so much and costs so much. It could even remind the shopkeeper to stock up."

"How does the computer read the bar-code?" I asked.

"Well, that's all done with lasers," Clifford explained. "There's a sort of little window built into the counter near the cash-till. The person who's sitting there passes the box of Maltesers – or whatever – over it. Now, behind the window there's a laser scanner. The shop assistant could use a light-emitting diode which is the same sort of thing, but either way, the light hits the bar-code. Are you with me so far?"

I wasn't sure, but I nodded anyway. If I'd learnt one thing from science lessons at school it was this. When scientific types start explaining things, it's hard enough to follow. But when they start explaining the explanations, that's when you really get lost.

"All right." He nodded. "The light beams hit the bar-code. Now, the dark lines don't reflect light. Only the white ones do that. So only some of the light gets reflected. And somewhere inside that little window there's a photodetector which is a clever machine that produces a pulse of electricity whenever you shine a light on it. Do you see? As you slide the bar-code over the window, the shining light hits the lines. Some of it is reflected back on to the photodetector which gives out a 'bleep' for every white line. It's the 'bleep' that's the digital information sent to the computer. Almost like Morse code. And that's how the computer knows what the product is!"

He stopped triumphantly and sneezed. Lauren reached out for the Maltesers and he gave them to her. She turned them over and examined the bar-code.

"Could you use the bar-code like a ... key?" I asked. That was the word the Fat Man had used. He had said he was looking for a key.

"Absolutely!" the journalist said. "That's just what it is, really."

"But could it open something – like a safe?"

"It depends how you programmed your computer. But the answer's yes. It could open a safe. Play Space Invaders. Make the tea…"

"*They open the…*" I'd asked the Professor what the Maltesers did and that was what he'd said before he caught himself. It was all clicking together. A key. A code known only to the Falcon. A safe. Johnny Naples had guessed the day he went to Selfridges. Now I remembered the words he'd written down on the scraps of paper I'd found in his room. Digital … photodetector … light-emitting diode. Clifford Taylor had used them all in his explanation.

I'd always thought that it was the Maltesers themselves that were the answer to the riddle. But I'd been wrong and I could have guessed. When Johnny Naples had bought the envelope at Hammetts, he'd done something else. He'd bought a pair of scissors. Why? To cut out the bar-code. That was all he needed. He just had to feed it into… But that was one thing I still didn't know.

"I do hope I've been helpful," the journalist said.

"Sure," I said. "More helpful than you'd guess."

"Is there a story in it?"

I nodded. "An international master-criminal, a gang of crooks, a fortune in diamonds? There's a story OK."

Clifford Taylor sighed. "I'm afraid I can't

use it. It's much too exciting for the *Fulham Express*. But look out for the next edition. I'm doing a very interesting piece on the effectiveness of one-way traffic systems in Chelsea."

"I can hardly wait," I said.

We left him at his desk and went back down the stairs. It was only when we got to the bottom that Lauren's hand flew to her mouth. "I've left the Maltesers upstairs!" she exclaimed. "Hang on, honey..."

I watched her run up the stairs and into the newspaper office. About a minute later, she reappeared, waving the Maltesers. "I must be out of my mind!" she said. "How could I leave them?"

I thought no more of it. That was definitely a mistake.

We were near Herbert's flat so I decided to go in and get some fresh clothes. It was easier for Lauren to take the tube straight to Baron's Court, so we parted company outside Fulham Broadway Station. It was a beautiful day. Cold but with a brilliant sun. Lauren stopped outside the station almost like she was afraid to go in.

"Nick..." she said.

"Yes?"

"What I said that night – I want you to know that I meant it. You're a nice boy. You deserve the best."

I stared at her, then laughed uneasily.

"What is this?" I said. "I'll only be an hour or so. You're talking like I'm never going to see you again."

"Sure." She shook her head. "Forget it."

She went into the station.

I walked all the way up the Fulham Road, past the cemetery and on to the flat. As I walked, I thought. I understood so much now. What the Maltesers meant and why everybody wanted them. The only trouble was, if the Maltesers really were a sort of digital key, how was I to find the digital door? And there was something else that puzzled me. Who had shot Johnny Naples in the first place? My money was on the Fat Man. If it had been Gott and Himmell, they'd have told me when I was their prisoner. After all, they'd told me about Lawrence without blinking an eye. But at the same time, I couldn't believe it. I just couldn't see the Fat Man getting his hands dirty that way. It wasn't his style. So if not him – who?

I checked the bag. At least the Maltesers were safe. Right now that was all that mattered.

It was around three when I reached the flat. I slipped in as quickly as I could. The fewer people who saw me go in the better. I didn't mean to stay there long – just long enough to pull on a fresh shirt and a new pair of socks and make a clean getaway. I went up the stairs. The office door was open. I went in.

There were four thugs in there waiting for me. One was behind the door. He kicked it shut after I'd gone through it so when I turned round there was no way out. I'd have given my right arm for a way out. If I hung around there much longer they'd probably tear it off anyway. The four thugs were all wearing extra large suits. That was because they were extra large thugs. I was once taught at school that Man evolved from the ape and all I can say is that these four had a long way to catch up. They were big, heavy and brutal with unintelligent eyes and thick lips. They were all chewing gum, their lower jaws sliding up and down in unison. "Are you Nick Diamond?" one of them asked.

"Me?" I said. "No ... no! I'm not Nick Diamond. I'm ... er ... the delivery boy."

"What are you delivering?" a second demanded.

"Um..." I was having to think on my feet. Any minute now I'd be thinking on my back. If I was still conscious. "I'm a singing telegram!" I exclaimed, brilliantly. "Happy birthday to you, happy..." I tried to sing but the words died in my throat. The four thugs weren't convinced. "Come on, guys," I pleaded. "Gimme a break."

"Yeah – your legs," the third one said.

They all laughed at that. I'd heard more cheerful sounds on a ghost train. They were still laughing as they closed in on me.

"You're making a big mistake," I said.

The man behind the door was the first to reach me. He grabbed my shoulder with one hand and lifted me clean off my feet. "There's no mistake, sunshine," he said. "The Fat Man wants to see you."

IN THE FOG

I discovered that the four thugs were called
Lenny, Benny, Kenny and Fred. Lenny was in
charge. He was the one with the driving
licence. They'd parked the car outside the flat.
It was a Morris Minor. After we'd all piled in
it I was surprised it was able to move. I certainly wasn't. I was on the back seat between
Benny and Kenny. Things were so tight that if
they'd both breathed in at the same time, I'd
have been crushed. The Maltesers were still in
my shoulder-bag but now the shoulder-bag
was on Fred's lap. Lenny was driving. I was
being "taken for a ride" as they say. And I had
a nasty feeling I'd only been given a one-way
ticket.

We drove out of town, west towards Richmond. Lenny had made a telephone call from
the flat before we left so I knew the Fat Man
would be waiting for me. It looked like he was

going to have a long wait. These heavies really were heavy and the Morris Minor could only manage thirty miles an hour on the level. Not that I was in any hurry. In fact, my only hope was that the engine would finally explode under the pressure. I could hardly see them "taking me for a ride" on a bus.

"You can't do this to me," I protested. "I'm under-age. I'm only a kid. I've got my whole life ahead of me."

"That's what you think," Lenny sneered.

"But I've got money," I said. "I could make you guys rich."

"Sure." Lenny swung the steering wheel. "You can leave it to us in your will."

The car turned off the main road and began to follow a winding lane through what looked like the remains of an industrial complex. It was still pretty complex but I reckoned it hadn't been industrial for a hundred years. It was a network of Victorian buildings, most of them burnt out. Another bit of London that was falling down. The lane led down to the river. Suddenly we came to the end of the tarmac and I could hear gravel crunching underneath the tyres. The Morris Minor bounced up and down. The four thugs bounced in their seats. The springs screamed for mercy. We drove right up to the edge of the river. Then Lenny put on the handbrake. We'd arrived.

"Out," he ordered.

He'd produced a gun from somewhere and I don't need to tell you what it was pointing at. If you've ever looked into the single eye of a gun barrel, you'll know it's no fun. The devil must have an eye like that.

"Walk," Lenny said.

I walked. We'd stopped in a space about the size of a car-park, only the Morris Minor was the only car parked there. It was another building site, more luxury houses for the Thames. But they'd only got as far as the foundations and a few pieces of the framework. The iron girders hemmed us in like we were on the stage of a Greek amphitheatre, only there was no audience. The light was fading and to complete the picture – or maybe to obliterate it – the fog had rolled in across the water. It carried the smell of salt and dead fish in its skeleton fingers and when it touched my neck I shivered. I couldn't see across to the other side of the Thames. Which meant that anyone on the other side couldn't see me. I was alone with just about the four nastiest customers you could ever hope not to meet.

There was a low hiss as one of them lit a paraffin lamp. It threw a circle of hard, white light. They'd set it all up in advance. I didn't understand it – but somehow I didn't like it much. There was a wooden chair about four metres away from the edge of the river and an old iron bathtub right in front of it. The bathtub was quite deep. It came to about the same level as the chair. Nearby, there was a pile of brown paper sacks. Kenny picked one up and tore it open. Grey powder flooded out. At the same time, Benny walked forward carrying a hose. Water was already spluttering out, liquid mercury in the strange, harsh light. Cement, water, a bathtub, a chair and the River Thames. Now I understood it – and I liked it even less.

"Sit down," Lenny said.

He waved the gun towards the chair. I walked forward, the soles of my shoes squelching on the wet gravel. The four men never stopped watching me. They weren't getting any pleasure out of this. They were just doing a job. Mind you, I wasn't getting any pleasure out of it either – and I wasn't being paid. But there was nothing I could do. I sat down on the chair. It was so close to the bathtub that my legs had to go in it. Out of the corner of my eye I could see Kenny and Benny mixing the cement. If I ever get out of this one, I thought to myself, I'll take the first flight to Australia. My parents might not have been ideal company, but they'd never tried to kill me. At least, not so you'd notice.

"Look, Lenny…" I began, trying to be reasonable.

"Button it, kid," he snapped.

Kenny and Benny came over, each carrying a large bucket of wet cement. They glanced at Lenny. He nodded. As one, they tipped them up. The stuff poured out sluggishly, like cold porridge. It splattered down into the bath, covering my shoes and rising about fifteen centimetres up my legs. I could feel it seeping through my socks. It was icy. And it was heavy, too. My shoes were pressing against my toes. They were only sneakers and already the cement was oozing through them. I wiggled my toes. Lenny pressed the gun against the side of my neck. "Keep still," he said.

"But it's wet..." I complained.

"Don't worry, kid. It's quick-drying. You keep still and it'll set in no time."

Two more buckets followed the first and two more went after them. By the time Kenny and Benny had it finished, the cement came all the way up to my knees. If anyone had seen me – sitting there with my legs in a bath staring out across the Thames – they'd have thought I was mad. But nobody would see me. It was dark now. And the fog had got thicker. Like the cement.

Lenny wasn't even bothering to massage my neck with his gun any more. The cement had almost set. I experimented. Carefully I tried to lift my right foot. I couldn't do it. That was when I began to get really afraid. Talk about having one foot in the grave – I had both feet

191

and most of my legs. I was glued to the bathtub and I knew that any minute now they'd pick it up and drop it into the river. I – it – we would sink like a stone. I'd spend the rest of eternity in an upright position.

They say that when a man drowns, his whole life flashes before him. Mine did that now but it was all over in about five seconds. That made me sad. It had been a short life and I'd spent far too much of it at school.

I heard a sort of glugging sound coming from the Thames. That made my ears prick up. A boat. It was getting closer. For a moment I was hopeful. It might be a river police boat. Or perhaps a dredger of some sort. But Fred had been waiting for it. The grey curtains of fog were pushed aside by the bow of a sleek, white cruiser. A rope was thrown out of the darkness. A gangplank was slid over the edge and made steady on the bank. The Fat Man walked down it.

He was dressed in a dinner jacket with a mauve bow tie and a white silk scarf hanging loose around his neck. He nodded at Fred and the others and then strolled over to me. Without saying a word, he leant down and tapped the concrete with his knuckles. That made my heart lurch. The stuff was already solid. I couldn't even feel my feet. He straightened up. The four thugs formed a rough circle around us. And I can tell you now, circles just don't come any rougher.

"No wisecracks today, Nicholas?" the Fat Man demanded. "Nothing funny to say?"

"You're a loony, Fat Man," I said.

"And you, my boy, are a fool. You were lucky to escape alive from the Hotel Splendide. But now your time has run out."

"What have you got against me?" I asked. "What did I ever do to you?"

"You lied to me," the Fat Man said. "Worse still, you defied me. I gave you forty-eight hours to find something for me. Find it you did not."

"Well..." I said. "How about a second chance?"

He sniffed. At the same time, Fred moved forward. He'd opened the shoulder-bag and taken out the Maltesers. He handed them to the Fat Man. The Fat Man looked at the bottom, holding them to the light so that he could read something. "Perfect!" he whispered. That threw me. How had he found out about the Maltesers? He'd never mentioned them before. He must have read the expression in my face because he smiled. "You're wondering how I discovered what was inside the dwarf's package?" he asked. He turned round to the boat. "Professor!"

I peered through the swirling fog. A second figure appeared at the top of the gangplank and made his way unsteadily down. He stood at the edge of the circle of light, blinking at me. Quentin Quisling, the Professor. He shook his head. "You gave me the wrong box, sir," he said in an accusing tone of voice.

"So the Professor came to me," the Fat Man continued. "A wise decision. A very wise decision. Did you know that the Professor designed them in the first place? You see, the Falcon needed a key – but a key that didn't look like a key. He had too many enemies. The Professor created the bar-code—"

"But why Maltesers?" I asked. The information wasn't going to be much use to me, but I wanted to know.

The Professor shrugged. "I like Maltesers," he said.

"And now I have them." The Fat Man smiled. The smile stretched his skin across his cheekbones like an elastic band. "And soon, very soon, the Professor will tell me what they open—"

"And then you'll kill him too," I interrupted. I had nothing to lose. I was only minutes away from the end. I could feel the chill of the cement spreading through my entire body. I turned to the Professor. "You don't think the Fat Man will share the money with you, do you?" I said. "Once you tell him your secret, you'll be joining the queue at the bottom of the Thames."

"It's fifty-fifty..." the Professor mumbled

but I could see he had his doubts.

"I'll see you in Hell, Professor," I said.

The Fat Man was furious. His face had gone white and the veins in his neck were standing out so far they were threatening to snap his bow tie. "Throw him in!" he yelled.

He stepped back. At once, Lenny, Benny and Kenny moved in on me. They bent down and a moment later I was in the air, bath and all, being carried towards the Thames. Don't let me kid you. I like to think I'm smart. Sometimes I act older than I am. But right then I would have screamed and cried and torn my hair out if I'd thought for a single second that screaming and crying and tearing my hair out would do any good.

The river drew closer. The Fat Man watched. The three men shuffled forward.

They were about two metres from the edge of the water when the spotlight cut through the fog and the darkness. It came from high up, somewhere behind me. It was hard to tell. The night seemed to rip apart, torn into shreds by the beam. The fog boiled furiously in its grip. The gangsters stopped as if frozen.

There was a crackle in the air. Then a voice boomed out, amplified by a loudhailer.

"This is the police. Stay where you are. You're surrounded."

Lenny, Benny and Kenny dropped me. I crashed to the ground but remained standing up. The Fat Man ran for the boat. He still had the Maltesers. The Professor stumbled after him. Lenny took out his gun and fired in the direction of the spotlight. I tried to dive for cover but I was about as capable of that as an oak tree. There was an answering shot. Lenny was blown off his feet. His gun clattered to the ground.

"Don't move," the voice commanded. "We're armed." It was a bit late to be telling Lenny that.

The Fat Man had reached the boat and turned round, stretching out a hand for the Professor. But the Professor was nowhere near him. Half-drunk and short-sighted he ran forward, missed the gangplank and dived into the Thames. Benny, Kenny and Fred scattered and ran for cover. But now the whole area was swarming with men. They were throwing black shadows as they sprinted through the glare.

The Professor couldn't swim. He was floundering in the water, shouting for help. But the Fat Man couldn't wait. The police had almost reached the boat.

The boat's engine roared and it swung away from the bank. At the same moment the Professor let out a ghastly scream. He'd been in the water. He'd been close to the propellors. Too close. I was glad I couldn't see what the Fat Man had accidentally done to him.

Benny, Kenny and Fred were arrested. I saw them thrown to the ground. The whole building site was lit up. And I was still standing in the middle of it all, knee-deep in cement.

And then I felt the bathtub being dragged slowly towards the river. I couldn't believe it. There was a figure squatting, struggling, pulling the bathtub along the gravel. With me in it.

But then I heard a familiar voice. Snape's voice.

"No, Boyle," he said. "You can't push him in. We've come here to rescue him. Go to the car and get a chisel."

IN THE BATH

Snape and Boyle drove me back to the flat. I was cold. I was wet. And I was fed up. My trousers, shoes and socks were ruined and my legs weren't feeling much better. My throat was sore and my nose was blocked. They'd got my feet out of the cement but I could still feel the cement in my blood and there was nothing they could do about that. And I'd lost the Maltesers. It had been a bad day. I was glad it was over. If I'd known it was going to be a day like that, I'd have stayed in bed.

They came in with me and I made them some coffee. While the kettle was boiling, I tried to call Lauren. I thought she might be worried about me. But there was no answer. I flicked on the hot-water tank for a bath and went back downstairs. Snape and Boyle had made themselves comfortable in the office. I fixed us three cups of coffee and took them in.

I didn't like them and they didn't like me. But like it or not, they'd saved my life. The least I could do was give them a cup of coffee.

"All right," I said. "How did you find me?"

"We were watching the flat," Snape told me. "We saw you go in and we saw you taken out. Lucky for you. We followed you to the Thames. When we saw what was going on, Boyle here called for back-up on the radio."

"Why were you watching the flat?" I asked.

Snape let out a sniff of laughter. "Why do you think? In the last few days we've been receiving some of the craziest reports I've heard in thirty years. A young boy blows up a hotel in the Portobello Road. A young boy pushes a grand piano out of a fifth-floor window. A young boy goes berserk in Selfridges and leaves forty hysterical children and a dead Santa Claus behind him. You'd think London was crawling with lethal young boys. Except they all fit the same description. Yours."

"I can explain," I said.

"I'm delighted to hear it. You've been making life very difficult for me. You've upset Boyle..."

"I'm upset," Boyle agreed.

"...and you've done more damage than the Germans managed in two world wars. And I thought your brother was a menace!"

"Where is Herbert?" I asked.

Snape's eyes narrowed at that. "We released him at lunchtime. We couldn't hold him. To be honest, we didn't want to."

"Well, I haven't seen him."

I wasn't particularly bothered just then. It was strange that Herbert should have just disappeared, but I could understand it. He'd probably gone to Aunty Maureen in Slough. He'd hide out there until the heat was off. I shivered. Herbert hadn't paid the gas bill for the flat. The heat had been off for two weeks.

"Did he tell you everything?" I asked.

"Well … Herbert and canaries have a lot in common."

Snape held out a hand. "I want the Maltesers," he said.

"I don't have them," I said. "The Fat Man took them." Snape's eyes narrowed a little more. "If you don't believe me, you can search my bag."

"I already have," Boyle muttered.

"The Fat Man took them," I repeated. "When you arrest him you can get them from him."

"Arrest him?" Snape twisted his neck until the bone clicked. "That may not be so easy."

"Why not?"

"It's a question of evidence, lad. We haven't got anything on him. Nothing concrete—"

"What about the stuff he was burying me in?"

"You don't understand!" Snape was distressed. "He'll deny he was ever there. He'll say it was a case of mistaken identity ... in the fog. He'll have an alibi."

I shook my head in disbelief. "So that's it, then," I said. "If the Fat Man goes free, he'll find the diamonds and that'll be the end of it."

"You should have given us the Maltesers in the first place," Boyle said.

"Sure." I nodded. "And if the Fat Man had come strolling in and claimed them as lost property I suppose you'd have handed them over."

That made Boyle scowl again. But Snape stood up. "You've got a lot of questions to answer," he said.

"Are you arresting me?"

"No. You've had enough for one day. We'll talk to you next week. Like you say, the Fat Man has the Maltesers and that's the end of it. We'll be in touch."

I showed them to the door. Snape stopped in the doorway and turned round. "Happy Christmas," he said.

I'd forgotten until then. It was Christmas Eve. "Yeah ... Happy Christmas, Chief Inspector," I said. "And to you, Boyle."

Boyle grunted. He probably didn't even know what Christmas was.

An hour later I was lying in the hot water with

the soap bubbles up to my neck and Herbert's plastic duck floating around my feet. My body wasn't a pretty sight just then. What with the ropes, the cement and the general man-handling, I had more bruises than I cared to count. But it felt good in the bath. I needed to relax. It was time for some serious thinking.

What did the Maltesers unlock?

I knew the answer. I knew I knew the answer.

It had to be something near Herbert's flat. Johnny Naples had left Notting Hill Gate with the Maltesers and a pair of scissors. By then he'd found the answer. He knew where he was going and he went to Fulham. But he'd been followed – and rather than lead anyone to his destination, he'd come to us. So it had to be something near. But what was there near the flat connected with the Falcon?

Four days later we'd found Naples dying. He'd managed to say two things: "The Falcon" and "the sun". I assumed it was sun. Henry von Falkenberg didn't have a son ... at least, not one that we'd heard about. But what had the sun got to do with the Falcon? Noth-ing ... unless he'd been talking about another falcon. Maybe not a man. A bird. Or a statue of a bird.

And then I thought about the Maltesers themselves and about a phrase that Clifford Taylor had used. The journalist had described the laser as "the shining light". The sun was a shining light, too. But the phrase bothered me. I'd seen those words somewhere before. The Maltesers.

When the Fat Man had taken them, he'd looked on the bottom. I'd already tricked the Professor once. He'd told the Fat Man to find something, to check that they were the real ones. Henry von Falkenberg would have had to mark them in some way. And there was an easy way.

"You'll see that there's a number with thirteen digits underneath."

That was what the journalist had said. And I knew that number. I'd read it so many times that I'd learnt it off by heart: 3521 201 000000. That number was the final clue.

I pulled the plug out with my toes and wrapped a towel round my body. Then, still dripping water, I went downstairs. It took me an hour before I found what I was looking for but there it was – a piece of paper with another number on it. I'd written that number myself on the day of the Falcon's funeral.

There were thirteen digits on the Maltesers box – but the last six of them were all zeroes. Cross those out and you'd be left with seven digits.

A telephone number. And I knew which telephone it rang.

That was when our own telephone rang.

203

The noise of the bell was so sudden, so loud, that I almost dropped the towel. I went into the office and picked it up.

"Nick Diamond?"

The voice was ugly with hatred. I didn't believe a voice could hate that much.

"Gott," I said.

"We have your brother."

That took me by surprise. Herbert? But that was the way Gott worked. He'd snatched Lauren, then me. Why shouldn't he add Herbert to his list?

"If you don't give us what we want," Gott snarled, "he dies."

I didn't have what they wanted, but I wasn't going to say that. Because suddenly I knew everything. It all made sense. I should have seen it a long, long time before.

"Come to the cemetery," I said. I was talking even before I knew what I was saying. "I'll meet you at the Falcon's grave. Tomorrow at twelve o'clock." I hung up.

I didn't want to get into any arguments.

Then I opened the drawer of Herbert's desk. On the day we had first met the Fat Man, he had given us a card with his telephone number. I called it now, hoping there would be someone in.

"Yes?" It was a flat, neutral voice.

"I want to talk to the Fat Man," I said.

"He's not here."

"It's important I get a message to him."

"Who is this?"

"Nick Diamond."

There was a pause. Then the voice said, "What is the message?"

"I know what the key opens," I said. "And I'm willing to do a deal. Tell the Fat Man to be at Brompton Cemetery tomorrow. At the Falcon's grave at five to twelve exactly. Alone. Have you got that?"

"Yes."

"Good." I hung up on him too.

After that I made one last call. That was the hardest to make. It cost me three and a half million pounds. But the way I looked at it was like this. The Fat Man had the Maltesers. Gott (and maybe Himmell) had Herbert. And I had the answer. If I'd planned things right, it would all sort itself out the next day at noon.

If I hadn't ... well, we were meeting in a cemetery. At least they wouldn't have to carry me far.

I just hoped it would be a sunny day.

THE SHINING LIGHT

There are only about three or four days in the year when the Brompton Cemetery is more or less empty – and Christmas Day, of course, is one of them. That would suit my plans. Witnesses were one thing I could do without. It was eleven forty-five when I walked up to the Falcon's grave. There was nobody in sight. Fortunately it was another crisp, cloudless day. The sun had no warmth, but it was bright. At least the weather was on my side.

I stood beside the Falcon's grave. The earth was still fresh where they'd buried him, like a sore that hasn't healed. It would take the grass time to grow over it – but where better to find time than in a cemetery? I looked at the memorial, that Victorian telephone box with the stone falcon perched on top. There's an old saying. I thought of it now. "You can't take it with you." But the Falcon had – or at least, he'd tried his best to. I read the inscription on the memorial. I'd read it before.

THE PATH OF THE JUST IS AS SHINING LIGHT,
THAT SHINETH MORE AND MORE
UNTO THE PERFECT DAY.

The Falcon must have smiled when he had that cut in. I wondered if he was still smiling in his grave.

I heard the gate grind open down at the Fulham Road. That had to be the Fat Man. Sure enough, he appeared a few moments later, wearing a camel-hair coat with real humps. He carried a shooting stick and walked at a jaunty pace, for all the world like a man taking a little exercise before his Christmas lunch.

He saw me standing by the grave, raised the shooting stick and sauntered over. He was smiling, but only with his lips. His eyes didn't trust me.

"Happy Christmas, Fat Man," I said.

"I hope so," he replied. "And I hope you're not wasting my time, my boy. You should know by now that I don't take kindly to—"

"Have you the Maltesers?" I cut in.

He nodded. "In my pocket."

"Let me see them."

He took them out but held on to them like he was afraid I was going to grab them.

207

"Read me the number on the bottom," I said.

He turned the box over. "3521 201 000000." It was the right number. "You say you know what these chocolates meant to the Falcon," he said in a graveyard voice. "You say you want to make a deal. What deal?"

"We'll split the money," I said. "Fifty-fifty."

"Eighty-twenty."

"Sixty-forty."

We were juggling figures. It didn't matter to me. I knew that once I showed the Fat Man what to do with the Maltesers, I'd be dead. But it was important that he hung on to them. They had to be out in the open.

"Seventy-thirty," the Fat Man said. "It's my last offer."

It was his last offer. There was a movement on the path behind him, and when he turned round there were Gott and Himmell with Herbert between them. It had been a week since I'd last seen him and Herbert had lost weight.

I smiled at him. "Hello, Herbert," I said.

He looked at me reproachfully. "The name is Tim," he muttered.

There are times when my brother really amazes me. I'd been kidnapped, tied up, chased around London, threatened and half-killed. He'd been arrested for murder and kidnapped himself. We were unarmed and surrounded by three psychopathic killers. And he was worried about Christian names. "How are you ... Tim?" I asked.

"I'm OK," he said. He considered. "Actually I've got a runny nose and—"

"All right," the Fat Man interrupted. "What is this?"

"It's a cemetery," Herbert said.

The Fat Man gritted his teeth.

"Do you know them?" I asked him.

He glanced at Gott and Himmell. "I know them," he said.

"If that little swine is trying to trick us—" Gott began.

"I'm doing what I said I would," I cut in. "I promised I'd lead you to the Maltesers in return for Herbert – I mean – Tim." I pointed at the Fat Man who was still holding them. "There they are. And I promised the Fat Man that I'd tell him their secret. If you'll let me, I will."

Nobody said anything. The wind ruffled my hair. I was wearing a body-warmer but my body was far from warm. I just wanted the whole thing to be over.

"Go ahead," Gott said.

"Yes, go ahead," the Fat Man repeated. "And it had better be good."

"All right," I said. "This is how it goes. Henry von Falkenberg was a very careful man, a man who trusted no one. He had three and

209

a half million pounds in diamonds stashed here in England. It was in a safe that had been specially built for him. Even the key to the safe was special. It was designed so that nobody would even know it was a key. Only the Falcon knew. It was the only way he could feel safe himself.

"The Professor built the safe for him – the late Quentin Quisling. I guess we'll never know, but I suppose he built in some sort of device so that Henry von Falkenberg could choose his own combination. That wouldn't have been difficult. The key was a bar-code. It could be on a tin of baked beans, a pack of playing cards – a box of Maltesers. The Falcon brought the key with him every time he came to England. If he was searched by the police, he had nothing to fear. Who would suspect that a few black lines on the bottom of a box of sweets could open up a fortune?

"There was one thing, though. One fail-safe device. There was a number written on the box. I don't know why. Maybe it appealed to the Falcon's sense of humour. Or maybe it was a clue – a puzzle for his heirs to fight over. But that number was 352 1201 with a few zeroes added to stretch it out. I wrote that number down for my brother on the day of the Falcon's funeral. It's the phone number of this cemetery."

I walked forward to the monument.

Nobody spoke but their eyes followed me like so many gun barrels. I stood on tip toe and wiped the cuff of my shirt across the eyes of the falcon. As I had guessed, they weren't made of stone. They were glass.

"And where is this ingenious safe?" I asked. "You're looking at it. The Falcon had it designed like a memorial. You see the inscription? The 'shining light' it's referring to is the light beam that opens it. Johnny Naples tried to tell me about that – the sun.

"I won't try to explain to you how a bar-code works. I only half understand it myself. But what you're looking at here is the first solar-powered bar-code reader. You've got to hand it to the Professor. He may have been crooked. He may have been a drunk. But he was clever.

"The sunlight goes in through the eyes of the stone falcon. You run the bar-code – at a guess – across the open beak. Somewhere inside all this there's a photodetector, a small computer and an opening device – all solar-powered. If you've got the right bar-code, it'll open the safe." I pointed at the Maltesers, still clutched in the Fat Man's hand. "That's the right bar-code," I added. "It's as simple as that."

I stopped. Nobody spoke. Only Herbert looked puzzled. He obviously hadn't understood a single word I'd said.

I wasn't exactly sure what was going to

happen next, but I'll tell you the general idea. The Fat Man isn't going to share the diamonds with Gott and Himmell. Gott and Himmell clearly have no intention of sharing the diamonds with the Fat Man. But now everybody knows the secret. Herbert and I are forgotten. Nobody cares about us any more. We slip away to live happily ever after, leaving our three friends to sort themselves out as best they can. That was the general idea. But obviously I'd been talking to the wrong general.

It all happened at once.

Almost casually, the Fat Man had lifted his shooting stick so that the end was pointing at Himmell. At the same time, Gott's hand had slid quietly into his jacket pocket. The two shots were almost simultaneous. Himmell looked down. There was a hole in his chest. The Fat Man lowered his shooting stick. And it was a shooting stick. The smoke was still curling out of the hole at the bottom. He smiled. The smile faded. He frowned. He raised a hand. He'd only just realized that he'd been shot in the neck. This time Gott hadn't used a silencer.

The Fat Man and Himmell slid to the ground together. The Maltesers fell on the grass. The last of the chocolates rolled out.

"Pick it up," Gott said.

I picked up the box. Something was chattering. I was just thinking that it was a bit cold for grasshoppers when I realized what it was. It was Herbert's teeth.

"Give me the box," Gott said.

I gave it to him, then stepped back a pace. Now Herbert and I were standing close together. Gott's gun was out of his jacket. There were too many plasters on his face to be sure, but I think his smile had grown even wider.

"I'm going to enjoy this," he said.

There were two gunshots.

Herbert's hands came up to his stomach. He groaned and lurched forward. "Nick..." he whispered. He pitched on to the grave.

I stared at him.

"Get up, Tim," I said.

"But I've been shot."

"No you haven't."

He held his hands up to his face. There was no blood. He lifted up his shirt and looked underneath. There were no bullet holes. Now he was blushing. "Sorry..." he muttered.

Gott had watched this performance with strange, empty eyes. Suddenly, he toppled forward. There were two holes in the back of his jacket. He hadn't had time to fire his own gun.

A figure appeared behind him, moving towards us. And that was the biggest surprise of the day.

It was Betty Charlady.

"Ello, Mr Nicholas," she gurgled. She was

still in her fluffy bedroom slippers, with a forest of artificial flowers on her head. "Wotcha, Mr Timothy. Blimey! What a turn-up ... innit!"

"Betty!" Herbert exclaimed. "What are you doing—" But then he plugged his mouth with his thumb, stopping himself in mid-sentence.

Betty was holding a gun. The gun had just killed Gott.

With a smile, she pulled off her hat and threw it on to the grass. Her wig, with the electric curls, went next. Once more her hand reached up and this time it pulled at the very skin of her face. It stretched, then tore loose, carrying the wrinkles and make-up with it. The gun in her other hand remained steady but otherwise, in front of our eyes, she was changing.

Betty Charlady was gone. Another woman stood in her place.

"Who is she?" Herbert whispered.

"Beatrice von Falkenberg," I said. "The Falcon's widow. Snape told us that she used to be a great actress. It looks like Mrs Charlady was one of her performances."

"That's right, boys," Beatrice said.

I took a quick look round the cemetery. The way things were going, I wouldn't have been surprised if the alligator had turned up – perhaps disguised as a hedgehog.

"But ... but why?" Herbert asked.

"I had to find the diamonds," she said. "My late husband's fortune. When the dwarf gave you the package, I had to get close to you – to find out what you knew. Then I saw your advertisement for a daily. That gave me the idea."

"And Gott and Himmell were working for you," I said.

"That's very clever of you, Nicholas," she muttered. "How do you know?"

I shrugged. "I told you we were going to the Casablanca Club. You were the only person who knew. But somehow Gott and Himmell managed to turn up just in time to snatch Lauren Bacardi. We led them to her."

Herbert looked at me in astonishment. "That's brilliant," he said.

"There's more. They learnt about the Maltesers from Lauren and they told you. That's how you knew what to ask for when I visited you in Hampstead. You were all in it together."

"Until their use ran out," Beatrice said.

"It's incredible," Herbert said.

"Not really," I said. "I almost guessed when I visited Beatrice. She knew your real name. She called you Herbert – not Timothy. And she was wearing the same perfume as Betty. Lavender. That was something she forgot to change."

"You're very clever," Beatrice said.

"Maybe. But there's one thing I don't get. Why did you kill Johnny Naples in the first place?"

She shrugged. "It was an accident. Gott and Himmell had tracked him down to the Hotel Splendide. They were going to snatch him, but I went to see him first. I walked in as Betty Charlady. Nobody looked twice. I wanted to persuade him to share what he'd found with me. I told him I was his only hope. I could keep Gott and Himmell off his back. And I could use them to stay ahead of the Fat Man. But he was greedy. He wouldn't listen. He had a gun. There was a fight. Like I say, it was an accident." She sighed. "There can't be any more accidents. You two can't leave the cemetery. No witnesses." For a moment she slipped back into her Betty Charlady voice. "Cheerio then, Mr Nicholas. Ta, ta, Mr 'erbert."

She lifted the gun.

"Oh, no!" Herbert whimpered.

"I don't think so, Beatrice." I said.

She looked beyond me and her face jerked back like she'd been slapped. But then she lowered the gun and laughed. Suddenly, the cemetery was full of uniformed policemen. They were springing up everywhere – out of the long grass and from behind the gravestones. At their head, running to be the first one to reach us, were Snape and Boyle.

"Well ... that's a lucky coincidence,"

216

Herbert said.

"What do you mean – coincidence?" I said. "I called Snape last night. I told him everything." Herbert's mouth fell open. "Well, I wasn't going to come here alone."

By this time Boyle had reached Beatrice von Falkenberg. She stretched out her hands elegantly for the cuffs but he threw himself at her anyway – a flying rugby tackle that sent her crashing to the ground.

"You could have come out sooner, Chief Inspector," I said as Snape arrived. "We were nearly killed."

"That's true, laddy," Snape agreed. "But ... well, it was Boyle. He wanted to see what would happen. He asked me to hold back. And as it's Christmas..."

The policemen began to clear away bodies. Snape leant down and picked up the Maltesers box.

"Now, let's see about this," he said.

The three of us gathered around the memorial. The stone falcon waited, its wings spread, its beak open, its glass eyes blinking in the sun. Carefully, Snape tore off the bar-code. He threw the rest of the box away. Then he laid the strip face up in the falcon's beak and pulled it through.

Behind the eyes, inside the falcon's head, a lens focused the sun's beams on to the bar-code. The white stripes reflected some of them back on to a photodetector hidden inside the falcon's body. We heard the click as a connection was made. There was a soft hum. A solar-powered generator had sprung to life. It activated a motor. There was another click and the entire front of the memorial – along with the inscription – swung open to reveal a solid metal container.

And that was the last surprise of the day. There was to be no Christmas bonus for Snape, no reward for us. Because there weren't any diamonds. There wasn't even a lump of coal. The container was empty. We were looking at three and a half million pounds worth of nothing.

THE FALCON'S MALTESER

"But Nicholas, I still don't understand."

"I've gone through it all twice, Herbert."

"Well, if you wrote it all down... That would help."

"Maybe I will."

It was the second day of the New Year. It didn't feel much different to the old year. It was cold. There wasn't any gas in the flat. And, as usual, we were down to the last handful of change. We'd had a great Christmas, Herbert and me. Two frozen turkey croquettes and the Queen's speech – only we'd missed the Queen's speech. Mum and Dad had sent us a card and a couple of presents but they hadn't cheered us up. The card showed two koalas in a Christmas tree. The presents were a boomerang for me and a hat with corks for Herbert.

I threw the boomerang away. It came back.

There were still a couple of weeks until term began and I'd have liked to have gone skiing. A lot of the guys in my class had made it to Switzerland or Austria or wherever and they'd be full of it when they got back. It didn't seem fair. After all I'd been through I couldn't even afford the bus fare to the travel agent.

And then the parcel came. Special delivery. From the South of France. It was addressed to me.

I think I knew who it was from before I opened it. There was only one reason I could think of why the Falcon's safe had been empty. I hadn't mentioned it to Snape or Boyle. I hadn't even mentioned it to Herbert.

"What is it?" he asked.

"I don't know."

"Well, open it."

I opened it. Inside the brown wrapping-paper there was a carton about the same shape and size as a film-box. It was filled with tissue paper but nestling in the centre was a round ball of milk chocolate...

"A Malteser!" Herbert said. The colour walked out of his face. Herbert didn't much like chocolates any more. And he hated Maltesers.

There was a card attached to the box. The message was short and not so sweet. It was written in a flowing, looping hand.

No hard feelings?
L.B.

No hard feelings? I wasn't so sure. Lauren had sold me the sob story of her life – and OK she hadn't had the breaks – but then she'd double-crossed me. All along she'd known more than she'd let on. Maybe she'd worked it out for herself or maybe Johnny Naples had told her. But she'd known about the cemetery and she'd known about the Falcon's memorial. I'd given her the last piece of the jigsaw when I told her about the bar-code. And that day, in the office of the *Fulham Express*, she'd made up her mind to steal the diamonds. She'd accidentally left the Maltesers upstairs. And when she'd gone up to get them, she'd made a simple copy of the key: photocopy.

She'd never gone into Fulham Broadway Station – at least, not down to the trains. The moment I'd left, she'd doubled back to the cemetery. Perhaps she'd overtaken me in a taxi. The sun had been shining that day. She'd slid her photocopy through the falcon's beak. And the diamonds had been hers.

I reached down and squeezed the Malteser between my finger and thumb. I was angry. I wanted to see it shatter. But it wouldn't. There was something hard in the centre.

"Herbert..." I said.

He looked. The chocolate had squashed. It

wasn't a Malteser at all. There was something sparkling inside. "What is it?" he asked.

"What does it look like?" I said.

The last of the chocolate had crumbled away. I was left holding a diamond the size of a peanut. What would it be worth? Ten thousand pounds? Twenty thousand? Certainly not peanuts.

So we would go skiing after all. And Herbert would break his leg as he got on to the plane and we'd blow all the money we got from the diamond before we'd even got round to paying the gas bill. But what did I care? It was the New Year and we'd come out of it all alive, and although diamonds may be for ever, you've got to grab every good minute and enjoy it while it's there.

ANTHONY HOROWITZ is one of the most popular contemporary children's writers. Both The Power of Five and Alex Rider are number one bestselling series enjoyed by millions of readers worldwide.

When Anthony launched the Alex Rider series he created a phenomenon in children's books, spurring a new trend of junior spy books and inspiring thousands of previously reluctant readers. Hailed as a reading hero, Anthony has also won many major awards, including the Bookseller Association/Nielson Author of the Year Award, the Children's Book of the Year Award at the British Book Awards, and the Red House Children's Book Award. The first Alex Rider adventure, *Stormbreaker,* was made into a blockbuster movie in 2006.

Anthony's other titles for Walker Books include the Diamond Brothers mysteries; *Groosham Grange* and its sequel, *Return to Groosham Grange*; *The Devil and His Boy*; *Granny*; *The Switch*; and a collection of horror stories, *More Bloody Horowitz*. Anthony also writes extensively for TV, with programmes including *Foyle's War*, *Midsomer Murders*, *Collision* and, most recently, *Injustice*.

Although abandoned by both his sons, Anthony Horowitz continues to live in Clerkenwell with his wife, Jill Green, and the ghost of his dog, Lucky.

You can find out more about Anthony and his books at:

www.anthonyhorowitz.com

www.alexrider.com

www.powerof5.co.uk

Contents

Foreword

When I was asked to contribute to this book I immediately agreed. The work, which addresses areas of growth for gay people in some of the most important aspects of life with which they must deal, is long overdue and badly needed. The need for a book like this is especially acute because of the climate of repression current in this country and, indeed, in other parts of the world as well.

Thirty years ago, when I first became aware of homosexuality, there would have been no market, no audience for a book like this. There was no gay community, no gay consciousness seeking growth or new ideas then. The word *gay* was not even used. Heterosexual and homosexual alike used the term *queer* and other pejorative terms. In my case, homosexuality meant the section of the textbook on abnormal psychology from which I taught; a smuggled copy of *The Well of Loneliness* when I was still in college; all the nonsense that everyone else talked. But I really knew absolutely nothing about homosexuality.

It was not until the end of World War II, I had the extraordinary accident of having a student who was gay (initially not to my knowledge). Then I began to learn about homosexuals. The atmosphere, the emotional and intellectual climate of the war years and of the McCarthy era which immediately followed were such that homosexuals had an intense and legitimate fear of being known, of being known on the job, of being known to me.

A long period of social interaction between that student and his friends, and my first husband and myself had to pass before there was enough confidence for them to open up to me. When we were dinner guests in Sam Fromm's home the first time, his then-lover was introduced as his "cousin." At that first dinner everything was so proper—like a dinner meeting almost—and there wasn't a hint that any of those present were gay. But what an incredibly diverse cross-section of people was represented—university professors, writers, artists—you name it, they were there.

It wasn't until they came increasingly to feel that I had no prejudiced attitudes, that I simply enjoyed them as people, as I enjoy anybody, that they gradually began to feel free. And only then did they begin to urge me to undertake a study of homosexuals, to make a beginning at destroying the myths that surrounded their lives.

I recall attending a meeting of the board of directors of The Mattachine Society when it was first formed in 1952. The meeting was held in

Positively Gay

Editors
Betty Berzon, Ph.D.
Robert Leighton

CELESTIAL ARTS
Millbrae, California

CELESTIAL ARTS
231 Adrian Road
Millbrae, California 94030

First Printing, April 1979
Made in the United States of America

Library of Congress Cataloging in Publication Data

Main entry under title:

Positively gay.

   Bibiliography p.
   1. Homosexuals—United States—Addresses, essays, lectures. I.   Berzon, Betty.
II. Leighton, Robert, 1938-
HQ76.3.U5P68 1979   301.41'57'0973   78-72287
ISBN 0-89087-240-6
1 2 3 4 5 6 7 — 84   83   82   81   80   79

Cover Design by Robert Hu

a home high in the Hollywood Hills. All of the men were dressed in suits and ties and the meeting was conducted very formally. I finally exploded: "For God's sake! You're acting like the directors of Chase Manhattan Bank." They acted that way, of course, because they felt they had to be more respectable than anybody else.

In those days guilds were formed, discussion groups which met in individual homes and were operated along the lines of communist cells. Members used pseudonyms. No one knew their real names. No one had a mailing list. I know men today who can describe the absolute terror with which they went to their first guild meeting, fearful that they were being followed by the FBI or the police.

During the late '50s I went to a huge English Department party at UCLA. A young professor came up to me and talked of his great pleasure at our meeting. The next day I had a letter from him apologizing profusely if he had in any way offended me by anything he had said. I could not understand what he was talking about and wrote to tell him so. He asked if he could come to call and only then did he tell me he was gay and that he'd looked forward to coming to UCLA because I was there. He had felt he had to so disguise what he said at that party that not even I knew what he was talking about.

Five years ago I went to another party at UCLA and guess who was there—that same young man, now openly gay and accompanied by his lover. He was also, by then, chairman of the English Department.

This immense change took place over ten years. In that time he could become openly accepted as a gay man, become chairman of the department, give parties at his home with his lover present.

I've recalled the fear and paranoia of those times in order to make the point of what has happened not only in the gay community but in the larger community since those days. The freedom with which people can now be openly gay, to hold positions of great responsibility—particularly since 1969, the ability of gay people to say openly "I am gay" on the job or in social situations—is to me just mind-blowing.

One of my proudest nonachievements is that I didn't lift a finger to get the American Psychological Association to change its policy on homosexuality being an illness. I didn't have to because gay people did it. With dignity and pride, gay people initiated the whole action, went to the APA, got a task force started and got the APA involved. They didn't have to depend on straight people to do the research. A lot of the best research on human sexuality today is being done by people who are openly gay.

Perhaps one of the most positive changes in attitude among straight people that I have observed over the years has occurred in my role as an expert witness in security cases and as a consultant.

I remember an instance in the military which illustrates the way it was. I appeared as a witness in a court-martial involving an Air Force technical sergeant. It was a tragic case. The sergeant was within one year of retirement. He had gotten drunk one night and it was alleged he had engaged in homosexual activity in a public restroom or someplace. He didn't even remember. His record showed him to be clearly heterosexual.

The hostility of the court-martial board was so palpable that you could feel it. During my testimony there was no effort to listen to what I had to say. Today when I testify—whether in a military hearing or elsewhere—there is a good cross examination, but the atmosphere is different. They really want to hear what I have to say.

The same is true of the media. Now when I'm asked to consult on a television show or film, it's totally different. The attitude of the writer who comes to me for help—for instance, when the young actor Brad Dourif came to me about the show on the Matlovich case—the attitude now is one of really seeking information and being receptive to it.

I frequently think about the positive contributions that homosexuals make to society. Our democratic system believes strongly in pluralism. In a pluralistic society, individuals and minorities are valued highly. I believe that the gay minority is the last minority to finally begin receiving the recognition it deserves for the many creative contributions it makes.

As I see it, the freedom of the gay person to be increasingly and openly gay is not a steady march upward, but follows a cyclical curve. Progress in civil rights movements is always threatening to the status quo of the majority. So for all forward action there is always some reaction that slows down progress. We see that happening now with the anti-gay crusades of Anita Bryant and California State Senator John Briggs.

Worldwide, as well as nationwide, we are moving toward increasing freedom for all minority groups. And the gay group, along with other minorities, will no longer stand for, nor tolerate for very long, any backlash.

What I look forward to and what I hope this book will help accomplish is to show the gay community that as important as sexuality is, it is also the most unimportant thing. A lot of people will disagree with me and I know it. I should preface this by saying that I have led a very active sexual life, a full sexual life. Sexuality to me is one of the most recreative experiences when it is good, when it is with someone one loves, of any experience in life.

Despite that, I still say that what keeps some gay persons from growing is that they get locked into this prison of defining themselves as first of all gay, meaning that they focus on sexuality and how to get sexual gratification. Therefore, the richness of life—within the gay community and related to nongay people—passes them by.

The great philosopher Kuhn said that to understand the past is to re-define the present. I think it is absolutely essential that gay people do this. They must understand what they have been doing in allowing themselves to be victimized. They are victims of themselves, really. The attitudes are out there, of course, but many gay people have allowed themselves to be imprisoned by those attitudes. They focus on being gay, being different, being outcasts, being ostracized. There are those who say they feel safe only with gay people, who are as hostile toward straight people as many straights are toward gays. The tragedy is that they are cutting themselves off from many people who might be sources of extended or rich relationships in which they could expand and grow.

It is equally important for straight people to realize that by stereotyping gay people, by not knowing what gays are really like, by not having the privilege of knowing gays and having them as friends, they too are depriving themselves.

Homosexuality serves in contemporary society as a threat and a challenge and a reminder. A reminder that sexuality is a form of recreation, not just procreation; that the diversity and variety of sexual pleasure and of human love—affectional and sexual—is a constant.

It is a threat because gay people dare to engage in forms of sexual behavior which are nonconformist, unconventional, illegal. Homosexuality has been repressed because it stands for impulses which may be close to the conscious surface and which to individuals who are homophobic are deeply threatening. Very attractive, but threatening.

Homosexuality challenges both the laws and the moral precepts by which straight people, by and large, live. And that is a healthy challenge.

Evelyn Hooker, Ph.D.
Santa Monica, California

Preface and Acknowledgments

In the letter sent with his chapter Protestantism and Gay Freedom, Rev. William R. Johnson wrote:

> I have agonized over this chapter, attempting to reach deep within me to embrace the pain I have encountered in the lives of gay Christians over these eight years and put into words those things which

> seem to me, from my knowledge and experience, to be most needful
> and healing.

In some measure that is what each of the authors in this collection has
done with regard to achieving a positive identity, new social opportunities, successful gay coupling, improving family relationships, resolving
religious issues, effective gay parenting, adjustments to aging, growing
as a gay professional, developing gay art, strengthening legal protections
on the job, sound financial planning and organizing for political influence.

This book does not pretend to represent all or nearly all of the concerns
and issues relevant to lesbians and gay men. There are no chapters on
third-world gays, disabled gays, rural gays or gay youth. There is not
equal representation of all points on the gay political spectrum nor are
all regions of the country represented.

What we believe we have is a book of general interest to lesbians and
gay men and the nongay people who want to understand gays better. We
hope it is a book that will help put the dreamer and the dream together
in a new way, one that yields options never before thought of, opportunities never before believed in, hope for an open and integrated, positive
gay life never before seen as possible.

We particularly like what Loretta Lotman has written with regard to
gay art. We think it applies, even more broadly, to gay life in general:

> Right now, we should be building among us a Voice that will be
> heard through succeeding generations of gay people. Without a leg-
> acy of understanding, we could easily lapse back into an era of fear,
> hate and bigotry. This must not be allowed. It is time for us to show
> the world that. . . we have reached a point in our history when we
> will record, explain, ornament, and yes, damn it, glorify our lives as
> a bequest to the future. That gay is so good we want to sing, per-
> form, write, paint, sculpt, and otherwise rejoice about it.
>   The only way this will happen is if you and I, my artistic sistren
> and brethren, get off our asses and do it. We must create and share
> without fear. You see, we have a world to change.

We want to thank the women and men who contributed chapters to this
book. The time, effort, thought and care they put into their work is an
indication of the growing concern that lesbians and gay men feel for
each other. And to us, that is an indication of change within the gay
community that is, indeed, positive.

We are each blessed with loving partners, Betty with Teresa, Bob with
Bill. To each go our special thanks for their loving encouragement and
support during the preparation of this book.

                                                    Betty Berzon
                                                    Robert Leighton

Developing A Positive Gay Identity

Betty Berzon, Ph.D.

Who am I? Am I okay?

Two questions that plague all of us eternally. The answers are elusive and everchanging, clearer and more dependable at some times, less trustworthy at others. We grow older and find new layers of definition in ourselves. Our values change. Society's values change, or at least shift in emphasis. Our own reference point moves, and moves again. We are greatly affected by external events. We, in turn, affect those events by the way we relate to them. Our lives involve a constant interplay of feelings and behavior, past and present, fantasy and reality. We are the sum of all our parts, but only for a moment. Identity is a moving, changing process, not a fixed, established point. But, this is an intolerable truth. Our sanity requires a compromise. We select components of ourselves to relate to in awareness. We arrange them into a semblance of order and think of ourselves as this configuration as long as it makes sense to us and to those around us.

This is what personal identity is about. It is not immutable. It is not totally fluid. It is somewhere in between. It is amenable to change by design. It is ours to reorder if we have the courage to accept the challenge.

It does take courage.

It takes courage to consult one's self for the direction to take in life rather than consulting tradition. It is often easier to be defined by what other people expect of you, to merge into a stereotype, to yield individuality, to abdicate responsibility for being who you are and becoming what you want to be. But the price for giving up the prerogative to grow is devastating in spirit, in energy and in integrity. Forever, it seems, gay people have been giving their power away to others: define me, explain me, structure my behavior, decide for me what I can and cannot hope to

1

achieve in my life, make rules for my participation in society, let me know the limits of tolerability if I happen to go beyond the boundaries set for me.

It takes uncommon courage to reclaim power once it has been given away. It is uncommon courage that is called for in developing a positive gay identity in an antigay society.

Such courage has been aroused for many by the accomplishments of the new gay rights movement. Many gay people have been inspired to seek a better life through increasing self-definition and self-determination. Many of us are now rejecting tolerance, rewriting the rules, defying the boundaries, embracing the challenge of change by design and implementing that challenge with personal and political action.

It has not always been so for me.

I lived my young adult life in the 1950s and 1960s. I learned to deny my homosexuality almost totally with more than a little help from a series of well-meaning, kind, smart, skillful, miserably misguided psychotherapists. But I had a fantasy. I decided that if I should ever be told that I had a terminal disease and only had a short time to live I would go to another city and become gay. It would no longer matter what others thought of me or what I thought of myself. The fantasy was a pleasant one. Having given myself permission to think homosexually, in the fantasy, I could yearn for the closeness and the passionate connection with women I was deprived of in real life.

I thought I had to die to live.

I found out I was wrong. I'm not sure how that happened exactly. Perhaps I had enough of the kind of loneliness that goes beyond experiencing the absence of other people, that begins at one's core and permeates the entire field of one's being. It is the loneliness of alienation from the true self, as if deep in one's center there is a truth pleading for acknowledgment but lost in denial and dread of exposure to the unknown. Risking the acknowledgment of my gay feelings, the expression, the being known for what is true and so long denied, had been terrifying for me.

I was helped, I think, in moving toward the discovery of my true self by the profession I happened to be in. I was accustomed to asking difficult questions of other people. I finally got around to myself.

I will never forget the anguish of the day when I actually made the final decision to leave my comfortable, secure, conventional existence and move to another city, other work, a new life. Luck provided an unexpected visitor that day, an old friend, the late psychologist Sidney Jourard. I had not yet told my employers of my decision to leave. I told Sid, and all the anxiety I was feeling came out with the disclosure. I broke down. I cried. "Am I crazy? Look what I'm giving up. What am I going to? Am I making a terrible mistake? What am I doing?"

Sid smiled and said in his quiet way, "You are re-inventing yourself."

He was right. I didn't know how wonderfully right until the day I arrived in my new city. That day I met the woman I was to be involved with for the next year and a half. I began to live the truth so long defended against, the fulfillment so long denied. With the living out of that truth came a sense of new strength and optimism, came new prerogatives I had only dared dream of before. I could open my life to lesbian women, the one category of persons I had consistently shut out of my experience, almost out of my awareness. I could (and did) make myself available to deeply involving emotional and sexual experience in which I could give up control for the first time and allow another human being access to the inner reaches of my sensuality. When that happened, and it was really different than it had ever been before, I knew I had made the right decision, that my re-invented self was one I would want to spend the rest of my life with, hold up to others as evidence of the rewards of stuggling for truth in self-definition.

The struggle was not over, however. In my fantasies I had longed for intimate connections with women, but when I began to meet many lesbian women I found to my surprise that the old program was still operating. I was often afraid of them. Or, more correctly, I was afraid of the feelings they aroused in me even though there was no longer any reason to deny those feelings. The interplay of past and present, fantasy and reality. Making friends with these women was like making my way back through a mine field that I had myself set. I had to be very cautious for fear I might be destroyed. The old program was very strong in me, and from the outside it looked very different. My cautiousness was seen as aloofness, my manner was interpreted as condescending and rejecting. Insight did not often catch up with experience and I felt alienated from the very people I wanted so much to accept me. It was an exceedingly painful part of the coming out process. It still is.

I was lucky though to have had some women friends who were able to decode my signals, or ignore them, who reached out to me and encouraged me to continue to move among women. Gradually, I learned to let them in, to let them know me, to let myself be touched by them, sometimes very deeply. I am thankful for these women friends. Their's is the kind of understanding and support that all of us need as we learn to identify and replace our old antigay programs.

Deprogramming ourselves is a long and arduous process. In our formative years we were all exposed to the same antigay jokes as our nongay counterparts, the same stereotypes of lesbians and gay men, the same misinformation from our peers. For we gay people who have swallowed all this toxic material, it works against us from the inside while society's homophobes (persons who fear homosexuality and have an antagonistic and punitive attitude toward gay people) work against us from the out-side. In the long run, I am convinced, we will be able to do something collectively about societal oppression. In the short run we each owe it to ourselves to do something now about our self-oppression. We must work to rid our thinking of destructive stereotypes and depersonalizing myths: "Gay people are superficial/immature/disloyal/flighty/narcissistic." "Gay men think only of sex." "Lesbians are angry and over-aggressive." "Gay men can't form lasting relationships."

How often have you heard a gay person stereotype another gay person? Every time we unthinkingly use one of those cliches we tarnish our image. We pay tribute to bigotry and ignorance. Just as we must stop reinforcing the straight world's homophobia by laughing at their fag and dyke jokes, we must stop reinforcing our own homophobia by perpetuating these harmful generalizations about ourselves.

In addition to deprogramming our homophobia, we must also begin to reprogram our thinking about ourselves as gay people. One of the most effective ways we can do that is to substitute accurate for inaccurate information regarding homosexuality and the lives of lesbians and gay men. For instance:

(1) *Homosexuality has existed in every society since the beginning of recorded history, and in many it has been more accepted than it is in our society.* Ford and Beach's classic cross-cultural investigation of sexual behavior found that in 64% of the human cultures studied nomosexuality was considered to be a normal variant of sexual behavior.[1]

(2) *There are over 20 million adults in the United States who are predominantly homosexual in their sexual and affectional orientation.* This widely accepted estimate is supported by statistics provided in 1977 by the (Kinsey) Institute for Sex Research: 13.95% of males and 4.25% of females, or a combined average of 9.13% of the total population, had either extensive or more than incidental homosexual experience.

(3) *It is not known what determines a homosexual or heterosexual orientation.* Many different possibilities have been studied, including genetic and pre-natal factors, hormonal makeup, and early learning experiences.

There is no conclusive scientific evidence that explains how sexual orientation is determined, but there is general agreement (a) that it happens very early in life, well before the age of five, (b) that individuals do not choose their sexual orientation, and (c) that a conscious choice to suppress behavioral expression of one's sexual orientation is possible but is unlikely to be successful over a long period of time.

(4) *Homosexuality is not immoral or unnatural.* To quote Dr. William Reagan Johnson, minister and religious scholar, on the origins of antigay attitudes in Judeo-Christian tradition:

Before we look at the evolution of the antigay bias of the Tradition, we need to acknowledge that the Gospel writers and the missionary Paul did not possess the psychological, sociological, and sexological knowledge which now inform our theological reflections about human sexuality. They knew nothing of sexual orientation or of the natural heterosexual-bisexual-homosexual continuum that exists in human life. They did not postulate that persons engaging in same-gender sex acts could have been expressing *their natural sexuality*. We now know that homosexuality is part of the created order, same-gender sex acts having been observed in a multitude of species from sea gulls to porcupines.[2]

(5) *Homosexuality is not illegal.* There is no state where homosexuality per se is against the law. While there are laws in many states against sexual acts associated with homosexuality, these laws pertain just as much to heterosexuals. However, these laws are enforced in such a way as to discriminate against gay people, gay men in particular. Repeal of these laws, which too often provide the rationale for other forms of discrimination, has been urged by the American Law Institute, the International Congress of Criminal Law, the American Law Committee, the National Commission on Reform of the Federal Criminal Laws, the American Civil Liberties Union, the National Institute of Mental Health and the American Mental Health Foundation.

(6) *Homosexuality is not a mental illness.* During the nineteenth century many social issues previously regarded as moral problems were recast in medical terms. For instance, Benjamin Rush, the father of American psychiatry, proclaimed in print that the color of Negros' skin was due to a mild form of congenital leprosy from which they all suffered.[3] Therefore, according to Rush, whites should not intermarry with Negroes in order to protect posterity from this disorder. Obviously, his diagnosis served as a way to control social conduct. Similarly, homosexuality became a psychiatric diagnosis, and medical stigma replaced religious stigma as a means of social control of a feared and misunderstood group of people. Though homosexuality was erroneously institutionalized over a period of time as a psychiatric problem, it was not until the last few decades that actual research was conducted that demonstrates no greater incidence of mental illness among homosexual persons than among nonhomosexual persons. The most famous of these studies was conducted by Dr. Evelyn Hooker, Chairperson of the National Institute of Mental Health Task Force on Homosexuality.[4] In 1973 the American Psychiatric Association ruled that homosexuality be removed as a mental disorder from its official diagnostic manual. In 1975 the American Psychological Association voted to support the American Psychiatric Association action and passed the following resolution: "Homosexuality per se implies no impairment in judgment, stability, reliability or general social or vocational capabilities."

(7) *Since homosexuality is not an illness it has no cure.* Over the years various mental health practitioners have claimed that they have success-fully re-oriented the sexuality of their patients. There is, however, no sci-entific evidence to back up these claims, nor have objective studies been conducted to test them. To quote Dr. John Money, Professor of Medical Psychology, Department of Psychiatry and Behavioral Sciences, Johns Hopkins University School of Medicine, author or editor of 14 books and over 200 papers in the field of sex research:

> Until the determinants of the complete sequence of human psycho-sexual differentiation have been discovered, any claim to be able to intervene and influence the outcome will be based not on theoretical logic, but on trial-and-error probability. This means that any claim to be able to change homosexuality into heterosexuality will be only as valid as the validity of its counterpart, namely the claim to be able to change heterosexuality into homosexuality.[5]

Of interest here is the following statement by Dr. George Weinberg, author of *Society and the Healthy Homosexual:*

> From what I have seen the harm to the homosexual man or woman done by the person's trying to convert is multifold. Homosexuals should be warned. First of all, the venture is almost certain to fail, and you will lose time and money. But this is the least of it. In trying to convert, you will deepen your belief that you are one of nature's misfortunes. You will intensify your clinging to conventionality, en-large your fear and guilt and regret. You will be voting in your own mind for the premise that people should all act and feel the same ways. . . Your attempt to convert is an assault on your right to do what you want so long as it harms no one, your right to give and re-ceive love, or sensual pleasure without love, in the manner you wish to.[6]

(8) *Gay men are not oversexed and have as much control over their sexual impulses as nongay men.* Until recently the penalties for male homosexual behavior were so severe that gay men generally had no place to meet each other except the most clandestine of environments. Such environments put drastic limits on the ways in which people could re-late. This, added to the fact that men have been socialized to sexually ob-jectify others, created a tradition of clandestine sexual activity as the main social mechanism through which gay men made contact with one another. The increased opportunities for social interaction now avail-able in the more open gay community have supplemented these secret sexual settings as meeting places for gay men, much to the relief of the many individuals who had always felt uncomfortable pressure in situ-ations that were strictly sexual. Lesbians, psychologically less drawn to casual sexual encounter, and socialized to reject multiple sexual contact,

have typically had to meet through established friendship networks, or not at all.

I believe the large numbers of formerly married women coming out as lesbians in the 1970s demonstrates the historical need for more ways for lesbians to meet each other. Now there are such ways and women are using them. Prior to this time, no doubt, countless women, have lived their lives without ever being able to do anything about their lesbian sexuality.

(9) *Gay people are no more prone to molest children than are nongay people.* The facts, according to the National Center on Child Abuse and Neglect, Department of Health, Education and Welfare, are that 90% of all child abuse is committed by heterosexual men on minor females.[7] This myth about gay people is one of the most destructive. It has no basis whatsoever in fact.

(10) *Gay people are not limited in the kinds of careers they can pursue.* I offer a simple device to illustrate this point. The following is a partial listing of gay professional organizations and gay caucuses within professional organizations. I use it to indicate the fields in which lesbians and gay men have established careers and are actively working to protect those careers:

National Lawyers Guild Gay Caucus
Gay Law Students Association
Gay Medical Students Association
Gay Nurses Association
Gay Caucus of the American
  Psychiatric Association
Association of Gay Psychologists
Gay Public Health Workers
Gay Historians and Political
  Scientists Association
Gay Anthropologists Association
Gay Task Force of the American
  Library Association
Association of Gay Social Workers
Association for Gay Seminarians
  and Clergy
Gay Public Employees Federation
Assocation of Gay Educational
  Consultants

Gay Caucus for the Modern Languages
Gay Caucus, American Association
  of Geographers
National Association of Gay
  Gerontologists
Triangle Gay Scientists
Gay Airline Pilots Association
Gay Prizefighters of America
  Association
Gay Academic Union
Gay student groups (on every major
  American college and university
  campus)
Gay teachers groups (in nearly every
  major American city)
Gay business and professional
  organizations (New York, Los
  Angeles, Chicago, Seattle,
  San Francisco, among others)

Obviously, as we have come to say, We are everywhere! And we have been everywhere for a long time. Gay people have been among the world's most renowned and accomplished citizens. Following is a list of prominent individuals who have announced or publicly discussed their homosexuality, compiled for Wallechinsky, Wallace and Wallace's *The Book of Lists.*[8]

Women
Sappho (flourished c. 600 B.C.),
   Greek poet
Christine (1626–1689),
   Swedish Queen
Madame de Stael (1766–1817),
   French author
Charlotte Cushman (1816–1876),
   U.S. actress
Gertrude Stein (1874–1946),
   U.S. author
Alice B. Toklas (1877–1967),
   U.S. author-cook
Virginia Woolf (1882–1941)
   British author
Victoria Sackville-West (1892–1962
   British author
Bessie Smith (1894–1937),
   U.S. singer
Kate Millett (b. 1934,)
   U.S. author
Janis Joplin (1943–1970),
   U.S. singer

Men
Zeno of Elea (fifth century B.C.),
   Greek philosopher
Sophocles (496–406 B.C.).
   Greek playwright
Euripides (480–406 B.C.),
   Greek dramatist
Socrates (470?–399 B.C.),
   Greek philosopher
Aristotle (384–322 B.C.),
   Greek philosopher
Alexander the Great (356–323 B.C.),
   Macedonian ruler
Julius Caesar (100–44 B.C.),
   Roman emperor
Hadrian (76–138 A.D.),
   Roman emperor
Richard the Lion Hearted
   (1157–1199), British king
Richard II (1367–1400), British king
Sandro Botticelli (1444?–1510),
   Italian painter
Leonardo da Vinci (1452–1519),
   Italian painter-scientist
Julius III (1487–1555), Italian pope
Benvenuto Cellini (1500–1571),
   Italian goldsmith
Francis Bacon (1561–1626),
   British philosopher

Christopher Marlowe (1564–1593),
   British playwright
James I (1566–1625), British king
John Milton (1608–1674),
   British author
Jean-Baptiste Lully (1637–1687),
   French composer
Peter the Great (1672–1725),
   Russian czar
Frederick the Great (1712–1786),
   Prussian king
Gustavus III (1746–1792),
   Swedish king
Alexander von Humboldt
   (1769–1859), German naturalist
George Gordon, Lord Byron
   (1788–1824), British poet
Hans Christian Andersen
   (1805–1875), Danish author
Walt Whitman (1819–1892),
   U.S. poet
Horatio Alger (1832–1899),
   U.S. author
Samuel Butler (1835–1902),
   British author
Algernon Swinburne (1837–1909),
   British poet
Peter Ilyich Tchaikovsky (1840–1893),
   Russian composer
Paul Verlaine (1844–1896),
   French poet
Arthur Rimbaud (1854–1900),
   French poet
Oscar Wilde (1854–1900),
   British playwright
Frederick Rolfe (Baron Corvo)
   (1860–1913), British author
Andre Gide (1869–1951),
   French author
Marcel Proust (1871–1922),
   French author
E.M. Forster (1879–1970),
   British author
John Maynard Keynes (1883–1946),
   British economist
Harold Nicholson (1886–1968),
   British author-diplomat
Ernst Rohm (1887–1935),
   German Nazi leader
T.E. Lawrence (1888–1935),
   British soldier-author
Jean Cocteau (1889–1963),
   French author

Waslaw Nijinsky (1890–1950),
  Russian ballet dancer
Bill Tilden (1893–1953),
  U.S. tennis player
Christopher Isherwood (b. 1904),
  British author
Dag Hammarskjold (1905–1961),
  Swedish U.N. secretary-general
W.H. Auden (1907–1973),
  British-U.S. poet
Jean Genet (b. 1910),
  French playwright
Tennessee Williams (b. 1911),
  U.S. playwright

Merle Miller (b. 1919),
  U.S. author
Pier Paolo Pasolini (1922–1975),
  Italian film director
Brendan Behan (1923–1964),
  Irish author
Malcolm Boyd (b. 1923),
  U.S. theologian
Allan Ginsberg (b. 1926), U.S. poet
David Bowie (b. 1947), British singer
Elton John (b. 1947), British singer

How affirming it would be for young gay people to learn of such things early in the development of their gay identity. What a difference it would have made for me to know in my formative years that the thoughts and feelings I was having were not sick and unnatural, that they need not condemn me to a shadow existence outside the mainstream of life. How supportive it would have been to know that so many had gone before me, that so many shared my experience. But to be open to that kind of information I would have first had to label myself as gay, and that I was unwilling to do.

The labeling issue is an important one with regard to the formation of a positive gay identity. Attaching a label to yourself tends to bring that which you are labeling into your consciousness. It becomes a part of your sense of self at a given time. If you are trying to *deny* some aspect of yourself you are unlikely to label yourself in terms of that aspect. Refusing to adopt a particular label will not make that aspect of self less true. It serves only to prolong the process of denial. For years I labeled myself heterosexual. That did not make me one bit less homosexual. It simply delayed resolution of my identity dilemma. And, not incidentally, it also wasted years of my life in an energy-consuming battle between my true sexual nature and the fictional one I devised with the help of my psychoanalytic "friends." I wanted so to please them and all the others who claimed to care about my welfare. But I am convinced that I am diminished as a person because I missed out on those early adult experiences of connectedness in love that expression of my true sexual nature would have brought me. I am very much saddened by the loss of opportunities for natural love in those precious young years.

Many gay people are reticent to apply the labels *lesbian* or *gay* to themselves because they feel they are not ready to integrate that concept into their sense of identity. Or if there is readiness at the private level, they are resisting the label at the interpersonal level. "Why do I have to tell anybody I'm gay? Why do I have to call myself that? What does it

matter?" It matters for two reasons. The first involves personal growth·
the second is political.

First, personal growth. I believe the ability to be self-disclosing is
especially important to the mental health of gay people who have been
subjected to longstanding societal directives that say: be silent, be invisible. The repressive effect on one's ability to communicate about self has
to be a strong one. In general, the ability to make one's self known to
others is critical to the successful establishment of relationships with
other people. It is not only critical to one's social development, it is essential to the growth of intimacy in close, loving relationships.

Self-disclosure tends to reduce the mystery that people have for one
another. In so doing it facilitates honest communication and builds trust
between people. It brings people out of isolation and makes possible understanding of that which was previously perplexing or even frightening.
For gay people, this is particularly important—the demystification of
gayness through personalized disclosure: The simple words, "I am gay."
The affirming act that says, "I will no longer be silent. I will no longer be
invisible. I am understandable. I am natural. I have the right to live my
truth rather than living a lie to preserve someone else's fantasy of how
the world should be." It is the acceptance of reality that is the hallmark
of the healthy personality.

There is a subtle variation of the labeling dilemma that also deserves
attention. It is the situation in which a person says, "Why do I have to
call myself gay (lesbian)? The people I work with know. My family
knows. My straight friends know. We just don't *talk* about it." Let's
think of this arrangement as an unspoken contract that might read something like this:

> Party of the first part agrees not to identify reality: "I'm gay.
> _____ is my lover."
>   Parties of the second part agree not to withhold social invitations/
> job advancements/respect/admiration/acceptance/love/etc.
>   Parties of the second part are allowed the luxury of never having
> to deal directly with the *awful* reality of homosexuality in their
> midst.
>   Party of the first part is allowed to remain in their midst.

What is wrong with this? I believe what is wrong shows up in the small
print, this unspoken contract where party-of-the-first-part's conduct is
even further restricted. It's the statements that are censored before they
are spoken because they're too revealing of intimacy. It's the second
thoughts about who else to invite. ("He's a little too obvious for Dad to
take.") It's the pictures put away, the books slipped to the bottom of the
pile, the word *gay* carefully left out of the conversation. It's the caress

cut short, the kiss never given, the thousand little compromises that mean nothing individually but add up to the blunting of experience, the demeaning of love, the spoiling of identity that are too much a part of our gay lives already. I think it is time to break this deadly contract, to negotiate a new one that enables love and trust rather than fear and embarrassment to determine the limits of relationships with those we care about.

The second reason why it matters for gay people to identify themselves as gay is political. As an individual you may or may not be ready to make this your business, but you should at least be aware of it. The changes that are needed in social policies and in laws in order to improve the quality of life for gay people will come only when there is a political and economic gay constituency that is visible and identifiable. We have the numbers of people but as long as we remain a "phantom population" the numbers are useless. The politician will continue to say, "I don't think I have enough gay constituents to warrant my support of your proposed legislation." The regulatory agency will say, "Gay people are not a significantly large enough segment of the community to justify a change in the regulations." The corporate decision makers will say, "There is not enough of a gay buying public to pay attention to your demands or your protests." The social agencies will say, "There is not a demonstrated need for special programs for gay people."

Voting power counts only when the constituency is a visible and identifiable one. Buying power counts only when the consumer group is a visible and identifiable one.

Only when we begin to come out of the shadows in large numbers will we be seen. Only when we begin to speak up and identify ourselves in large numbers will we be heard. Only when we tell them who we are, what we are, and where we are in large numbers will they pay attention to our needs and concerns. Not before. That is the political and economic reality. We will have to confront it sooner or later.

Finally, I would like to look at the development of personal identity in the context of what life is about for most gay people, and what it might be about in the future.

In heterosexual society there is a tendency to measure the progress of one's life according to a predetermined pattern revolving around the development of the nuclear family: mother, father, children. Much that happens for an individual from about puberty on, takes on meaning in relation to eventually becoming a marriage partner and a parent. This is one of the major "tracks" of modern life. Progress along this nuclear family track is marked by certain events that signify how far one has come and how far there is yet to travel. Because of their symbolic importance I shall call them ritual events: first dates, courtships, engagements, weddings, childbirth, etc. There is comfort in the knowledge that someone has passed this way before, that there is precedence for one's experience, that something is known about the passage ahead. These ritual events give form to one's life and the notion that it is all about something quite understandable.

For gay people it is different. Without the nuclear family track to move along, how do we know if we're making progress as we go? What does give form and continuity to our lives?

First of all, gay people have the same needs that nongay people have. We too need to feel worthwhile, to feel safe, to feel free of pain and suffering. We too need to achieve and acquire. We too need to love and be loved. We too need to do for others and to generate projects that will endure beyond our own lifetime. These are the internally generated needs that motivate most of human endeavor, including involvement in the nuclear family drama.

Where we *are* different is in some of the mechanisms we are developing to meet our needs when heterosexual mechanisms won't work for us. The nuclear family arrangement is one heterosexual mechanism that doesn't work for us, so we are developing other ways of meeting our needs for affiliation, security, altruism and immortality. For instance, we have replaced the straight marriage with the same-sex lover partnership. Many of us have replaced or supplemented our straight family of origin with a gay friendship/support group with whom we can more easily share the joys and struggles of our gay lives. The gay movement itself is a resource for support and positive identification, offering opportunities for involvement in a collective effort to change the quality of life for gay people in our lifetime and beyond.

What we have been lacking is a way of formally calibrating our progress through life. To remedy this we should begin to think in terms of our own special, life-affirming, gay growth track. The end point of the track is the validation of our gay existence just as the nuclear family track validates the heterosexual existence of those who follow it. As with the nuclear family track, ritual events would be the symbolic markers of forward movement along the gay growth track. Such ritual events have the purpose of signaling the end of one period in a person't life and the beginning of another. They give us permission to leave behind many of the thoughts, feelings and behaviors that belong to the period that is ending and to adopt new ones for the period being entered into. Some of these ritual events by which we might calibrate our gay lives are:

(1) The first acknowledgment of gayness to one's self.
(2) The first sexual experience with a person of the same gender.
(3) The first disclosure of gayness to a nongay person.
(4) Beginning the first lover relationship.
(5) Moving into the first domicile shared with a lover.

(6) First involvement in the organized gay community.

(7) Other important disclosures to family, friends, co-workers, and so on.

Just as nongay people plan a life to include courtship, marriage and the arrival of children, gay persons should plan for the ritual events of gay life that move them toward the validation of gayness and its complete integration into their identiy. The organizing principle of such a plan would be to develop the ability to live one's gayness openly at home, on the job, in the family of origin and in the world generally. The process of putting the plan into action is what would give form and purpose and continuity to our gay lives.

Achieving the goal of an open and integrated gay identity might mean starting work on it early. For instance, careful vocational planning would include preparing, while still young, for an occupation or profession in which there is maximum freedom from constraints imposed by other people. Or it might mean restructuring one's income-producing activity later in life to enable such freedom. It would also mean planning and preparing early for disclosure to family and friends that one is gay, so that deception does not have to be a way of life with those closest to you. It might also require a shift in one's value system. For instance, a lifestyle designed to bring primarily material reward might have to be refocused to give higher priority to projects that would yield personal freedom. No longer could one say, with credibility, "I've got the house with the swimming pool, the cars, the trips, and everything else I ever wanted. Why should I jeopardize it all?" In the well-designed gay life no one will have made it until they are able to be as openly gay as they choose to be, in any area of their life, at any given time.

The challenge of achieving such a free and validated life is the crisis of courage out of which our gay future will be born.

FOOTNOTES

1. Ford, C. S., and Beach, F. A. *Patterns of Sexual Behavior.* New York, Harper & Brothers, 1951.

2. Johnson, W. R. "Protestantism and Gay Freedom." In *Positively Gay.* Berzon, Betty, and Leighton, Robert. (eds.), Millbrae, Calif., Celestial Arts, 1979.

3. Rush, Benjamin. "Observations intended to favour a supposition that the black Color (as it is called) of the Negroes is derived from the LEPROSY." *Transactions of the American Philosophical Society,* 289–297, 1799.

4. Hooker, Evelyn. "The adjustment of the male homosexual." *Journal of Projective Techniques,* Vol. 21, 18–31, 1957. Also published in Ruitenbeek, Hendrik M. (ed). *The Problem of Homosexuality in Modern Society.* Dutton, 1963.

5. Money, John. "Bisexual, homosexual, and heterosexual: society, law, and medicine." *Journal of Homosexuality,* Vol. 2, No. 3, Spring 1977.

6. Weinberg, George. *Society and the Healthy Homosexual.* New York, St. Martin's Press, 1972. (Paperback Edition: Anchor Books, 1973).

7. *Child Abuse and Neglect: The Problem and Its Management.* Washington, D.C.: U.S. Dept. of Health, Education and Welfare, National Center on Child Abuse and Neglect, DHEW Publication No. (OHD) 75-30073.

8. Wallechinsky, David; Wallace, Irving; and Wallace, Amy. *The Book of Lists.* New York, Bantam Books, 1978.

The Changing Lesbian Social Scene

Teresa DeCrescenzo, M.S.W., and Lillene Fifield, M.S.W.

"Please send a copy of your bibliography. Or, if not that, please send help!" Those are lines from a letter sent to Barbara Gittings, a lesbian activist for more than 20 years. This is one of many such letters from lesbians throughout the country, women who live in remote locations far from large cities, who feel isolated and without social contact resources.

While there are unique problems encountered by women living in areas of the country far removed from large cities, the lesbian social milieu of today offers more options for social contact in a wider range of settings than ever before.

There was a time in our not too distant past when the lesbian social scene consisted of softball and bowling leagues, private parties and secret organizations that were accessible only through personal introduction. Many lesbians still play softball and join bowling leagues, attend private parties, and join secret lesbian groups. However, we are no longer restricted to these few choices and we find increasing support and validation for the many varied lifestyles we choose.

Many of us have chosen to work in national gay and women's political organizations, most of which have chapters in large cities throughout the country and often in smaller communities. Here, we find opportunities to work on meaningful women's issues and lesbian issues, while broadening social contacts at the same time.

In addition to reaping the benefits of expanded social contacts individually, our increased lesbian visibility has provided the impetus for considerable attitude change within the women's movement. For example, many chapters of NOW (National Organization for Women) have formed lesbian rights task forces, where NOW members work specifically on issues of concern to lesbians, provide a setting for valuable contributions of time and energy, and are an excellent forum for gay/straight dialog. As a result, the perception of lesbians as a "lavender menace" in the Women's Movement is diminishing and the once-sharp lines of division between lesbian and nonlesbian women are disappearing.

This broad change was perhaps best illustrated at the International Women's Year conference in Houston, in November 1977. The overwhelming majority of women from all economic, social, racial, political, ethnic, cultural, educational and religious backgrounds were in support of the resolution to eliminate discrimination on the basis of sexual and affectional preference. That assemblage went further to urge that state legislators reform penal codes and repeal state laws that restrict private sexual behavior between consenting adults.

But what about those of us who do not have the choice of working in the gay or lesbian movement, those of us for whom IWY was only a television event? Where are our options for work and play, for meeting new people and making new friends, or for finding a lover? For women who can't move to a large city, Gittings suggests we have to do it for ourselves. Often, when our loneliness and isolation are based mainly on geography, we just don't do enough for ourselves. For purely social contact, Gittings advocates the *open house* model, originally developed by a Washington, D.C., lesbian. The format is simple; there are no games, no structured raps and no entertainment. Lesbians, and those who think they might be gay, are free to just drop in on the specified evening. There is a relaxed feeling in this kind of setting that is often lacking in the sometimes rigid, structured organizational gatherings. And the woman who undertakes this type of outreach need have no special political credentials.

Publicizing this kind of ongoing social event is a major problem. People who are not a part of a movement and who have no organizational ties often only read mainstream newspapers or watch television. Consequently, unless you can afford an ad in your local newspaper, a more creative approach is needed. Gittings suggests posting notices in places we all use, such as supermarkets and laundromats.

The gay movement offers additional opportunities for contact with other women, though some lesbians are hesitant to work in it. Their concern usually centers around the necessity of confronting sexism in gay men that is also found in the larger heterosexual male society. As more men's attitudes change and more gay men ask for lesbians to conduct consciousness-raising sessions, larger numbers of gay women are working in the movement, expanding not only their social outlets, but their horizons as well.

Perhaps the broadest area of increased social options for lesbians in the 1970s is our emerging and growing culture, especially a very real and clearly defined lesbian perspecitve within the arts. We are producing cultural forms which truly reflect a lesbian consciousness—art, dance, music, poetry, fiction and theater—all vehicles for reflecting the uniqueness of the lesbian perspective. They have given rise to some of the most popular social events in our environment.

Women's concerts, dances, peotry readings, comedy and theater provide social experience with content that, for some of us, speaks to our lives. Women's concert production companies have emerged throughout the country, and whole networks for tours are now possible for lesbian performers. Yearly, there are two National Women's Music Festivals (largely lesbian) held in Champaign-Urbana, Illinois, and in Mount Pleasant, Michigan.

These products of our emerging culture—the music, the theater, the comedy and the poetry—are usually feminist in orientation and tend to reflect our daily lives. The price of admission is usually modest and women often feel a sense of pride and sharing by spending their money in support of women artists. However, for those of us who do not enjoy the current dances, or who find that women's music and women's bands do not speak to our lives, some of these events can be a nightmare of ear-splitting sounds, relentless in their attack on our eardrums.

The traditional lesbian bar remains intricately woven into the fabric of our social lives. Despite political objections against allowing ourselves to be ghettoized, bars survive as a staple gay social contact, though in a slightly different form than previously. For those who enjoy bars and disco dancing, the quality of lesbian bars is being upgraded. Women are no longer accepting substandard decor or limited music selection.

The impact of disco music has not been lost on some entrepreneurial lesbians. Portable disco and D.J. shows complete with strobe lights and pulsating sound systems, are available in metropolitan areas to provide a comfortable environment for social interaction.

Lesbian publications are an important source of information about events and happenings within the women's community. They are often the main advertising vehicle employed by openly lesbian businesses and entertainers, since they are guaranteed to reach a lesbian audience. They frequently provide the only source of news information of importance to the lesbian community, and they generally calendar social events open to, or exclusively for, lesbians.

Probably the best known, and certainly the longest lived, lesbian publication is the *Lesbian Tide*, a Los Angeles–based bimonthly newsmagazine published by the Tide Collective. Though dominated by a political point of view, the *Tide* provides excellent coverage of newsworthy events, both local and national.[1] A newer publication, also national in scope, is the *Lesbian Connection*. It has the advantage of a less constricted political agenda. This monthly newletter is free, though it requires donations of money and time to keep afloat and it provides space for the most radical political thought and for the most timid inquiries from lesbians who are just beginning to reach out for support. The *Lesbian Connection* is one way for isolated lesbians to keep in touch with other lesbians.[2] A number of new magazines and newsletters have recently begun to take hold, and the prospect for growth in the area of lesbian-oriented publishing looks promising.

For lesbians who enjoy sports and the outdoors, there is an ever-increasing range of choices for recreational activities, from inexpensive hikes with an all-lesbian group to luxury excursions arranged by lesbian travel agents.

In addition to softball and bowling leagues, we now find gay ski clubs, backpacking groups, bicycling treks, sailing clubs and tennis clubs, and competent women ready to teach these skills. In Los Angeles, for example, it is possible to take sailing lessons from United States Coast Guard certified lesbian sailors who are experienced in coastal piloting and celestial navigation. In addition to teaching theory classes onshore and a shipboard practicum, Seaworthy Women offers day-long pleasure trips, weekend cruises and week-long excursions on the 31-foot mariner auxiliary ketch Esperanza (hope). The women who operate this enterprise, Ellen Power and Jeanine Talley, are as seaworthy as their fully outfitted vessel. They believe that the experience of living outdoors while acquiring sailing skills gives women a feeling of increased competence that transfers to other areas of our lives.[3]

Another California recreational endeavor, Women in the Wilderness, offers a wide range of outdoor activities, and also approaches recreation with a feminist perspective. In Whitewater Rafting Self-Confidence Workshop on the Klamath River, participants are able to compare individual and team effort on an oar-powered paddle raft. Women from around the country have joined in such unique adventures as a Sea Vegetable Workshop, in which participants combed the Marin County (California) beach, gathering and preparing edible sea vegetables for later use in multiple-course meals. Women in the Wilderness also sponsor work parties on the Jug Handle Nature Preserve in Mendocino, California, where they do their bit to preserve the natural environment. A mother/daughter trip on the Stanislaus River is another popular outing and offers an unusual opportunity for lesbian mothers to make social contact with one another in an atmosphere sure to be a hit with their children.[4]

Camping Women is a feminist venture that blends social activities with an outdoor program structured to enhance self-awareness and build confidence. From their base in Sacramento, California, Emily Mast, Charlotte Williams and Marsha Ross offer cross-country skiing, autumn hikes, bike tours of the Delta River area and a women's mountaineering course.[5]

Those of us who are not up to the rigors of the great outdoors, and who can afford the time and the money to travel some distance, can join the many luxury tours available through feminist and lesbian travel agencies. One such agency in Los Angeles is Womantours, where Estilita Grimaldo specializes in women's group excursions. One exotic trip organized by Grimaldo is an all-lesbian vacation on a remote island off the coast of Costa Rica. The tantalizing Jesusita Island (which translates "little female Jesus") has one hotel and miles of smogless, people-free beach to tempt the adventuresome.[6]

Of course, many of us are not able to afford luxury tours and may find that neither are we compatible with mother nature nor do we find dances to be our milieu. For some of us, the most viable means of making social contact with other lesbians is through gay caucuses or gay special interest groups of national professional organizations. There is a visible organized gay representation within many professions now. A partial listing includes: Association of Gay Psychologists; Association of Gay Social Workers; Bay Area Physicians for Human Rights, Caucus of Gay Counselors/American Association of Counselors and Guidance Personnel; Committee of Gay Historians/American Historical Association; Gay Caucus of the American Association of Geographers; Gay Caucus for the Modern Language/Modern Language Association; Gay Caucus for the National Council of Teachers of English; Gay Caucus of the National Educational Association; Gay Caucus of the National Lawyers Guild; Gay Cultural Festival; Gay Lawyers Guild; Gay People in Medicine; Gay Teachers Association; Lesbian Herstory Archives; Lesbians in Law; Triangle Area Gay Scientists.[7]

The list is extensive, impressive and heartening, since these groups generally meet in a setting designed to facilitate the social process, with format and content geared to the interests of those within a particular profession.

A gay organization whose interest encompasses all of the professional and academic disciplines is the Gay Academic Union.[8] Lesbian academics, college and university faculty, professionals and anyone interested in working toward the end of discrimination against women and gays will find GAU responsive. Some events sponsored by GAU are purely social, others are educational, and there is a panoply of projects designed to combine social connections with intellectual stimulation.

Some chapters have formed women's committees which have in turn formed lesbian research groups, theatre groups, art groups and lesbian history groups. GAU also sponsors a scholarship fund for lesbian and gay male students and it presents a major conference each year over

Thanksgiving weekend. The fifth GAU conference was held in Los Angeles in 1978 and included original theater, music, poetry readings, panels and research reportage. Lesbian visibility was high at GAU 5, and is likely to increase in the future.

Younger lesbians and lesbians on college campuses can usually find at least two opportunities for meeting other lesbians. Campus women's centers are frequented by lesbians and often provide lesbian support groups. Campuses throughout the country also have gay student unions. Some of the larger universities in urban areas have lesbian student organizations in addition, so that being a lesbian on a college campus today need not be the isolating experience it once was.

Women's centers outside of the academic environment are available in many cities throughout the United States and are another rich source of lesbian social contact. Perhaps the most notable is the Los Angeles Women's Building, which provides a forum for displaying lesbian art, poetry, theater, music and dance.[9] Like most women's centers, LAWB offers topics of interest to lesbians and sponsors workshops in many diverse areas, such as lesbian sexuality, consciousness-raising, self-defense, lesbian literature and lesbian therapy. One is also likely to find many courses, conferences and workshops on subjects and issues relevant to most women and certainly of interest to lesbians. Supporting a women's cultural center has not been a priority item for most American cities, so such centers are often on shaky financial grounds. We urge you to seek out and support a women's center in your community—or start one of your own.

We will not discuss the oppression suffered by gay people within most organized religions. However, a number of organizations have developed in response to those gay women and men who do not want to choose between their religion and the expression of their sexuality. Some of these groups exist with the official blessing of the mainstream religious institution, others without.

The largest and best known alternative church is Metropolitan Community Church, founded by the Reverend Troy Perry in 1968. MCC has grown in its nearly 11 years of existence to have several hundred branches throughout the United States and in many foreign countries. It has lesbian and nonlesbian women ministers and has undertaken the major task of examining scripture in an effort to ferret out sexist language.[10]

Dignity, an organization of gay Catholics, has provoked considerable dialog among the policy makers of the Catholic Church. Gay and sympathetic nongay priests celebrate Mass and offer the Sacraments to gay Catholics.[11]

Integrity, an organization open to gay Episcopalians, also has a number of branches providing religious counsel, Mass, meetings and social events.[12]

Temple Beth Chayim Chadashim, a member of the Union of American Hebrew Congregations, has many impressive achievements. Recently it sponsored the Third International Conference of Gay Jews. The conference was attended by nearly 300 Jews from around the country and the world. The fourth ICGJ is scheduled to be held in Israel in 1979.[13]

For lesbians for whom these resources are unavailable or impractical, there are getting-acquainted services and dating services. Undoubtedly the best known of these services is the Wishing Well, a California-based, national introduction service. For a small fee, the subscriber places an ad in the organization's magazine, indicating the kind of person she is and the type of women she would like to meet. Confidentiality, discretion and good taste are the trademarks of the Wishing Well. Subscribers have code numbers; responses from interested readers are channeled through the Wishing Well offices to the original advertiser. Conspicuously absent is the explicit sexual language that typifies male-oriented publications.[14] For some women, especially those living in isolated geographic areas, this type of service is a valuable option. The Wishing Well is clearly successful, for its services have recently expanded to include travel and tour arrangements.

There are also a number of directories listing women's organizations and groups, lesbian groups, gay organizations and groups, as well as bars and showrooms. Specifically of relevance to lesbians are those directories which limit their listings to organizations, groups, places and events that interest us. The best known lesbian directory is GAIA's Guide,[15] which lists travel agencies, bars, clubs, political organizations, churches, services and special interest groups by state and city. It is nearly impossible to keep a current listing of resources for lesbians.[16] Despite heroic efforts to be current, the 1978 edition of GAIA's Guide had inaccuracies in it. However, it is unquestionably the most reliable directory of lesbian-oriented groups throughout the world.

Too often, there is little attention paid by any of the resources we've mentioned thus far to reach black, Asian and third-world lesbians. When there is an outreach, you can almost count on its being political. So, it is refreshing to note that there is at least one *purely social* club, Debreta's in Los Angeles with an outreach to black lesbians. While Debreta's welcomes all racial and ethnic groups, their membership is mainly black. They have sponsored a variety of events, including cruises, family picnics, theater and dinner parties, house parties and two New Year's Eve dances.[17]

As we continue to expand our social contact options, we seem also to expand the variety of alternative living arrangements. While most of us still live in cities, some of us are living in collectives and communes and many of us have moved to the country, to farms and land trusts. We seem to be moving away, many of us, from patterning our lives after the traditional family structure, our only model until quite recently. Lesbians are beginning to realize that the isolation that sometimes occurs in a one-person or two-person household is not a model we must follow. As we continue to reclaim our lives and find ourselves wanting to share more of ourselves with more women, we are increasingly able to broaden the variety of living arrangements with which we are willing to experiment.

For those of us who do not move to the country, farms and land trusts offer a temporary haven for respite from taxing city life. Many women's retreats permit weekend or longer visits for lesbians who just want to get back to themselves and make contact with other women in a pastoral setting.[18]

Is it possible that our trek from softball leagues to the floor of International Women's Year, from autumn hikes to the demanding rigors of lesbian politics has left you still feeling isolated and alone? We asked Ivy Bottini[19] the question: "What if there just isn't any organized gay or lesbian group in a given geographic area?" She advised joining any group of women you see involved in social action, and you will likely find a lesbian.

Gittings admonishes: "We can't expect deliverance. We must do more for ourselves. Don't be discouraged if you don't meet someone congenial on the first outing. Stay around. Come back again. As soon as you walk out of the door, another lesbian may walk in, look around, feel uncomfortable, and also leave."

In conclusion, we can safely say that we no longer seem destined to be socially and geographically isolated from one another, finding each other only by fortuitous accident or through someone who knows someone. The barriers are coming down, the laws are changing, and neither social custom nor prejudice can keep women in an inferior position or away from one another. We are moving toward each other, we are moving forward, together, in a spirit of self-affirmation. We are becoming more and more self-defined. Our friendships, our support networks and our social contact points reflect our definitions of what a lesbian is, what a lesbian wants and what our lives can be.

FOOTNOTES

1. *Lesbian Tide*, 8706 Cadillac Ave., Los Angeles, CA 90034
2. *Lesbian Connection* is published by Ambitious Amazons, P.O. Box 811, East Lansing, MI 48823
3. Seaworthy Women, 2210 Wilshire Blvd., Suite 254, Santa Monica, CA 90403
4. Women in the Wilderness, 13 Columbus Ave., San Francisco, CA 94111
5. Camping Women, 2720 Armstrong Drive, Sacramento, CA 95825
6. Womantours, 5314 No. Figueroa St., Los Angeles, CA 90042
7. For information on any of these caucuses, or any material in this chapter,

please send a stamped, self-addressed envelope to: Teresa DeCrescenzo, P.O. Box 633, Hollywood, CA 90028

8. Gay Academic Union, National Headquarters, P.O. Box 927, Hollywood, CA 90028

9. Los Angeles Women's Building, 1727 No. Spring St., Los Angeles, CA 90012

10. For information on locations of Metropolitan Community Churches, please write: M.C.C., 1050 So. Hill Street, Los Angeles, CA 90015

11. For information on Dignity chapters, please write: Dignity/LA, Box 27516, Los Angeles, CA 90027

12. For information on Integrity chapters, please write: Integrity/LA, 5629 Monte Vista, #37, Los Angeles, CA 90042.

13. Temple Beth Chayim Chadishim, 600 W. Pico, Los Angeles, CA 90035

14. The Wishing Well, P.O. Box 664, Novato, CA 94947

15. GAIA's Guide, 115 New Montgomery St., San Francisco, CA 94105.

16. See *Our Right to Love*, Ginny Vida, ed., Prentice-Hall, 1978

17. Debreta's, P.O. Box 4232, Inglewood, CA 90302

18. Some land trusts, retreats: Ozark Women on Land, P.O. Box 521, Fayetteville, Ark., 72701; Nourishing Space, Cave Canyon Ranch, Box D-11, Vail AZ 85641; Womanhill, 6517 Dry Creek Road, Napa, CA 94558

19. Ivy Bottini, long-time lesbian activist is currently Director, Women's Resource Center, Gay Community Services Center, 1213 No. Highland Ave., Hollywood, CA 90038

For Men: New Social Opportunities

Robert Leighton

The modern gay liberation movement is about ten years old. It has been a turbulent period, with freedoms opening up to gay people as never before. The ability of increasing thousands of men and women to say openly and proudly, "I am gay," to their parents, their employers, their non-gay friends, is just short of miraculous.

For a man of my generation, the changes that have taken place in that short span of time are nothing short of mind-boggling. I first recognized my homosexuality 26 years ago, at the age of 14. It was a devastating experience. Although I had only a vague idea of what the term *homosexual* meant, I knew it applied to me and that it made me somehow different from my family, friends and schoolmates. I felt alone, an aloneness so singular that for a short period of time I felt sure that I was the only homosexual in the world, with no one to turn to, no one to confide in, nowhere to go for understanding or help.

I recall walking down a street in the small Ohio city where I grew up. It was early evening. The implications of my newly discovered identity were racing through my mind. The terror that I felt must have shown clearly on my face and in my eyes, for a man stopped to ask what was wrong, saying I looked as if I had just lost my best friend. Even though only a short time had passed since the realization of my homosexuality, I knew intuitively that I could not tell this kindly stranger the truth. I mumbled some excuse and continued my walk on a darker, less trafficked street where my features couldn't be so easily seen.

The thoughts racing through my mind on that fateful evening were horrifying—and remain so in recollection. I felt more than alone in the world—I felt that I was sudenly so different that my life held no future. I seriously contemplated suicide for the first—and thankfully the only—

24

time in my life. At that point in my life I could not face the idea of a life that seemed so radically different from that of my family and friends. I felt cursed; death seemed the only way to dispel the curse. I was fortunate. I managed to overcome that self-destructive impulse.

An early interest in the theater had led me to the local community theater where there were other gay men, their gayness unknown at that point to me. One of them recognized what was happening to me and offered help and understanding. He confided the fact of his own homosexuality and assured me that I was not nearly as alone as I thought. This reassurance was enough to lift my spirits. As I slowly became aware of other men and women who were also homosexual and came to know them, I realized that I was far from alone in the world. Although that knowledge did not make me feel less guilty about who and what I was, and I continued to deny my true identity to my family and nongay friends, I was able to enter the clandestine world of homosexuality that existed even in that small city. I learned to cope, to lie, to lead the double life forced upon us by a disapproving society.

By the time I was graduated from high school I was adept at hiding myself, having two sets of friends, each ignorant of the other's existence. In a few short years I had adapted to my closet and was reasonably happy there. I had no choice. No other avenues were open to me.

At 18, though, I was ready for a larger world, one where I was sure life would be easier. I set out for New York City and for college, like thousands upon thousands of other young men, certain that in that huge metropolis I would find more than the two dingy gay bars my hometown had to offer; more than the few friends I had made who were even more firmly ensconced in their closets than I.

To my disappointment, I found New York was not much different from Youngstown. Granted, there were far more gay people (the term *gay* was just then coming into general use) but they weren't much easier to find. For the most part they, too, were locked firmly in their closets. The few gay bars in New York at the time—surprisingly few, considering the population of the city—were just as unsavory and dingy as those I had known at home. For the most part Mafia-owned and operated, the bars were difficult to locate because the police closed them regularly. And just as regularly, they would reopen a day or two later at a new address. But the staff remained the same, including the doorman, who always looked as if he had just stepped out of a Hollywood gangster film. (And if you didn't look gay enough to him, you didn't get in!)

The only other social/sexual meeting places then were clandestine settings where you exposed yourself to the very real possibility of arrest.

Unless one had gay friends, the bars, the baths and the parks were the main outlets available to gay men in the largest city in the country.

Again I was fortunate. In summer stock, I had met gay theater people from New York. Since I had the distinct feeling I was putting myself on the auction block every time I entered a gay bar, and since the baths were unknown to me, and since I was much too frightened of arrest to risk cruising the parks, I relied on my small circle of theater friends to introduce me to new people. And through them I eventually met a young man, fell in love and began a relationship modeled after heterosexual marriage—monogamous, uptight and ultimately unworkable. Except for mutual acquaintances, we shut ourselves off from the world and clung to each other for companionship and security. My closet had become a little larger, but it was still not all that different from Ohio.

The story of my coming out is not very different from the stories of thousands of other men of my generation. I knew this and took comfort from it while still yearning for a different world, a world where I could be myself—the same self—to everyone I knew, rather than one person to my gay friends, another to my nongay friends.

I am continually amazed at the changes in gay life I have witnessed over the past few years. How different my life would have been if gay youth groups had been available to me at 14, when I was facing my own gayness. My initial reaction might not have been very different, but I'm certain that had I found peer support, accepting myself as gay would have come far sooner and with much less trauma. Today, of course, gay youth groups exist in almost every sizeable city in the country. Where a gay community center exists, or the Metropolitan Community Church, young men and women will find youth groups and counselors providing outreach and support that simply didn't exist a few years ago. In some cities, even high schools have gay student unions that offer support groups and discussion groups, as well as social outlets.

One of the continuing goals of gay liberation has been the establishment of a gay community, a concept unknown in my youth. To a remarkably large measure, that has happened and continues to happen. The establishment of gay liberation groups around the country, in response to the Stonewall rebellion in New York City, was the first step in creating a community of gay women and men, and establishing social, as opposed to sexual, meeting grounds for members of the community.

Some readers can perhaps only imagine the sense of wonder, excitement, purpose and fulfillment that the movement created, seemingly overnight. For the first time it was possible to meet other gay people in a nonsexual atmosphere, an atmosphere charged with courage, vision, selflessness. Suddenly gay people had new considerations, new goals and commitments that permitted interactions on levels previously unthought of. Suddenly gay people were thinking and planning for the future. The possibilities appeared endless, the horizon unlimited. Gay people were discovering the joys of communication, of sharing, of dreaming. And they began to realize that it wasn't enough to educate the nongay world; gay people as well had to become educated, had to reevaluate themselves and learn about themselves, had to cast off the guilt they were cloaked in and begin to see themselves as whole human beings.

Rap groups formed, at first in individual homes, as a first step in bringing together people seeking to learn and communicate with like-minded people. For the first time, gay people were sharing, learning and meeting for the common goals of self-education and self-realization.

As these private groups began to proliferate, the need was seen for a more open outreach to other gays. In Los Angeles, out of the early gay liberation movement came the country's first gay community center. It seemed another impossible dream—a building to house the many services which the new gay community sorely needed. When the idea was first put forth, it seemed to many like pie-in-the-sky. How would it ever be accomplished, where would the money come from, who would come?

With vision, selflessness and an inability to concede defeat or recognize the word *impossible*, with a bank balance of $18 and an uncertain future, the Gay Community Services Center of Los Angeles was born. To humble beginnings, to be sure. A ramshackle old house was found on Wilshire Boulevard, in a decidedly seedy part of town, and a sign proclaiming its existence was erected in front of the building. Its ambitious projects included health clincs for men and women; an employment program; rap groups (open to anyone interested) on myriad subjects; a speakers bureau; outreach to both older and younger gays; and referral services for housing, welfare, counseling, legal services, and alcohol and drug abuse programs. First one building, then two, were acquired to house the homeless gays who pour into Los Angeles yearly.

The primary question—Would anyone come?—was quickly answered. They came in droves, with a sense of community that had never before existed. The center grew and grew and grew, continually expanding its services and facilities, and today it occupies its own building in the heart of Hollywood where it is a center of activity from early morning until late at night.

Gay community centers rapidly appeared in cities across the nation, providing services and social outlets that had not existed before, while building gay communities in those cities. Since then have come special-interest groups to meet the various needs of gay people. Today there exist in the United States over 2000 gay organizations, according to the National Gay Task Force, 80 Fifth Avenue, New York, NY 10011.

In Los Angeles alone there are over 300 gay groups and organizations, including two gay political clubs affiliated with the Democratic Party; a gay Republican club; the ACLU Gay Rights Chapter (one of the largest

ACLU chapters in California); the Community Guild, comprised of business and professional people; gay outdoors clubs (sailing, hiking, prospecting) and gay ski clubs; an organization for black gays and two organizations representing gay Chicanos; two organizations for handicapped gays; a classical music listening group; a Bible study group; 14 separate gay student organizations. The Gay Academic Union, for academics and professional persons, is presently headquartered in Los Angeles and has chapters in many cities, as well as affiliates in several foreign countries and satellite groups that feature speakers and rap groups.

Reflecting the diversity of interests within the gay community, there are also such organizations as Gay Overeaters Anonymous (and the Fat Underground), 28 gay male motorcycle clubs and at least one lesbian motorcycle club. Gay Teachers of Los Angeles was one of the first such organizations in the country.

The Metropolitan Community Church, founded in 1968 in Los Angeles by the Rev. Troy Perry, today has several hundred branches around the world, which provide an astounding array of services. For other denominations there are organizations like Dignity (for gay Roman Catholics); Integrity (for gay Episcopalians); Lutherans Concerned; gay study groups within the Unitarian Church; temples and study groups for gay Jews.

Almost every conceivable interest has spawned at least an informal group, if not a formal organization. To find a group to satisfy your individual needs and interests, scan the classified ads in gay publications or obtain a copy of the GaYellow Pages (published by Renaissance House, Box 292 Village Station, New York, NY 10014), probably the most complete listing of gay organizations, businesses and publications available today.

It is unfortunate that most of these social outlets are available only in major cities and in smaller cities and towns with universities and colleges. I believe, however, that in the not too distant future the present situation will change.

Despite the proliferation of groups and organizations, bars and baths remain the primary meetings places for many gay men. But even the bars and baths have changed in the past ten years. They are no longer dirty, dingy, poorly lit rooms to be entered through back alleys. Whether discotheque, nightclub, cocktail lounge or restaurant, it is always a pleasant surprise to enter one of these establishments and find a smart surrounding, courteous staff and open, friendly atmosphere. The gay disco scene in particular has set trends in music, has established stars in the music world and has attracted nongay customers to their uninhibited, freewheeling interiors.

The gay bath house has changed for the better. My first such experience took place in New York in the early '60s. The bathhouse was big and crowded; it was also dirty, unsavory and repressive. Today, in major cities, gay men have a choice of baths to attend that are clean, open and relaxed, with snack lounges, TV lounges, exercise rooms and other areas for relaxation. Many bath houses sponsor outings, special events and benefits for various gay community causes. Even these sexual hunting grounds have developed a gay social conscience.

How much easier my life might have been had the many services and possibilities of today been available when I first came out. Still I feel fortunate to be involved in the growth of a free and open gay community. I can't relive my life, but I am thankful for the sense of spritual rebirth that our new gay community has given me and millions of my gay brothers and sisters. These expanded social horizons are a definite and pleasurable part of our continually developing community.

Achieving Success As A Gay Couple

Betty Berzon, Ph.D.

Very few among us have been fortunate enough to have had homosexual parents who could model for us the ideal gay love relationship—caring, growing, fun, mutually supportive—in the context of a burgeoning gay culture. Most of us were stuck with mamas and papas of the heterosexual variety—good, bad or indifferent as mates to each other and parents to us, but no help at all in fashioning our gay love life.

Lacking marriage manuals, parental guidance and models of conjugal bliss on film and television, we've had to wing it when it came to putting together workable love and life partnerships. Intimate relationships are a tricky business at best. Without the sanctions and supports of society's institutions (no positive messages at all), same-sex coupling presents a special challenge to the courage and ingenuity of lovers trying to build a life together.

At times, that challenge involves the same hassles that bewilder every couple trying to make a go of it. At other times, it involves bedevilments seemingly reserved only for gay lovers in an uptight and intransigent straight world. We'll look at both in this chapter.

Same-sex couples? Unnatural, unsanctionable, unconscionable, immoral, sick and immature. Can't work. Won't last. Doesn't count.

Negative messages undermine, subvert and scare us into pale versions of our dream of love. Sometimes we internalize the messages and they work against us from inside: "*I'm* immoral. *I'm* sick. *I'm* immature. My relationship can't work, won't last, doesn't count." We undermine our own efforts by echoing society's baseless pronouncements about us. Too often we allow these cliches to become self-fulfilling prophecies. The prophecy of doom comes true, in turn, reinforcing the cliches and making them appear as truth. We swallow these nontruths and the cycle is complete.

If we are ever going to bring order, reason and sense to our lives as gay people, we must learn to interrupt that cycle. We must learn to identify our own homophobic messages. We must become alert to their presence in our thinking, to the ways in which we incorporate them into our view of ourselves and other gay people. "It was so *gay* of him," I heard someone say recently when describing a piece of inconsiderate behavior. We must catch each other at this, work together to break the vicious cycle. Only then will we be able to really honor our deeply felt need to love and affiliate with persons of the same sex. Only then can we learn to believe in the rightness of gay love relationships because they are, for us, the morally correct, emotionally healthy and socially responsible ways to live our lives.

Many nongay people would argue with that statement. Some gay people would argue with it. Going against prevailing beliefs is always threatening, even when doing so is ultimately to our advantage.

One of the most influential of such beliefs is the notion that monogamous marriage is the ideal arrangement for satisfying one's affection, affiliation and security needs. This, despite an astronomical divorce rate in this country, despite increasing evidence that the tensions and frustrations of monogamy are more than most people can cope with and still maintain their equanimity or sustain their love for one another. Despite the closet door's swinging wide open on child and wife abuse, despite sexual dysfunction, identity foreclosure (masculinity overkill annihilating the multifaceted real self it defines), communication breakdown and all the other ills attendant upon straight marriages today, most gay people are still looking to that format as the model for their own relationships: Find the right partner. Commit to live ever after (if not happily) with each other. Expect devotion, fidelity, unconditional love, understanding and security. Establish a routine, agree on ground rules, have nonthreatening friends, make plans for the future. It has to work. It's supposed to.

But it *doesn't* work as often as it *does* these days. And importantly, the accommodation to that failure isn't always apparent. All too often, it takes the form of a quiet closing down of personality—functioning—retreats into alcohol, sexual abstinence, passivity or silence. It looks okay on the outside, but it's a very different picture on the inside. It is not good enough, I say, for gay lovers to follow the straight marriage model without doing some serious questioning.

Let's start with the motivation to be in a coupled relationship in the first place. Why do it? After all, variety is the spice of life. Courtship is exciting. Freedom and independence feel good. So why couple up? The reasons are very much the same in the gay and nongay communities and they produce the same problems. Being alone has never been a valued condition in American society, being paired is, and the pressure to do so is almost as great in the gay world as in the nongay.

So, people seek coupling because:

1) *It's important to find a partner so others (and you) will know that you can do it.* Even though I am ten years out of the heterosexual husband-hunting scene, I still cringe inside at the term *old maid.*

External social pressures add to the internal pressures:

2) *Searching is boring*—all that small talk, game playing, insincerity, superficiality.

3) *Searching is risky.* You can get set up, ripped off, done in by strangers who don't know or care about you.

4) *Searching is time consuming.* I could be building, earning, learning, planting, painting, . . . doing.

5) *Searching is nerve wracking.* You can be put down, found out, written off.

6) *Singles are socially out of it*—unsafe to have around a carefully homogenated couples scene.

7) *Loneliness feels bad.*

When the partner search is motivated by such pressures, chances are the selection process will be short and probably short-sighted. That's not a disaster, since the willingness to work on a relationship can overcome such a beginning. The real problem is that short-circuited partner selection too often results in the fallacy of "if only I had a lover, then . . ." turning into the folly of "now that I have a lover, I will . . .": I will be loved, involved, safe, using my time constructively, emotionally supported, socially sought after and lonely no more. And then you aren't. At least not enough, not often enough.

You have invested your partner with enormous, usually unwanted power over your life. Few of us hold up under such a burden. If it has to be because of me that you feel adequately loved, meaningfully engaged, safe from the cruelties and crudities of boors and evil-doers; if it's because of me that you will be enabled to meet the intellectual and creative challenges of your own potential, feel comfortable in your dealings with the world, invited to the most desirable parties and freed of the pain of aloneness, well, I don't think I can handle all that responsibility. If all of this is happening in the underground of our relationship, we don't have a chance to deal with it, to become aware of it, to understand it, to express how we feel about it, to divest ourselves of the awful responsibilities of it. So, we have to find a way to make these implicit expectations you have of me explicit.

What we have to do is open up awareness of our own and our partner's expectations and learn to communicate about them. This is particularly important for gay couples whose relationships have to be made strong from within, since the culture without contributes so little to their stability. So how do we open up awareness and communication between us? How do we get to our fantasies and illusions about each other? Here's one approach.

Each of us has a personal mythology. That is, we have certain uncritically held beliefs about life, the basis for which may or may not be ill-founded. (It doesn't matter.) These beliefs make up our view of the world. They shape our expectations. They guide us in our decisions. They influence the way we behave with other people. The myths themselves come from a multitude of sources: the folklore of our culture, ethnic group, family, or adopted subcultures. Our personal myths may come from books we've read, movies we've seen, stories we've heard, people we've known. They may be (and often are) amalgams of all these.

The myths we have about romantic love and conjugal relationships are very important influences on how we go about making these things happen in our lives. They often determine when we are successful and when we fail in our endeavors as lovers and partners. For that reason they are worth looking at. Here's a way to do that.

1) On a piece of paper, write three uncritically held beliefs you've had about how it would be for you in a love relationship. The beliefs may be mainly about the relationship itself, about your partner or about the effect on your life the relationship would have.

2) Rank order these three beliefs for their importance to you.

3) Assess your present, or most recent, relationship (or partner) for the degree to which these beliefs are holding up. In those instances where the beliefs have not held up, think about the reasons. It may be useful to think about where these particular beliefs originated and how this influences their importance to you.

You may want to use this exercise to begin to sort out the contemporary person you are dealing with from the illusions and fantasies you've had about any partner you would have in a love relationship. Or, you may want to update your expectations, integrate them with what you know about life, your partner, or yourself.

One way to approach this is to think about the ways in which they myths you have about yourself and a partner have translated into unspoken agreements or "contracts" with regard to how the relationship is conducted. If I have always believed that I would be the strong, worldly-wise caretaker in a relationship, I will probably choose someone who needs this strong, worldly-wise caretaker for a partner. Or, at least, I will convince myself that this is what the partner needs. It may be only partially so. Or, the person with such needs may outgrow them. If I continue to operate in terms of my myth, without making room for my partner's growth, I am in trouble. This kind of trouble happens most often when two people in a relationship don't talk about what is happening between

them, when their relationship is conducted mostly in terms of their "con‑
tracts."

We develop these contracts in order to short-cut discussion around
issues of potential conflict. We all have a tendency to try to keep our re‑
lationships as safe and comfortable as possible. Sometimes we overdo it.
For gay people there are particular dangers in heaviy heavily "contract‑
ed" arrangements. There are important areas of our relationships un‑
charted by traditional gender-role expectations. In the absence of such
guidelines there is often a tendency to respond even more to our fantasies
about how our partners should be. We need to keep communication open
so that we are relating, as much as possible, to a real person in the part‑
nership rather than an idealized image of a person.

Let's look at some of the issues that most often cause problems for gay
couples. Some of the following will have more relevance for couples who
live together. Many of the issues overlap, but each is important enough, I
believe, to be looked at separately. If you are part of a gay couple, I sug‑
gest you and your partner use the device below to get at your unspoken
"contracts." Remember, a "contract" in this use is an arrangement that
has been arrived at either by mutual consent or by default, and which
determines how things are done in the partnership. Consider the ques‑
tions posed for each item before you describe the contract as you see it,
and as you would like to see it.

On a piece of paper, write out your responses to each of the items in
the contract. The partner should do this independently.

THE CONTRACT

ITEM I. FINANCES:

> Question 1. How important are the relative earnings of one partner over the
> other's?
> Question 2. How are decisions made about how money is spent?
>
> A. *Right now I think the contract is:*
> B. *I would like it to be:*

ITEM II. PLANNING JOINT ACTIVITIES:

> Question 1. Which partner most often initiates plans for social occasions,
> trips, projects, etc?
> Question 2. How are final decisions on plans arrived at?
> Question 3. Which partner usually has the most influence on plans?
>
> A. *Right now I think the contract is:*
> B. *I would like it to be:*

ITEM III. DIVISION OF LABOR AT HOME:

> Question 1. Which partner usually does what?

Question 2. What is this arrangement based on?
Question 3. How rigid is this arrangement?

A. *Right now I think the contract is:*
B. *I would like it to be:*

ITEM IV. TIME SPENT WITH OTHER PEOPLE:

Question 1. How much time is spent with other people?
Question 2. Who is time usually spent with (family, straight friends, gay friends, business associates)?
Question 3. Which partner has the most influence on who time is spent with?

A. *Right now I think the contract is:*
B. *I would like it to be:*

ITEM V. DEGREE OF MONOGAMY:

Question 1. How sexually exclusive is the partnership?
Question 2. Does one partner have more freedom than the other?
Question 3. How is jealousy dealt with?
A. *Right now I think the contract is:*
B. *I would like it to be:*

ITEM VI. DEALING WITH CONFLICT:

Question 1. What are the typical areas of conflict in your relationship?
Question 2. How is conflict usually dealt with (avoidance, fighting, discussion and negotiation)?

A. *Right now I think the contract is:*
B. *I would like it to be:*

ITEM VII. SEPARATENESS AND TOGETHERNESS:

Question 1. How important are activities done independently versus activites done together?
Question 2. How O.K. is it for each of the partners to spend time alone, away from the other partner?

A. *Right now I think the contract is:*
B. *I would like it to be:*

ITEM VIII. INTIMACY:

Question 1. What is the usual pattern for expressions of intimacy in private?
Question 2. What is the usual pattern for expressions of intimacy in public?
Question 3. How willing is each partner to be known and vulnerable to the other partner?

A. *Right now I think the contract is:*
B. *I would like it to be:*

When you have finished, compare your answers with your partner's. Where there are differences, discuss them. Say how it seems to you. Say what you object to. Say what you want to happen. Say what you'll settle for. Negotiate for yourself a "contract" that meets your needs, that feels fair to you, that makes you feel as if you've been heard and understood.

Don't be afraid to do this. All too often gay couples will close off discussion about what is happening between them because they fear the bond that holds them together is too fragile to withstand the confrontation. Usually just the opposite is true. In confronting your partner with your true needs and wishes, you are performing an act of trust in this person, an act that is binding in itself, because it acknowledges the importance of the alliance to you.

Every gay relationship is flawed. Every human relationship is flawed. A male friend who has been married and now lives with a gay lover told me when he was married to his wife he could see the flaws in their relationship but then he'd think, "Oh, well, that's how it is with married couples. It's amusing. Look at all the situation comedies written around marital discord. It's okay. It happens to everyone." Now with his gay lover he reports, "It's frightening to fight. Discord might be signalling the end of the relationship." (Can't work. Won't last. Doesn't count. And we're dancing to their tune again!) But turning away from conflict is turning away from reality.

Denying anger, until it explodes unexpectedly at a later date, is bewildering and potentially very damaging to a relationship. Dealing with it as directly as possible, when it is happening, is strengthening though it may be painful and frightening to do so. Fighting is a necessity in a thriving relationship. Fighting fairly and to the finish is essential to the continuing growth of any partnership.

Unfinished fights are usually aborted because of fear of losing or fear of exposing hurt feelings or concern over letting go of one's emotions totally. Most of us have experienced all of these fears at one time or another. But unfinished fights leave the participants tense and anxious. If you feel that way when you stop fighting, your fight is probably unfinished. You should continue trying to work through to the finish—that is, until the real, underlying issues are confronted.

In a good fight, the partners are aware that they are risking themselves and they are willing to experience the discomfort that brings to resolve the conflict. In a good fight, the participants trust each other enough to be honest about their feelings, about their grievances and what they want to be different in the future. The good fight ends in negotiation, with both parties being clear about what is being asked for in terms of change. There is accommodation on both sides. Nobody loses. Everybody wins.

To sum up the above points and to make a few more, I've composed the following list of "Do's and Don'ts for Couple Fighting."

DO'S

1) *Do be specific about your complaints.*
("It's putting your cigarettes out only in clean ashtrays that I can't stand!"

And what about what changes you'd like to see in relation to your complaints.
("Use an ashtray that's already dirty, or clean your ashtrays after you use them!")

2) *Do send "I" messages, not "You" messages.*
("*I* feel ignored and put down when I ask you to do something and you ignore me." *Not "You* are an insensitive and uncaring clod!"

3) *Do try to get to underlying issues and feelings.*
("I don't feel like an equal partner in this relationship when you ignore my needs. When that happens, I feel angry and hurt!")

4) *Do finish the fight—Keep at it until the tension between you feels worked through.*

DON'TS

1) *Don't get stuck in the past.*
("You never did before, why should you start now!")

2) *Don't "kitchen sink" your partner.*
("And not only that, I also resent the way you . . . and the way you . . .)

3) *Don't deliver sweeping condemnations.*
("You are absolutely incapable of understanding me.")

4) *Don't abort the fight. Don't stop fighting while you still feel strong resentment or frustration or confusion.*

We must be willing to fight with each other to discharge the tensions that relationship building inevitably bring. We must be willing to fight in order to work through the control issues that are a part of every partnership. The more openly these issues are dealt with, the better chance the partners have for a lively, satisfying and enduring companionship arrangement.

Much of what I have written about so far is applicable to both male and female couples, for that matter, to nongay as well as gay couples. There are some ways, however, in which liaisons between two women and between two men are unique. I believe these differences are, primarily, outcomes of the ways women and men are differently socialized in this society.

Men are conditioned by the society to be strong, competitive, independent and sexually aggressive. Relationship skills are secondary to the ability to earn, win, achieve, make sexual conquests and show strength by not showing emotion. With regard to sex, men are taught to get all they can, that they should want it, that it is their right to have it.

The inclination is to do what we are taught. We tend to pay particular attention to the socializing lessons we learned early in life because with those lessons we usually learned that doing what we've been taught makes us okay. Good marks, good student, good person. At some level, we all need to experience ourselves as included, competent and loved (though some people have learned to deny these needs as a means of surviving especially harsh psychological conditions in their early life). At any rate, the early lessons stick, the early conditioning persists.

Two men in a couple tend to put a lot of energy into showing who is superior. The competition may be over physical strength, sexual prowess, intelligence, accountability, worldliness, earning power, social popularity, or it may be to see who is the most daring, most dispassionate, most evil-doing, or who is craziest. The revealing theme is *competition*, a competition that serves the dual purpose of providing a source of personal validation and of avoiding the intensification of intimacy in the relationship.

In the early socializing process, most males learned that nurturance, affection and caretaking were women's work, and that a woman would eventually do these things for them. Without that dream come true, where does the gay male look for those experiences? To another gay male? But, how do you ask for love and tenderness from your competitor? A lot of gay males don't, even though they want to. They haven't learned how to ask for the nurturing they want, or how to adequately express the deep and tender love they might feel for their partner.

As a counselor working with gay male couples, I try to help them get in touch with the ways in which they compete in order to cover up the intimacy needs they don't know what to do with. I encourage experimentation with cooperation and mutuality rather than competition. I suggest they try to end up agreeing, rather than winning or losing. I encourage them to figure out a way to do it together, rather than arguing which one's way is better. I push for increased expression of affection, even if it's uncomfortable at first. I try to get them to give themselves permission to ask for and give love to one another in deeper, gentler, softer ways.

Encouragingly, there is a new emphasis on relationship-building in the gay male community. As more fully functioning gay persons come out publicly, increased attention is being paid to personal growth and the development of relationship skills. There is much more meeting and relating as total persons, taking into account a broad range of emotional needs. I believe that satisfaction in relationships is being accorded more value among gay men than it was before. New sources of validation are evolving. Sex is no longer the only game in town. I consider this by-product of the gay rights movement a psychological bonanza for the embattled male seeking to build for himself a gay life that meets more than his most superficial social and sexual needs.

Lesbians, on the other hand, socialized as women, are rewarded early for the development of relationship skills. Typically, little girls take care of their dolls and play at being mothers. As adolescents, they dream about home, family and spouse. They are conditioned to equate being okay with acquiring and hanging onto a mate. They are trained and psychologically prepared to be nurturers. Little girls who grow up to be lesbians often do not deviate from their programming, aside from the gender of their partners. Their lives are centered on home and mate. Much emphasis is put on nurturing in the couple relationship. Having and hanging onto a partner is critical to their sense of acceptability.

While success at this makes for stability and continuity in one's everyday life, it does sometimes create an overdependency on the relationship for validation. Options for individual growth outside home and the partnership go unrecognized. One's drama becomes cast to type, with friends chosen to provide the appropriate backdrop to domestic tranquility. This is not an unworkable scheme of life given that both partners are equally accepting of it. But more and more often these days, this is not the case.

Women are generally less and less satisfied with domestic tranquility as a goal in their lives. Women are more and more rejecting of the limitation placed on their potential by too much emphasis on their nurturing abilities. Women are increasingly interested in being in the mainstream and making themselves felt in the world in a multitude of ways. Lesbian women are no different. The feminist and gay movements provide new opportunities for lesbians to meet outside of narrow social networks, to increase options for self-expression and productive involvement.

In counseling with lesbian couples, I encourage more outer directedness of their activities. I encourage a broadening of interests and of contracts. I encourage the development of individual as well as joint goals in life. I support assertiveness in the pursuit of personal growth. I applaud the evolution of independent frames of reference. This usually builds self-confidence in the partners, respect for one another's differing competencies and renewed interest in the partnership as a source of energy, strength and love.

To end where I began, we gay people must accept the fact that we're on our own when it comes to developing relationship arrangements that work the best for us. We have to help ourselves. One way we can do this is to stop hiding from each other. I strongly suggest the formation of informal self-help couples' groups. Meet in your living room. Talk to each other about your common concerns, your relationship problems and solutions. Share your defeats and triumphs. Support each other's efforts to grow in partnership. This is one way we can begin to build effective relationship models and a tradition of success in gay coupling. We need to do this in order to stop apologizing, once and for all, to anyone, for loving one another.

Lesbian Couples: Special Issues

Nancy Toder, Ph.D.

Lesbian couples: who are we? Descriptions range from the traditional homophobic view that sees us only in terms of our sexual activities, to the liberal heterosexual view that we are "just like any other married couples" (and that therefore no special effort is required to get to know us or to recognize and correct the injustices we deal with every day), to one version of the radical lesbian feminist perspective which states that our relationships don't or shouldn't have anything in common with heterosexual relationships. In fact, I find that many of our daily experiences as couples, many of our joys and difficulties, are similar to those of heterosexuals. However, we also have unique experiences, both as gay people and as lesbians, and must cope with unique issues in our couple relationships. In this chapter I will discuss some issues of particular relevance to lesbian couples. Throughout, I will explore both the extra stresses that we face and the singular advantages that are open to us. It is my belief that our relationships in couples can be vastly improved by our learning to recognize and deal with our unique stresses, and to celebrate and maximize our special advantages.

THE LESBIAN COUPLE IN THE HETEROSEXUAL WORLD: THE COMING OUT DILEMMA

Perhaps one of the most difficult decisions we lesbians face is to determine in which areas of our lives we can be ourselves, and in which areas we must wear a mask. If we stay in the closet, we risk never being known as we truly are, never having intimacy with family and friends, and losing self-respect and any sense of power and control over our lives. On the other hand, if we come out, we risk losing the love and support of our family and friends, forfeiting our jobs or curtailing our promotions, feeling the isolation of stigma, and in some places even getting arrested. Nevertheless, the advantages of coming out are great: a wonderful feeling of freedom, an increase in self-respect and integrity, the knowledge that we are doing something that may improve the lot of lesbians and gay men everywhere, and the opportunity to create friendships in which we are truly accepted for ourselves.

The stress on the individual who must make these decisions is obvious; what is not so obvious is the stress these decisions place on the couple. Not only do the additional pressures on the individual tend to bring more anxiety, confusion, anger and fear into the relationship, but the decisions that each woman makes for herself will directly affect the partner.

Couples run into the most conflicts when the two women are at different stages of the coming-out process. Thus, a lesbian who has come out with her family, who perhaps is beginning to feel comfortable about her lesbianism and to whom openness and honesty are very important, will have great difficulty pretending to be "the roommate" when her lover's parents come to dinner or for a month's visit. For many lesbians, home is sanctuary in an unsafe world, and even those who have not come out professionally or with their family may deeply resent the invasion of their home by people who are ignorant or disrespectful of their love relationship.

What is the impact of such situations on the couple? As in a juggling act, things have a tendency to fall and get broken. What may suffer here is the trust that eacy lover feels for the other as well as for herself. A few years ago, a friend with an important professional job threw a party at her house for some of her co-workers. Very few people knew she was a lesbian, so her lover's clothes closets were carefully shut, books hidden behind other books, a few pictures put away in drawers and other precautions taken to ensure that nobody would guess the household was lesbian. In addition, her lover, who works in the same profession, was invited to the party but had to pretend that she didn't live in the house.

This is a particularly dramatic example of how our fears can negate each other and invalidate our relationships. This happens all the time, usually in more subtle ways than we know. Chipping away at the trust, loyalty and respect that we feel for each other, these "little" betrayals can undermine the very foundations of our love relationships.

Problems with families—especially difficult around holiday time, when each member of the couple, seen as a single person, is expected to go home to her own family—do not automatically disappear when we come out to our relatives. Most family members react somewhere between the two extremes of horror and approval, and the lover, usually is not treated as one of the family, at least initially.

The couple may take out on each other the frustration and anger they feel in response to their families' treatment of them: "Why did you let her get away with that? Why didn't you confront her on the shit she was saying?" "Why didn't *you*?" "Well, she's *your* mother." Many such fights revolve around disagreements on how to handle family. Each woman may feel torn between loyalty to the lover and fear of confronting parents or other relatives. Often the partner who is more open with her family will not be able to understand why the other partner is so "cowardly." The two lovers can become pitted against each other, making it more difficult for them to fight the real enemy: the homophobia in the world and in themselves.

Additional stresses in the relationship can arise from differences between the lovers' attitudes about being seen together publicly—as a function of different vulnerabilities in their work situations or different degrees of self-acceptance. These stresses range from inconvenience ("Can we go to the movies together on a Friday or Saturday night, or only on a weeknight?") to serious differences between the social and political activities the two lovers want to engage in: Does one lover want to go to the bars, while the other is afraid to be seen there? Does one lover want to become involved in lesbian/gay organizations, and is this a threat to the other lover? Again, these issues are a problem mostly for lovers who differ considerably in their attitudes and interests. However, even for a couple that shares similar goals and values on such issues as coming out, political activity and visibility in public, many conflicts can arise from smaller differences and from the difficulty of coping with such emotion-laden issues.

How can we deal with these conflicts? The lover who has come out more fully must be as patient and supportive as possible, trying not to put demands and pressures on the more fearful partner, yet at the same time encouraging her to take risks. Try to recognize that you and your lover are different individuals with different capacities, needs and circumstances.

The lover who is further in the closet must try not to be threatened by her partner's decisions and not to invalidate or belittle what is important to the partner. Try to keep some separation between your identity and your lover's identity, and try not to sabotage your lover's growth because of your own fears. If you are frightened that your lover's political activities will give her less time for you, that the two of you may eventually find your differences irreconcilable and have to separate, or that your lesbianism will be exposed as a result of your lover's activities, then express your fears to your lover, rather than attacking her with statements like "Gay liberation is stupid!" or "NOW meetings are a waste of time."

In situations where it seems impossible to come out, each lover can still show basic respect for the other and for the relationship. This means, for instance, not telling your mother about the fantastic (and invented) date you had last weekend when your lover is sitting with you at Thanksgiving dinner; it means making sure that people know your lover is important to you (even if you don't want them to know she is your lover) and that they treat her with respect and courtesy; it means avoiding situations where people who don't know about your relationship come to your house.

Our love relationships can be a tremendous support in separating reality from paranoia. By discussing the pros and cons of coming out in each situation, by role-playing (one lover plays the parents, boss, friend, etc. in a dialog intended to test the possible consequences of coming out), and by brain-storming for new ideas and strategies, the two lovers can be of great help to each other in making coming-out decisions. At best, each lover can give the other some of the courage that coming out requires and some of the support that dealing with the outside world necessitates. If desired, both lovers can be present in a potentially difficult coming-out scene, so that the one who is under fire will have support. In addition, each lover can help the other put things in perspective when something goes wrong, for example, in a family situation. We tend to be so vulnerable with our families that we have trouble sorting out craziness from reality, and our lovers can provide a voice of sanity and reason.

THE COUPLE IN THE LESBIAN WORLD

Some couples choose to remain relatively isolated from the lesbian support systems of friendship circles, bars and the political community. For many lesbians in rural locations and small towns, a peer group is not an option and isolation is chosen only to the extent that they chose to live in such a community in the first place. I think that choosing isolation often reflects homophobia ("We just don't find other lesbians *interesting*") or fear of losing one's lover as a result of exposure to other potential partners. In such an isolated couple, the two lovers often will become over dependent on each other, the homophobia of each will tend to reinforce the homophobia of the other and the resulting self-hate can lead to alcoholic pacts and other self-destructive and couple-destructive activities.

I firmly believe that some connection with the political lesbian community is essential to our individual and collective mental health. It takes an incredible strength to combat the homophobic pressures we deal with daily. Much of that strength comes from our inner resources and from the love and support of our partners. But within the couple relationship it is very easy to drain these resources and to feel overwhelmed by the huge obstacles we face.

The knowledge that there is a lesbian community, that our numbers are large and that we represent a positive political force is a great help in dealing with the fear and ignorance around us. It is through interactions with the lesbian community that we can begin to feel pride in ourselves and hope for our future.

I have heard lesbians say that going to their first meeting of a lesbian or gay organization, or marching in a gay demonstration, did more for their self-esteem than months and even years of psychotherapy. There is no equivalent for such an experience—for many of us, nightmares begin to recede and we begin to reclaim parts of ourselves that have been lost almost as long as we can remember.

Even in the healthy context of our own community, however, numerous pressures exist that can have an adverse effect on the couple. These peer-group pressures range from the pressure to stay together till death do you part (if all your friends are in couples—"How can you do this to us?"—or if you are seen as a model couple—"You two give me hope that someday I'll have a relationship like yours"), to the pressure in the radical lesbian community to be nonmonogamous and not to "act couple-y."

THE RELATIONSHIP ITSELF

Many lesbians are afraid to commit themselves to a relationship, not only because of a general fear of making commitments but also because of a more specific fear: that they are indeed gay. For those who have not fully accepted a lesbian identity, making a firm commitment to another woman cements the notion that they are actually adopting a lesbian lifestyle and must formulate a lesbian identity. This is no small step, particularly in our first same-sex love affair. In response to our fear, we may deny the implications of the relationship ("I'm not a lesbian, I just happen to be in love with this person and this person just happens to be a woman") or generally not believe in the viability of the relationship or fight for its survival against the obstacles that two women will encounter.

Money and Commitment

Money is likely to be a problem in a lesbian couple because of job discrimination against women. When money is scarce, there is more stress on the relationship than when it is plentiful; the two partners are generally more tense about financial matters, and each partner, frustrated by not being able to do or buy the things she wants, tends to blame the other.

I would like to devote most of this discussion, however, to an assump‑
tion that seems to be accepted without question in most lesbian couples:
the assumption that money is not to be shared. In the heterosexual mar‑
riage, it is usually assumed that money will be shared. As many feminist
writers have correctly pointed out, marriage is not a good model and is
in many ways inappropriate to the lesbian couple. However, heterosex‑
uals have one advantage in what is otherwise quite an oppressive pack‑
age: the ease with which they can make a commitment to a love relation‑
ship by sharing their material resources. (Of course this is not always the
reality, but generosity is supposed to be the spirit of the arrangement.)

The fact is that many of us who would not be opposed to the *idea* of
sharing money with a mate, are actually very hesitant to do so with a
same-sex lover. It is not uncommon for two women who have been living
together for a number of years to keep strict accounts of who owes whom
how much for what. Why is this?

Some lesbians argue that they need to have their own money; they
want to know that they are financially independent and have a way out
of the relationship if necessary. This seems reasonable. But sharing
money with your lover does not necessarily mean that you cannot have
your own checking or savings account. It simply means that the two of
you share expenses in proportion to your income, either by pooling all
your money or by working out a percentage agreement. ("I earn twice as
much as you, so I'll pay for two-thirds of our rent, utilities, food, vaca‑
tions, etc.")

Sharing money is not much of a problem when the two partners earn a
similar income: each one pays 50% of the couple's expenses. However,
when incomes differ or when an inheritance is involved, many problems
can arise. Whose standard of living should be adopted? How can resent‑
ments be avoided? The less affluent partner often finds herself "owing"
money to the other partner, and the longer the relationship, the less like‑
ly this debt will ever be paid off.

It is hard to imagine this happening in a committed heterosexual rela‑
tionship. I think that lesbians are more cautious, more afraid of getting
ripped off, less willing to trust in the durability of the relationship. In my
opinion, this extreme cautiousness is often the result of internalized ho‑
mophobia and the resulting fear of making a commitment to the lover.

Some may argue that keeping money and possessions separate makes it
easier to divide things should the couple break up. I'm not sure that this
is true. However, I am sure that never making the commitment to share
money, always feeling on the edge of disintegration, may result in pre‑
mature separation when problems arise. (In heterosexual marriages, the
opposite is more often the case: the two partners feel that their lives and
finances are so hopelessly intertwined that they stay together long after
the time has come to separate.)

I believe the core of this issue is a question of family. When a woman marries a man, they become family to each other. The question is: When does a same-sex lover become family? Is it when you fall in love? live together? buy a house together? raise a child together? Is it when your blood family accepts your lover as a family member? We have no rules by which to answer these basic questions. And in this society, money is usually shared, if at all, only with family.

We need to ask ourselves certain questions: Is it my belief that two women in a committed relationship should share their money? If so, how and under what circumstances? If I am not living the way I believe, why is that? Do I have a good reason? For example, I don't believe my lover is trustworthy about money, or she doesn't work as hard as I do, or I don't believe we're going to be together much longer. Or am I responding to fears and deep-seated insecurities that may not apply to this situation, and in fact may be antithetical to what I want in this relationship?

I am not advocating that every couple share finances, simply that we look at our assumptions and attitudes about money, see whether healthy realism or unconscious homophobia is influencing our decisions and take responsibility for our financial choices.

Monogamy and Nonmonogamy

One of the most common sources of conflict in lesbian couples is the issue of monogamy vs. nonmonogamy. Most often, problems arise when one partner wants to open up the relationship and the other does not. This frequently happens when two women have been together for several years, and one partner feels restless, bored with the relationship, less turned on to her lover than before and attracted to others. (In the heterosexual world this is known as the *seven-year itch*.)

There are no right or wrong answers to the question of how to deal with such feelings. It is natural to feel attracted to others in addition to your lover and these attractions do not necessarily mean that something is wrong with your couple relationship (as many lesbians assume). Yearning for an affair with someone new or unexpectedly falling in love with someone new can reflect a healthy desire to recapture the intense passion of a new relationship or the desire to experience yourself in new ways through sexual or emotional intimacy with different partners.

The potential growth of the individual and even of the couple that can result from outside affairs must be balanced against the potential loss of trust and safety in the primary relationship. In addition, there can be some less-than-healthy reasons for wanting to open up the couple relationship: new affairs can be a way to avoid dealing with problems in the primary relationship, to keep from making a commitment to the relationship or to distract yourself from a boring job or frustrations in your work. By putting the bulk of your energy into numerous emotional involvements, you may be putting off the expression of your creativity in some other form and you may even be avoiding confronting a feeling of emptiness and meaninglessness in your life.

The general consensus in the radical lesbian-feminist community is that nonmonogamy is more liberated and healthy than monogamy. The basic argument is that heterosexual monogamy has been used to regulate women's behavior and to protect the husband's proprietary rights over his wife. In addition, monogamy is seen as fostering jealousy, possessiveness and dependency, and creating closed units of two, thus setting artificial and unnecessary limits on our relations with each other.

As a result of these ideas, a large number of lesbian couples have attempted to open up their relationships. In many of these situations, although the two women in the couple may have agreed on what they wanted, the results have been disastrous for the couple and sometimes for the individual. Why is this? I think the main reason is that many of us have been naive about just how emotionally complicated nonmonogamy can be.

Sex and love go together for most women in our culture. Even what is intended to be a relatively casual and unthreatening affair can quickly evolve into an intense and complex emotional involvement. Believing that as good feminists they should be able to handle nonmonogamy, many women have acted according to theory without having a realistic idea of their needs, the extent to which they would suffer from jealousy and their personal limitations in dealing with potentially ambiguous, frustrating or complex situations. I think that women in the radical lesbian community have drastically underestimated the damage that can be done to their primary relationship when they try to live nonmonogamously.

Furthermore, we women have been socialized to believe that our self-esteem comes primarily from our relationships with other people. We traditionally think of this self-defeating need as being acted out in a monogamous couple relationship, where one or both women may be building their lives around their relationship. A variation on this theme, however, occurs when a woman engages in multiple relationships. These relationships can occupy most if not all of her time, and her sense of worth and identity may come to depend on the success or failure of many relationships instead of one! The point is that nonmonogamy does not guarantee a strong sense of self and independence, just as monogamy does not automatically mean an overwhelming dependence on your lover or a severe limitation on your freedom and growth as an individual.

If you or your lover wish to open up your relationship, it is very important to create conditions that will make this new "state of affairs" acceptable to both of you. Condition number one for most couples is the knowledge that the couple relationship is top priority and that any outside affairs are secondary. Then it is important to specify details of the arrangement so as to consider each other's needs and feelings. For example, how much time and which blocks of time will you spend with others; what time will you spend together? Do you want to hear about these affairs or would you rather not? Are any special conditions important to you (e.g., that your lover not relate sexually to anyone you know or that she not bring anyone into the house you share)? Once you have opened up the relationship, be sure to meet frequently to make sure that things are still feeling okay to both of you and to work out any additional conditions that either of you is discovering to be necessary.

The Effects of Sexism and Misogyny

In addition to dealing with homophobia, lesbians must also cope with discrimination against women and with misogynist attitudes. These pressures range from the more subtle and covert forms of antiwoman stereotypes to the more blatant misogynist acts of rape, economic discrimination and sexual objectification of women on the job, in the streets and in advertising. All these pressures tend to keep women in a second-class position in the society.

As can happen with any stress, our anger and frustration tend to spill over into our love relationships, and our lovers become the easiest target for our rage. In addition, misogyny and homophobia are internalized by all of us, and can have a devastating effect on our self-esteem and identity as lesbians, thus creating problems in our couple relationships.

Most of us have been taught from an early age that a woman needs a man—to be a real woman, to achieve safety in the world and to complete her identity. These messages sometimes linger long after we have begun relating to women and they make the formation of a positive lesbian identity very difficult. In a society that labels a "real woman" by her attachment to a man, lesbians are by definition not "real women."

Having internalized this message, many lesbians continue sexual rela' tions with men even after finding more meaningful relationships with women. Long periods of bisexuality are often a reflection of this conflict. Feeling that desirability is determined by their ability to attract a man, many lesbians find it necessary to prove to themselves that they could have a man if they wanted. This is almost always a losing battle, for as long as she believes that a woman without a man is not a real woman, the lesbian will not be at peace with herself, no matter how many men she attracts. The real question is not "Could I get a man?" but "Why on earth would I want to?"

Many women depend on men for protection. Because many men

respect the notion that a woman is a man's property, and because men generally expect a man to fight back, a woman in the company of a man is much less likely than a woman alone to be attacked or bothered. Lesbians are most often not in the company of men, so we can feel particularly vulnerable on the streets. Worried that our lovers cannot protect us and insecure about our ability to protect ourselves and our lovers, we sometimes feel resentful and cheated. Underlying these feelings is fear, a fear accentuated if we live in high-crime areas.

Women who have lived with men and experienced a sense of physical security in their presence often feel that being with a woman is a disadvantage: "A woman can't protect you; a woman can't make it easier for you in the world." In fact, women who live with men often have a false and dangerous feeling of security. Married women are raped as frequently as single women, and probably more frequently than lesbians. A woman who is dependent on a man may be more vulnerable and less prepared if she is attacked when her man is not around. And if her man is abusive, who protects her from *him?*

Breaking away from traditional notions of what women are or should be is simultaneously frightening and liberating—frightening because we are moving into uncharted territory, liberating because we are breaking free of stereotypes and because we are now engaged in the most challenging and exciting process we can experience as women: generating new definitions of ourselves and creating a woman-identified culture to support our new consciousness.

Internalized misogyny often sabotages our attempts to build a women's culture and to make satisfying relationships with each other. For example, most of us have difficulty feeling good about our bodies, partly because of the rigid standards that our male-dominated society imposes on female beauty and partly because our misogynist environment has taught us that our genitals are dirty, taste bad, have an offensive odor, etc. When you add into the bargain that we are seen as both sexually insatiable and frigid, it is no wonder that some of us have sexual problems! All of these negative attitudes influence our ability to express our sexuality freely with our lovers.[1]

Role-Playing in the Lesbian Couple

Role-playing has its roots in traditional heterosexuality. There is no more extreme role-playing than that which occurs in most married couples. Why have lesbians sometimes imitated this distorted notion of normalcy? It is no accident that in the "old days" there were many more butches than femmes. Role-playing is rooted in misogyny, and lesbians, who have always been aware of the raw deal that women get in this society and who were rebelling against the limitations of the prescribed female role, frequently chose to be identified instead with the male. The butch role in a lesbian couple is an attempt to cop some of the power and privilege that men get in the world. Because lesbians do not get that privilege in the outside world, home becomes the most important arena for acting out the wish for male privilege.

Wanting to be strong, independent and competent is not in itself a sign of role-playing or misogyny; on the contrary, it can be an important aspect of developing one's identity as a woman. Role-playing and misogyny come into the picture when a woman assumes that her strength must be pitted against the relative weakness of a femme lover or that her strength means that she is more like a man than like a woman. Underlying these assumptions is the association of femaleness with weakness and inferiority, and thus a self-hate and a disdain for the lover who is identified as more female.

In my opinion, the lesbian community is the best cure for internalized misogyny and the best defense against external misogyny. By talking with other lesbians about these issues (either informally or in consciousness-raising groups), by participating in the development of a woman-identified culture and by organizing to fight sexism, misogyny and homophobia in the outer world, we can take real pride in ourselves as women and as lesbians and we can bring this pride to our couple relationship.

Overloading the Couple

Because we feel alienated from and feared and attacked by the outside world, many lesbians in couples band together fiercely against the rest of the world. Our lover can become the only person to be trusted in an otherwise hostile and condemning environment. The additional fact that as women we have been socialized to believe that our principal worth comes from our love relationships further augments our tendency to make our lover the center of our life.

These forces put a tremendous load on the couple relationship, particularly the couple that is geographically or emotionally cut off from the lesbian community. Each woman in the couple is expected to meet all of the other woman's intellectual, social, and emotional needs. If one or both of the women are unhappy, they assume that something must be wrong with or missing from the relationship. The basic, unrealistic premises are that a good relationship guarantees individual happiness and that one person can meet all of another person's needs.

Because the world is perceived as an enemy, and because our lesbian realities and values are daily ignored or contradicted, we often feel an

extra need for our lover to validate our perceptions and beliefs. Any disagreement between the two women may be seen as a deadly threat; after
all, it is only through the support of the relationship that many women
feel they can tolerate their extreme isolation and alienation. Consequently, even tiny cracks in the couple's unity may precipitate major anxieties
and major conflicts until consensus is reached. Because so much is at
stake, the process of reaching consensus may involve bitter fighting, and
the women may seriously compromise their individuality in order to
achieve equilibrium in the relationship.

Individuality and growth may be severely limited in such a closed and
rigid relationship. For this and other reasons I feel it is essential that we
must reach out to other lesbians and develop friendships and resources
outside of our couple relationships. Doing so not only removes stress
from the couple relationship but also helps to build a stronger, more au-
tonomous sense of self.

Motherhood and Shared Parenting

Many lesbians have had children before discovering or becoming
ready to act on their lesbian feelings. Being a lesbian mother is difficult
not only in the straight world but also in the lesbian/gay community. Until very recently, child care was not provided at most lesbian/gay events
and the level of consciousness about the special needs and problems of
lesbian mothers was low. Being a single parent is hard enough; lesbian
motherhood has additional complications, of which the constant threat
of losing one's children is only the most dramatic.

Some of these complications are eased and others accentuated when a
lesbian mother becomes involved with a lover. The first issue that comes
up is, generally, how much responsibility will that lover take for the
children? Most mothers want their lovers to share this responsibility, and
some women who do not have their own children are pleased to be able
to relate to children without having to bear them or take on the responsibility that the blood mother usually has. In such situations, being a couple can be mutually beneficial; some of the strain of mothering is taken
off the mother, the lover gets the opportunity to share in the raising of a
child, and the child benefits from the attention of two adults rather than
one. In the case where both women have children, moving into a single
household can greatly improve the quality of both women's lives and
those of their children.

Many couples run into problems, however. Most typically, the needs
and expectations of the mother diverge from those of her lover. The
mother, who for years may have been assuming total economic and emotional support of her child, may count heavily on her lover to ease her re-

sponsibilities and in effect to become a second parent. The lover, on the other hand, may have no desire to assume such responsibilities. I have heard women say, "If I had wanted children, I would have had my own." The lover often feels that she "fell in love with the woman, not her child," whereas the mother often feels, "Love me, love my child." It is important to air these feelings rather than harboring resentments. The two women must negotiate a balance between their different needs.

Of course, each woman's attitudes toward mothering may change over time. The lover may grow fond of the child and want to assume more responsibility, or the mother may discover that she wants primary responsibility for her child. The change in the lover's attitudes will often correspond to a change in her feeling about the relationship: if her lover (the mother of the child) begins to feel like family to her, she is more likely to feel that the child is family, too.

Jealousy is another common problem when one of two lovers has a child. The mother is put in a pivotal position, with the partner and child feeling like competitors for her attention and affection. The age and dependency of the child and the maturity of the lover will greatly affect the degree of resentment between the child and the mother's lover. Many women, especially in the early phases of a relationship, hate the idea of anyone else getting the attention they want all to themselves. In addition, the presence of children usually means a considerable cramping of the couple's style: a babysitter must be found before the two women can go out, the child must be picked up at school, etc. A woman who never wanted children for exactly this reason may feel angry and bitter about having to take a child into consideration now.

Getting close to the child poses a series of dilemmas for the lover. What if she and the mother break up? She will not only lose contact with the woman she loves, but very likely with the child, too. She knows she has no legal rights in this situation, and even if she has helped raise the child for years, the child will go with the mother. There are no simple answers to these fears. All loving involves risks; at some point a risk is worth taking.

As in any family, once two women agree to assume mutual responsibility for the child, there may be disagreements about the details of child rearing. For the lesbian household, however, there is the additional question of how to present the relationship to the child. Of course, the age of the child will affect what and how much is said.

A surprisingly large number of women never discuss their lesbianism with their children: the two women live together, sleep in the same bed, but say nothing to the child to clarify what this means. Even some lesbian-feminist mothers avoid talking with their children about their love relationships and even about feminist issues. This reticence is usually a sign of internalized homophobia (although there are certainly practical considerations, too, such as the possibility that the child will get into trouble at school by mentioning the mother's lesbianism and even the possibility that the father will use the child's knowledge of the mother's lesbianism as a point in his favor in custody cases).

As lesbians we are often accused of proselytizing and even of molesting children. Many women overcompensate in response to these false accusations. They try so hard not to influence the sexual preference of their children that they give no information at all about lesbianism. Such behavior springs from hidden pockets of shame. In fact, if we look at the behavior of heterosexuals, we find that they are proselytizing all the time; not only do they individually laud the advantages of their way of life but they have even gotten the major institutions of society to present their message. By providing a healthy understanding of lesbian relationships, and letting your child experience the love between you and another woman, you can do some little bit to counterbalance mainstream propaganda and give your child something approaching a free choice.

Rearing a child in a nonsexist and nonhomophobic household can be a most challenging and valuable experience. It is wonderful to be able to offer a child some of the wisdom and freedom that most of us have attained only in adulthood, and with tremendous struggle at that. In sharing this process, a couple can greatly enrich their individual lives and their relationship.

ADVANTAGES OPEN TO LESBIAN COUPLES

The fact that we have no images or models for the "successful" lesbian relationship, though it causes anxiety and confusion, may really be a blessing in disguise. Once we break free of the vestiges of heterosexual imagery, we can experience a marvelous sense of freedom. Uninhibited by the narrow restrictions of cultural acceptability, we can create our own structures and values. For example, the fact that we are in a same-sex relationship means that the predetermination of roles by gender, so destructive a force in heterosexual relationships, is not relevant to our lives. Each member of a same-sex couple is free to act from individual interests, predilections, and skills, rather than having to choose between conforming to or rebelling against the cultural norm. We are able to see the mainstream culture from a greater distance and a healthier perspective. This means that we know that many of the oppressive messages of the culture are inapplicable to us, and that others are simply false or distorted. Thus, we are able to circumvent much of what is jokingly referred to as "The Battle of the Sexes"—really, no joking matter at all.

Ironically, it is the same-sex couple that can most clearly see itself as being composed of two human beings, whereas the heterosexual couple is constantly having to deal with the coercive personae of Man and Woman.

In many ways, we have an easier time of creating a truly egalitarian, mutual and mature relationship. In fact, some researchers are now beginning to look at the same-sex couple as a model for helping heterosexuals to create more human relationships.

In contrast with heterosexuals, who often feel alienated from their mates, we need only look inside ourselves to know much about our lovers. We are able to relax with each other in a much more trusting way than can most straight couples. The inequities in our relationships are individually made ones, for the most part, and not a function of historically sanctioned power imbalances that have created the fear and hatred in which many women and men coexist today.

In a lesbian couple, both women can freely develop strength and competence. In addition, having been socialized as women, we have been trained to be interpersonally sensitive, nurturant, gentle and compassionate. In a heterosexual relationship, these qualities are used primarily to serve the man and to oppress the woman, who often must bear full responsibility for the emotional quality of the relationship. These same attributes, however, can create a miraculously high-quality relationship when shared by two women who are matched in their capacities to share and to love.

Gay and Catholic

Brian McNaught

Growing up gay and Catholic can be like living in Northern Ireland with a Catholic mother and a Protestant father. Loyalty to one seems to preclude loyalty to the other. Not only do gay Catholics receive a consistently clear message from the hierarchy of the Catholic community that their sexual orientation is "seriously disordered" but they also hear from the other front that maintaining Catholic ties "perpetuates the oppresor." Although a decision between loyalties is frequently called for, there is no need to make a choice.

Traditional condemnation by the Church is based on a lack of understanding of homosexuality and upon an imposed understanding of human nature, justified by faulty interpretation of Scripture. Condemnation of the Church also reflects a limited understanding of the true meaning the Church has and can have in people's lives.

Theologians of the Roman Catholic Church in the United States take one of three basic positions on the morality of homosexuality. The traditional stand, as enunciated by the Vatican Decree on Certain Questions Concerning Sexual Ethics, insists that the basic purposes of sexual activity are procreation and expressions of mutuality (conjugal love). Insofar as homosexual lovemaking does not satisfy the requirement of procreation, it is a "misuse" of the genitals and therefore "disordered." (When confronted with the practice of blessing marriages of heterosexuals who are biologically incapable of procreating, the Church responds that there is at least the possibility of procreation, as with the story of Abraham and his wife Sarah, who though well beyond the possible years of carrying a child, nonetheless, through the intervention of God, did conceive.)

The second position, adopted by theologians such as Charles Curran, considers homosexual behavior the lesser of two evils *if* the individuals involve themselves in a permanent relationship. This holds true only if they are unable to maintain a life of sexual abstinence. Richard McCormick uses the word *non-normative* when describing homosexual relationships but argues that he would bless such a union rather than encourage promiscuity by condemning the relationship. The third position is that of Fr. John McNeill, the Jesuit who was silenced twice by Rome because of the popularity of his book *The Church and the Homosexual* and by Gregory Baum. Both men place homosexual relationships on a par with heterosexual relationships by arguing that the individuals are being true to their nature.

In a book entitled *Human Sexuality*, a sexuality study group of the Catholic Theological Society of America drew heavy fire from the American bishops for suggesting that not all homosexuality was morally wrong. Given the case of a "constitutional homosexual" (the individual who has made no choice of sexual orientation), the authors suggested that the same criteria be applied to the homosexual's relationship as are applied to the heterosexual's. Is it "self-liberating, other-enriching, honest, faithful, life-serving and joyous?"

How then do we gay Catholics reconcile ourselves with these three positions? The answer depends upon what we mean by "Catholic." Some persons who call themselves Catholic mean they were baptized Catholic but have had no ties with the Church since they left home. Some Catholics, like myself, enjoy participation in the Church for a variety of reasons totally unrelated to the do's and don'ts of man-made tradition. Others consider themselves Catholic because they go to Mass every Sunday and, while they don't especially like being Catholic, are afraid not to be for fear of eternal damnation. Michael, the pathetic character in *Boys in the Band* who rushed to midnight Mass at St. Malachy's after throwing his dehumanizing party, comes quickly to mind here.

There are Catholics who cannot act without justifying their actions with quotes from the Bible. There are Catholics who wait for direction from Rome or from the American bishops or who place the total direction of their spiritual life in the hands of their local priest. Therefore, in counseling Catholics who want to reconcile their homosexuality with their faith, it is not enough to share the processes which I went through in making my religion and my sexual orientation inseparable. Their age, their ethnic background, the number of years they spent in parochial schools, their knowledge of Scripture all contribute to make significant differences in the ease with which they will reconcile what seems to be irreconcilable.

From my perspective, I made no choice in becoming a Catholic. Yet, I have no regrets. A Catholic background is not unlike a strong Jewish background insofar as growing up with rules, rituals and cultural idio-syncrasies that separated you from many of your friends and provided common bonds with others which became fun cocktail conversation at even the dullest parties. The Latin Mass, no meat on Fridays, the rosary, the May crownings, your new St. Joseph Missal, the nuns' habits, being an altar boy and fainting from incense, traditional rivalries with the athletic teams of neighboring public schools, thoughts about entering a seminary or convent, holy cards, the "Decency Pledge" and a variety of other "typically Catholic" traditions are essential ingredients to my past which I share with other persons who grew up Catholic. And as with family, while I might privately be scandalized by some of their personal-ities or practices, I become incredibly uncomfortable when someone out-side the family holds them up for ridicule.

From the spiritual vantage point, I have traveled the same roads as most persons with 16 years of parochial education. In grade school I was considered by the nuns to be a "saint of a boy." For several years I con-sidered entering religious life and finally made a brief visit (eight weeks) to a monastery of teaching brothers. At Marquette I went through the fashionable stage of being an "academic agnostic." Today, I find that my life has more meaning if centered around the existence of God. Jesus holds particular significance as the individual who lived a perfect life of selflessness, thereby liberating us from the legalism of religion and from the siren song of overindulgence.

In the Roman Catholic Church I see millions of persons who shared my cultural background and who are therefore initially fun to be with; who like myself would not suffer torture at the hands of the "Commu-nists" in defense of the Immaculate Conception, the Assumption or papal infallibility, but who all the same consider themselves an impor-tant part of the "Pilgrim People" stumbling through life in an attempt to incorporate the message "Love God, love neighbor as you love self" into everyday transactions with grocery clerks, salespersons, parish priests, homophobic bishops or state representatives.

As Mass on Sunday can be more dehumanizing and alienating than staying at home, I frequently opt to celebrate and worship God alone or with friends in small community gatherings. I haven't been to confes-sion since the priest at Marquette insisted masturbation was not sinful. If I encounter a period of spiritual-emotional isolation, I either sit down with my lover Ray and talk it through (fully respecting his personal, though uncelebrated spirituality) or I call a friend (who happens to be a priest) but is more importantly a person I respect.

How can I call myself Catholic given all of these apparent transgres-sions against the rules? I can call myself anything I choose and there is no priest, bishop or pope who can tell me otherwise. Each person's life is a major gamble. People who choose not to believe in God are gambling that when they die there will be nothing. I gamble with my life that there will be. As a Catholic who is also gay I gamble that the Church has totally misinterpreted the Will and Word of God. If I am wrong then, the Church tells me, I will pay the price. Yet, I cannot conceive of a God who would allow a person to live on this earth as an emotional cripple when that person need not make that choice. Likewise, when the Church publicly condemns me and leads campaigns to eliminate my civil rights, they too gamble. If they are wrong (which I am sure they are), they will encounter a God who will greet them with "How in the hell could you do that to another human being?"

As anyone who plays poker knows, it is next to insanity to gamble without a winning hand. Gay Catholics sit across from a person with far more chips, with a reputation for being able to bluff countless others out of the game and with five cards which he insists are unbeatable: The Bible, Revelation, Tradition, the Keys to the Kingdom and Infallibility. Let's take a look at this "unbeatable" hand.

The Bible has been used to justify human actions since the first ink dried on Chapter One of Genesis. We have used it to condemn Jews, maintain slaves, keep women in what we imagine to be their "place," condemn non-Catholics, condemn borrowing money from banks, condemn masturbation, justify the Crusades, condemn inoculation and a variety of other practices or attitudes we weren't comfortable holding alone but insisted that everyone else hold too. The Church cites Genesis, Leviticus and Letters of St. Paul to Romans and Corinthians and Timothy to build its case against homosexuality.

A growing number of Scripture scholars (whose writings the Church has cited in the past but now discredits) insist, however, that all references to homosexuality have to be understood in context and that ultimately there is nothing in the Old or New Testament that speaks of behavior by "constitutional" homosexuals. Men of science insist that until a few decades ago, it was presumed that homosexuals were heterosexuals who were either emotional midgets or were deliberately deviating from their true orientation for the sake of "thrills." How then can the Bible have condemned something the writers of the Bible did not understand? Even given this argument, however, some persons believe that every word of the Bible is the word of God and that even if the writers didn't know about homosexuality, God did and planned their words for future reference. There is no arguing with these people except to point out the thousands of violations of the Bible which they commit in a single week. Anita Bryant, for instance, should know well the Bible's admonition against women speaking up to men! The first card of the "unbeatable" hand, therefore, shouldn't scare you out of the game.

Revelation is technically the revealing of divine truth through a variety of means. The Church has always insisted that it alone holds this card. While I personally have no doubts on the reality of revelation, I know for a fact that the Church is not the only recipient of divine truth. It has, for instance, been revealed to gay Catholics that God does not wish them to hate their homosexual orientation but to celebrate it in a manner consistent with the teachings of Jesus, i.e., to love selflessly. This knowledge has been put through a far more thorough test than the celibate teachers of the Church are able to engage in, for gay Catholics have had to *live* the truth and not merely talk about it.

If there is such a thing as "truth," then living the truth must result in internal wholeness and joy. This has been my experience and the experience of thousands of other gay Catholics who have lived the truth. Gustavo Gutierrez, the third-world theologian who is captivating the minds of millions with his *Theology of Liberation*, persuasively argues that the Gospel must have relevance to an individual's life in order to be acted upon. Put quite simply, you cannot say, "Blessed are the Poor" to starving people who live under a dictatorship. Christianity, in that context, makes no sense. Gutierrez instructs those who suffer persecution to examine the internal sources of their oppression and interpret the Gospels in a way which makes sense. Revelation for Gutierrez does not come to us by way of an early Church scholar who reasoned out the Will of God; it comes to us from our own real experience of the world around and within us. As a person who has experienced levels of selfless love by way of homosexual lovemaking, the truth revealed insists that to abstain from that vehicle would be a living lie.

The third card is Tradition. The Church believes that anything that has survived its long history of scholarly probing and has withstood the test of time, must indeed be the Will of God. Yet, traditions change by the weight of new discovery. Case in point is the Church's attitude toward women. The Church continues to cite tradition as a good reason for not ordaining women to the priesthood. In society however, women are successfully challenging their traditional role. While the past held the lid on opportunities for women in the professional world, observers today insist it won't be long before a woman is elected commander-in-chief of the Armed Forces. When that happens, Rome will release its tradition and ordain women to the priesthood, lest they appear totally irrelevant to people's lives. Likewise with the tradition which they insist condemns homosexual behavior. In a soon-to-be-published scholarly book, Dr. John Boswell of Yale University shows that the Church has not always condemned homosexuality and that in fact, many of its early writers defended it against repressive laws. The Church will no doubt ignore Boswell's findings but can't really rely on its tradition when it comes to a persistent denial of the moral neutrality of homosexuality any more than it could continue to condemn usury, Jews or condone slavery.

The Keys to the Kingdom is weak to begin with. It is based upon the recording of Christ's words to Peter that "Upon this Rock I will build my Church." His followers were told that whose sins they forgive are forgiven and whose sins they bind are bound. This power is handed down from Pope to bishop to priest through ordination, making each a representative of Jesus on earth. However, for a variety of reasons, this line of authority carries little ultimate weight in the lives of individual Catholics. To begin with, an essential teaching of the Church is that, above all else, conscience must be the ultimate guide for behavior. People cannot be told to do something or to refrain from doing something if that action is inconsistent with their own moral decision of conscience. The Church warns, however, that a conscience must be *developed* and that a means of developing your conscience is study of the Scriptures and the Revelation and Tradition of the Church. For the weak minded, this provides a convenient Catch 22. Do what your conscience tells you, but a truly developed conscience will tell you to do what the Church has just told you to do. Individuals who take their faith seriously have done the necessary homework. They respond that, while maintaining their allegiance to the Church, their conscience tells them they must disobey this particular instruction. According to statistics, over 80% of American Catholic couples use artificial means of birth control as a decision of conscience rather than follow the pronouncements of the Pope.

Contradicting a teaching of a person of spiritual authority in the Church is perhaps the toughest hurdle for the gay Catholic. Traditionally, Catholics with questions were always encouraged to "ask Father." While you never had the opportunity to ask the bishop, you jumped when the bishop spoke. And heaven forbid if the pope made a pronouncement! The seriousness of this is best illustrated with reports we received of gay Catholics who commited suicide after the Vatican Decree on Sexuality seemed to close the door to any further debate on homosexuality. What must be remembered, however, is that the practice of "asking Father" developed when the clergy was the best educated group of people in the world.

Today most clergy would acknowledge that their training in the area of human sexuality was next to nil and that most bishops are in worse shape when it comes to knowledge of homosexuality. Even priests recently ordained laugh about the fact that the section on sexuality was the only of their studies which was written in Latin. When I went on a water fast in 1974 to protest the sins of the Church against gay people, I sent a gallon of water to the five Detroit bishops, asking them to join me for a day. One responded positively and afterwards admitted that he read more on homosexuality in the 24 days that I fasted than in his entire career as a priest or bishop. Welcoming his honesty, I would have to admit major reservations about placing the Keys to my spiritual future in the hands of any individual who has no idea what a homosexual is.

There is not now, nor has there ever been, a spiritual blanket of divine truth hanging over St. Peter's in Rome which prevents the Pope or those who surround him from making mistakes. The final card of the poker hand, Infallibility, was a manmade institution invented to keep protestors from becoming Protestants. It states that when the Pope speaks *ex cathedra* (from the chair) on matters of faith, he will be free from error. From my perspective, this is sheer nonsense; that it has rarely been used perhaps reflects a similar feeling by those in Rome. The Pope has made mistakes throughout the history of the Church, as have bishops (Coleman Carroll of Miami comes immediately to mind) and priests. What the Church condemns today (Martin Luther), it embraces tomorrow. For that reason, there is no pronouncement that comes out of Rome, the bishop's office or the pulpit that should prompt any person to believe he or she is seriously disordered or condemned to hell.

Now that we have called the bluff of the "pat hand," what cards do *we* hold? To begin with, any person who believes in God and believes that Jesus was the perfection of humanity and the Son of God and who attempts to live a life based on the basic message of selfless love, approaches the poker table with an unbeatable hand; there is no gamble involved. Likewise, if we distinguish the externals of being Catholic from the essence that has been carried through the ages by tradition, a thirst for justice, an ability to forgive, an awareness of the Kingdom within, then our status as Catholics cannot be undercut. If we listen to the voice within and do not exploit the celebration of our homosexual orientation, then the pot is clearly ours.

Lest anyone be confused, I love the Church. While I find no meaning in Infallibility or the Immaculate Conception and while obligatory Sunday Mass has not created the sense of community for me that it was designed to create, I find no need to rid them of meaning in other persons' lives. While I am contemptuous of authority that bases its power over me on a magical formula, I believe in the potential authority and power of the priesthood if it is exercised by individuals who are called forth by the community to lead with consent and who fully realize that they are being called to serve, not to be served and feared. The Roman Catholic Church is not only an essential part of who I am, given my 30 years at its breast, but more importantly, I see it with adult eyes as a potentially powerful vehicle for transforming the face of the earth into a Kingdom where love replaces fear and hatred, and sharing eliminates want.

Gay Catholics are essential to the future of the Church. We are a test which strikes at the very nerve of Christianity. As society's lepers we are a continual indictment of the lack of Faith commitment of those who claim to keep all the rules but who are unable to reach out in love as they know they must. Our presence forces the decision between being a Church of the People of God and a Church of comfortable status.

Likewise, the unique beauty with which our trials have endowed us provides us with a vision to be shared with those whose eyes are scaled with contentment. The commitment to the Faith which gay Catholics personify by their determination to sit through a service that condemns homosexuality (not unlike staying at a party at which you are the constant butt of the host's humor); to pray with brothers and sisters who would hold back the kiss of peace if they knew you were gay; to proudly announce your religious affiliation when the leaders of your Church have condemned you to hell; is a persecution for the Faith which most Catholics have only read about in the *Lives of the Saints*. When the work of the Spirit is completed and gay Catholics are liberated from the fear and hatred of the nongay world, we will be celebrated.

Therefore, when we encounter representatives of the official Church who would have us believe God hates practicing homosexuals, it is important to convey by words and by actions the basic strength and pride that gay Catholics share. I make sure that any priest or bishop I encounter is made instantly comfortable with his fear of me. I assure him that I understand why he feels the way he does and am most willing to help him liberate himself from his anti-Christian sentiments.

We are making great strides forward. The hierarchy of the Church is more and more divided on the issue. While ten years ago the subject of homosexuality was too embarrassing to discuss, today there are many bishops who have made strong public statements in support of full civil rights for gay men and women. There are even a few bishops who will privately confide that they find nothing morally wrong with homosexuality in a love relationship. Likewise, theologians and other educators are spending a great deal of time studying the subject; many have changed their positions because of their encounters with happy and healthy gay Catholics. While the thinking of the hierarchy and theologians does not affect me personally, I rejoice in their change of attitude; it will make it that much easier for later generations of gays to grow up feeling good about who they are. As with all movements toward the Kingdom, everything will come to pass. It is merely a matter of patience and perseverance.

As for those gay persons who are as vile in their attacks on our religious affiliation as some religionists are with our sexual orientation, remember that many of these persons lash out because of anger. Most call themselves former Catholics and they seem disturbed that not everyone hates the Church as much as they do. Patience, again, is required in explaining why the Church continues to hold meaning for you; patience is needed in helping them discover why their feelings run so deep. Anger and bitterness confine more than they liberate.

If gay Catholics play their cards right they can enjoy the riches of both their faith and their sexual orientation, which when combined and fully integrated are priceless. Both are essential to my life and as such, no one will be allowed to bluff me out of the game.

---

1. For further reading on the subject, see *The Church and the Homosexual* by McNeill and contact Dignity, Inc. at 3719 6th Ave., Suite F, San Diego CA 92103 for a variety of related printed materials.

Protestantism and Gay Freedom

Rev. William R. Johnson

This is an exciting and challenging time for those of us who are gay Christians. More than at any other time in its history, the institutional church is confronting the injustices inherent in its traditional attitudes toward human sexuality, and toward same gender relationships and sexual expression in particular. The historical silence of lesbians and gay men within the church has been broken. Increasingly, we are speaking our truths as persons who affirm our sexuality and the sexuality of others and who celebrate our faith in the revelations and teachings personified by Jesus, the Christ.

We are well aware the systemic oppression of our people is rooted in the Judeo-Christian Tradition, that monolithic body of mythology, history, ritual, theological speculation, Biblical scholarship and interpretation rigidly institutionalized in the church, the law, the culture and the popular mind of Western culture. We are equally aware that many of our lesbian sisters and gay brothers think us foolish for daring to contend with that Tradition and the ignorance and fear of human sexuality it has fostered. Yet *faithfully contending* with injustice—in this case injustice perpetrated by the church itself—has always been fundamental to Christian discipleship. Human activity has created all institutions in our culture, including the church, and human activity inspired by the vision of freedom and respect for human dignity will constructively change them.

Those of us who are gay and Christian on this homophobic planet have a difficult but not impossible task. We are called to be true to our faith despite the popular mythology that posits we cannot be both gay and Christian. We are called to meaningfully claim the freedom from all that oppresses inherent in the Good News that we are loved of God and empowered by grace. We are called to live our lives with triumphant

65

faith and be witnesses to the power of love rather than servile to the stagnation of unquestioned authority.

The truth is we are gay; we are Christian to the degree we have chosen to be students of the Nazarene teacher of love, faith and freedom, living our lives according to *his* example. Christian discipleship invites a conscious commitment to active loving and to living with faith, not fear. In such vulnerability, freedom becomes reality. This is the life-nurturing, liberating dynamic of the life of Jesus which threatened the mortal power of the political and religious leaders of his time. While those around him, hungering for freedom from Roman tyranny, hailed him as the long-expected Messiah of the Messianic traditions of Hebrew sects, Jesus perceived his purpose differently. He acknowledged being the anointed one of God, through whose life on this physical plane the liberating power of God/love was revealed to humankind. He lived and died and lives victoriously because his power was not political, ecclesiastical, physical or social, his power was spiritual. He lived not to orchestrate an overthrow of Roman tyranny or to save humanity. Consistently he declared that *faith* in God/love (made manifest *through* him) is the doorway to life. As Howard Moody, pastor of the Judson Memorial Church in New York City, illuminated in a recent sermon, "The faith of the early Church was not about salvation for oneself but rather *a deliverance from that concern.*" For Jesus, faith in God's grace—the empowering, eternal, affirming, liberating love energy/spirit in the cosmic universe—rendered concern for personal salvation meaningless. Such grace embraces each of us without distinction. Although we know tyrannies on this physical plane, like the oppressed, whose common lot he shared, our spirits are free. That freedom is a living reality and is known to us according to our faith.

RELIGIOUS FREEDOM

In the sixteenth century, a young priest named Martin Luther dared to challenge the authority of the Pope and all hell broke loose. Luther was but one of many protesting Catholics who found no semblance of Christian discipleship in the exploitation by guilt of the faithful by the Roman hierarchy. Their willingness to stand with courageous faith and challenge the ecclesiastical status quo gave birth to the Protestant Reformation. Protestantism grew from theological concepts then considered radical. To be radical means going to the root of a matter and that is precisely what Luther did.

Luther shared with the people his vision of the priesthood of all believers. At a time in history when the hierarchy of the Roman Church was less subtle and was selling indulgences to sinners seeking to avoid temporal "punishment," Luther offered a testimony of faith in God's grace. He proclaimed the primacy of the Gospel, through which he believed the Spirit that is Holy nurtures the soul in faith. The buying of indulgences was not necessary; salvation of the soul, he set forth, is by grace alone through faith. This is the cornerstone of the Protestant heritage.

Christian faith is a profoundly personal, internal affirmation of confidence that the revelation of Jesus, the Christ, is true: we are free because the kingdom of love is within us, is made manifest in us, through us, and to us, by our personal faith in God's grace.

By going to the root of Christian discipleship—dynamic, intensely personal faith in God's continuing interaction with humanity—Luther well earned the accolade, "radical for Christ." His radical theology shifted the focus of some believers from ecclesiastical power systems to the most intimate of human experiences: the power within each individual life.

Luther's daring, and the Protestant Reformation it inspired, established within Protestant thought the imperative of religious freedom. His was a quest which gave to Protestantism the principle of freedom in witnessing to one's faith as well as in the interpretation of the scriptures.

It was a quest for religious freedom that caused our Protestant forebears to set sail for the New World and that spurred the expansion of Protestantism in America. When the Pilgrims left England, the renowned Congregational preacher, John Robinson, admonished them to be open to the continuing revelatory activity of the Holy Spirit with these timeless words: "The Lord hath yet more light and truth to break forth from His Holy Word." Often when disagreements arose with prevailing theology, Biblical interpretation or religious practice, colonial preachers and their followers formed religious sects, some of which became denominations known to us today. Other denominations evolved from Protestant traditions alive in Europe and brought to American soil by immigrants. The history of American Protestantism is replete with divisions initially made because individual persons exercised their religious freedom. The Constitutional separation of church and state in the United States originally was a *defense* of religious freedom.

The history of the early church is equally replete with divisions based on interpretations of the meaning of the life of Jesus, religious practice and jockeying for ecclesiastical power. The Christian Church, in its many forms throughout history as *institution*, has never been the *inclusive* community of faithful people committed to personifying love that Jesus envisioned. The intrapersonal and interpersonal dynamics of which Jesus spoke and personified in his life have been obscured by ecclesiastical mystification of his human sojourn and by the maintenance of patriarchal power. To the degree the church has been exclusionary, the church has adulterated the Gospel, which is given to all people with-

out distinction. Yet, throughout the centuries, there have been those individuals whose comprehension of the liberating Gospel of the Christ
have caused them to dare to challenge the church to subject its doctrine
and practice to scrutiny under the light of the Gospel. That Gospel pro-
motes love, demands faithfulness, and liberates. Such daring forced the
church to abandon its advocacy of segregation among races and today is
forcing the church to confront its Machiavellian role in the perpetuation
of injustices against sexual people.

   Many of us can remember boring sermons. When I was growing up in
Houston and attending church services weekly, I often found myself tun-
ing out the voice of the preacher, reflecting instead on the scripture lessons from my own personal experience, faith, and openness to interaction with the Spirit that is Holy. I felt I needed to sort out for myself what
it meant to be a Christian on a pilgrimmage of faith in order for my faith
to be real; viscerally mine. I now know I was exercising my religious
freedom, which is not only my birthright as an American citizen, but as
Luther would affirm, also my human right as a mortal/spiritual person.

LOVER PERSONIFIED

Living as we do in a time when myth-mongering exploiters of ignorance
and fear are claiming Christian identity and presenting a very real
threat to the rights of all persons, our reflections need to be focused on
the life of Jesus, the paradigm for Christian discipleship. His was a life of
love personified, sometimes love empowered in anger, but always active
for good, not ill, in human interaction. Genuine faith in the Christ event
shows itself in compassion, vulnerability, forgiveness, risk taking, honesty, humility, response-ability and reverence for the dignity of human life
and for all creation. It can be witnessed in human interaction. Those
who claim Christian identity but whose lives evidence hard-heartedness,
defensiveness, prejudice, rigidity, untruthfulness, self-aggrandizement,
fear and disregard for human dignity and all creation fail to comprehend the essential meanings of the life of the Christ.

   From the Gospels emerges the portrait of a man profoundly committed to human community. Jesus was a man attuned to his humanity and
to spiritual vitality. His teachings and his interaction with other persons
proclaimed clearly and resolutely the inherent worth and quality of
every living creature and the certainty of grace in the dynamic inter-
relatedness of all that is. In contrast to the ecclesiastical images of Lord
and King, Jesus identified himself as servant of the oppressed and revealed an androgynous humanness to a patriarchal culture in which women
were considered property and only male children had inheritance rights.
He was not a defender of the status quo, either socially, politically or

religiously. Rather, his was a revolutionary faith and radical love that transformed the lives of those he encountered and transcended concern for personal salvation. We discover in the demystified, human Jesus profound confidence in the grace of God, in the evolution of the spirit in life and beyond the experience of death, and in the liberating power of love. Firm in his certainty of grace in human life, he abandoned temporal concerns and in word and deed taught the imperative of losing one's life in the loving service of humanity in order to truly experience life in its fullest meanings. While those around him agitated for temporal salvation, he spoke of freedom that transcends the limitations of time and space. I am confident, were we to encounter him today, he would give us the same affirmative Good News: You are free! Live with faith in God's empowering grace! Do justice! Love God with your heart, mind, spirit and strength by loving your neighbor *and* your self and you will know life, and life abundant!

THE ANTISEXUAL TRADITION

As Protestant gay Christians, we have a responsibility to ourselves and to others to understand the popular dogmatic attitudes toward human sexuality in general and homosexuality in particular that have developed in the Judeo-Christian Tradition. In his enormously helpful book, *Embodiment*, Christian ethicist James B. Nelson offers a comprehensive examination of the anti-body, anti-sexual development of the Tradition.[1] Addressing the fact of sexual alienation, in both history and the individual, Nelson explores the ways sexist dualism (patriarchal subordination of women and the "feminine") and spiritualistic (body-spirit) dualism have contributed to a sex-negative, sex-for-procreation-only sexual ethic and theology.

The Hebrew culture in which Jesus lived was male dominated, men assuming themselves superior in reason and spirit to women, and thus destined to lead both civil and religious communities. In contrast, women were identified with emotionality, physicality and sensuality; their menstrual flow was deemed a sign of religious uncleanness and emotional instability. Women, with their procreative sexuality, were legally the property of men who secured and disposed of them. Fathering male heirs was the objective of sexual relations and because female reproductive processes were not visible, it was assumed the power of life resided with the male. Sexual expression was a male prerogative and male control over sexuality guaranteed continued male control over the culture; control established in religious law.

Pre-Christian Hebrew culture considered sexuality a good gift of God and spiritualistic dualism was minimal. In Greece, a body/spirit dualism arose after the death of Alexander the Great which held that "the true state of existence was devoid of any physical sexual activity."[2] In Rome, stoicism was the prevailing ethical philosophy. Though they did not devalue sex, the Stoics considered passionlessness the supreme virtue, especially the repression of visceral emotions such as sexual passion. All of these influences demanded asceticism, sexual alienation and denial of the human experience of embodiment.

Into such a world culture, Jesus proclaimed the imperative of fundamental equality of women and men and illuminated the primary importance of love and forgiveness in sexual and all other matters. He was clearly not an ascetic, being known for his drinking and acquaintance with persons from every strata of society. He openly defied the patriarchal cultural mores and religious laws; a living contradiction of the prevailing dualisms.

Significantly, Jesus spoke no word of condemnation against persons engaging in same-sex acts. Such acts were condemned in the culture because of the procreation-only demand; the condemnation being boldly *ascribed* to Yahweh (Jehovah), the one true God of the Hebrews. In the Hebrew mind, non-procreative sex acts were equated with the "paganism" outside Judea, and within her boundaries as well. This equation, a tenet of religious law, served to maintain male control of the social and religious life of the culture. Males who did not procreate were devalued. Given the general devaluation of women, same gender sex acts among women were ignored.

None of the Gospel writers, nor the missionary Paul, nor the formulators of the Tradition, possessed the psychological, sociological and sexological knowledge which now inform our theological reflections about human sexuality. They knew nothing of sexual orientation or of the natural heterosexual-bisexual-homosexual continuum that exists in human life. They did not postulate that persons engaging in same-gender sex acts could have been expressing *their natural sexuality*. They *presumed* that persons engaged in same gender sex acts were heterosexual, *presumed* only one purpose for sexuality (procreation) and *presumed* that anyone engaged in same gender sex acts was consciously choosing to pervert himself and what they assumed to be his natural sexuality (i.e., heterosexuality).

We now know that same gender sex acts have been observed in a multitude of species from sea gulls to porcupines and that homosexuality can justifiably be considered a minority expression, but a natural expression nonetheless, within the created order. We know such acts can be expressive of love in same-gender oriented human beings. Until this century human knowledge of the reality of same gender relationships was limited. Even though lesbians and gay males have survived centuries of repression and genocide, ours is the first generation to come out proudly into the sunlight of personal affirmation. Perhaps this is happening because we know we cannot allow the world to forget that half a million homosexuals perished in the ovens of fascism. Most certainly it is happening because we now have factual information about human sexuality never before known. From our twentieth century historical perspective we can assert with integrity that the Biblical writers, to the limited extent they addressed the subject, condemned specific sex acts that did not result in procreation from ignorance of human sexuality rather than a comprehensive understanding of its complexities, meanings and natural expressions.

For Christians, the religious laws of purification found in the Old Testament book of Leviticus are subordinated to the Gospel of Christ and rendered irrelevant to Christian discipleship. I mention them at this point only to remind us that in these laws the connection between idolatry (paganism) and same-gender sex acts was first established. It is in relationship to paganism that the condemnation of same-gender sex acts emerges in the writings of the missionary Paul.

After the death and resurrection of Jesus, the Apostle Paul traveled widely, establishing Christian churches throughout Asia Minor and maintaining contact with them through epistles and personal visits. A persecutor of Christians prior to his dramatic conversion on the road to Damascus, Paul was a Hebrew who became the primary interpreter of the Gospel of Christ in the first century A.D. His writings are replete with evidence of Roman and Greek influences and we can be sure that, writing as he was for Gentile (non-Jewish) Christians, Paul had a great cern that his followers not be led astray by the widespread idolatry of those who did not acknowledge Yahweh, the one true God of the Hebrews, as revealed in Jesus, the Christ. He valued celibacy as a means of Christian purification in preparation for the Parousia, the second coming of Christ, which he thought imminent. Though Paul affirmed a highly positive view of creation and as a Christian proclaimed the liberation of the whole person by Jesus Christ, his writings indicate he was influenced by the spiritualistic dualism of the Greeks in his belief that pure love for God necessitated divorcing oneself from earthly loves.

Paul's few references to same gender sex acts are made in the context of discussions of paganism. From his limited understanding, such acts were a sign of paganism and, indeed, the whole of the Hebraic tradition, in which he had been reared, sustained such a view. In discussing Paul's condemnation of homosexual acts, Nelson makes the following observation:

> What then should we make of Paul's moral judgment in this case?
> Perhaps we should just accept him for what he was: a faithful apos-
> tle and a profound interpreter of the central message of the Gospel,
> yet one who was also a fallible and historically conditioned human
> being. Paul's central message is clear: we do not earn righteousness
> by anything we do nor are we justified by anything we are—we are
> justified by the grace of God in Jesus Christ, and the gifts of the
> Spirit are equally available to all persons.[3]

Paul's teachings concerning the subordination of women and the
"moral" justification of slavery have been seriously re-examined by the
church in its effort to be faithful to the liberating Gospel of Christ. His
teachings concerning same-gender sex acts deserve equal scrutiny, especially in the light of our current knowledge of psychosexual orientations.

The church has applied flexibility and nonliteral interpretation to
many of the moral judgments in scripture and clung dogmatically to literal interpretations of references to same-gender sex acts. Following the
time of Jesus and Paul, the mystery and miracle of embodiment and affirmation of sexual expression were lost in a schizophrenic body-spirit
dualism. The sex-for-procreation-only dogma prevailed. In view of the
power struggles within the early church and ecclesiastical maintenance
of male prerogatives despite Jesus' egalitarian teachings, this is not surprising. Widespread belief in the Parousia was certainly another factor;
St. Paul had clearly denounced human physicality.

The negativism of the early church fathers degenerated even more
when Augustine equated sexual expression with lust and held that *every*
sex act is connected with original sin (though sex for procreation was en-
dorsed with regret because he considered its single purpose to be "right-
eous"). An affirmative attitude toward sexuality eluded Luther as well;
he echoed Augustine. Another reformer, John Calvin, introduced the
first semblance of enlightenment in the Tradition by proposing that
companionship rather than procreation was God's intention in the marital relationship.

In the centuries since the Reformation, Protestantism has evidenced an
increasing awareness that sexual expression within marriage has values
quite independent of procreation. Particularly with twentieth-century
knowledge of human sexuality has come a measure of affirmation of sexual expression as an important aspect of self-expression in human relationships. Although it would be premature to suggest that the church
now sacramentalizes sexual expression within marriage as pleasure,
communication and celebration, the evolution of the church's doctrine is
clearly in that direction. Such interpersonal experiences as the honoring
of the other, trust, tenderness, sensuality, caring, respect, vulnerability
and spiritual unity are all possible within human sexual expression, irre-

spective of the gender of the persons relating or the nature of their marital circumstance.

While there has been some degree of affirmation of sexual expression within marriage, the church's attitude toward gay sexual expression has remained largely unchanged. From the 13th century, when Thomas Aquinas declared same-gender sex acts "a crime against nature" until the 1950s when Derrick Sherwin Bailey engaged in research that facilitated decriminalization of same-gender sex acts in England,[4] the reality of gay sexuality and relationships remained seriously unexamined within the Tradition. Some people still believe the view offered by Thomas Aquinas that same-gender sex acts cause earthquakes, droughts, famines and other natural disasters. Amazingly, there are those who give credibility to such nonsense.

We, and all sexual people, are victims of the church's historic sexist and spiritualistic dualisms. We are fortunate to be living in a time when the Judeo-Christian tradition is being challenged with faith and intelligence in its narrow and culturally determined perspectives on human sexuality. We might well be witnessing the evolution of a second great reformation within the church, fostered by understanding and by abandoning the sexist and spiritualistic dualisms of patriarchal theology.

For many, the manner in which the scriptures are interpreted will be a stumbling block to full affirmation of God's grace in human sexual community. There are, essentially, two ways of interpreting scripture: literally and critically. Either can be employed by persons of faith; the difference between them is qualitative.

The Bible we read today has a complex history, having been translated and edited over a period of centuries. The claim that the words of the Bible are *actually* the "words of God" is a gross oversimplification and is intellectually dishonest. Though translators and editors of the Bible may have been inspired to undertake their tedious work, their work was not perfect and none could escape the adulterating cultural and ecclesiastical influences of their particular historical contexts.

Literalists, like Anita Bryant and her followers, are necessarily selective in quoting passages of scripture to denounce the "sins" of others—those realities in the lives of others *they* find *personally* repugnant. Recognizing they too are victims of the homophobic development of the Judeo-Christian Tradition, we may empathize with their ignorance and fear, but we cannot ignore the fact that their selective use of scripture out of context betrays their personal prejudices. They worship an authoritarian, not a liberating, God.

To be sure, Protestantism is not without its literalists, though historically the Protestant Tradition has adhered to a critical approach to the scriptures (literary and textual scholarship) informed by faith in God's grace, the continuing revelatory activity of the Spirit that is Holy, and contemporary knowledge through which God's intention for humanity is also made known.

United Methodist theologian Robert Treese has suggested five guidelines for Biblical criticism necessary for the appropriation of the scriptures for our time:

> (1) The Bible is not the word of God, but the words of men, in which and through which we believe the living, active, constantly con-temporary Word of God come to men. (and women)
>
> (2) A Bible passage is to be interpreted in terms of the experiences, life setting and problems of the specific writer and with respect to the purposes for which it was written.
>
> (3) A passage is to be further explicated in the light of our contemporary experience and knowledge. We must try to see it in relation to our social-psychological-historical-philosophical un-derstanding as well as to our existential knowledge. There may not be agreement, for sometimes—in fact, often—the Bible stands in judgment of our contemporary life, but the task is to discern, as nearly as possible, the meaning for us today.
>
> (4) Although the Bible writers faced the same basic existential questions we face, many of their answers are time-caught, as ours are, and valid only for them. But the values they affirmed by their answers are of significance to us.
>
> (5) The whole Bible is to be seen in light of the Gospel of Jesus Christ and the experience of the early Church.[5]

Believing, as I do, that the scriptures nurture the soul in faith in God's grace and impart to human understanding those things necessary for freedom, I do not advocate a retreat from the scriptures. I do believe the proof-texting used by literalists to justify *their* prejudice against gay peo-ple (and, historically, against other peoples) betrays an incomplete un-derstanding of the meaning of the life of the Christ. We who are gay Christians have a special responsibility not to be diverted by the wide-spread use of scripture to undermine our essential humanity imbued with grace and the capacity to love. Our task is to explore the scriptures with a keen commitment to understanding the central message of the Bible with regard to human sexuality: Sexuality is a good gift of God that is not a mysterious and alien force of nature but integral to an under-standing of what it means to be human in the fullest sense of embodiment of spirit. Its deepest meanings are made known in the honoring of ourselves and the personhood of others in loving. It is not to be abused in exploitative or manipulative relationships but celebrated in ourselves and in others as the most intimate experience of physical and spiritual communion. In affirming our sexuality, whatever our affectional and sexual orientation, we affirm God's grace to us and to all humanity.

FAITHFUL VISIBILITY

The rigid sexuality of the Judeo-Christian Tradition in its procreation-only emphasis has caused many of us to isolate our sexuality from other integral parts of our personhood. This compartmentalization is supported by the entire culture which causes many persons—gay and nongay—to feel sexuality must be kept in a closet of secrecy. Our intrapersonal struggle is one of reintegrating our sexuality into a meaningful understanding of ourselves as persons. For those of us who are gay this means affirming our emotional, psychological, social and erotic responsiveness to persons of our own gender as integral to our personhood. It means recognizing the expression of our same-gender feelings as congruent with our primary understanding of who we are, rather than accepting cultural or ecclesiastical definitions of our identity. Most important it means knowing that as sexual humans we have a God-given right to express our sexuality responsibly rather than repress it.

In using guilt to maintain ecclesiastical control over sexual people and the expression of sexuality, the church has created human suffering and violated the spirit of the Gospel. There is no condemnation in Christ. We are free. Each of us must define for ourselves the degree to which we will live with faith, not fear, in that freedom—and personify love. The church has offered to us a standard of value for personal integration and social intercourse but has failed in its responsibility to foster a person affirming understanding of human sexuality. We can appreciate the limitations of its knowledge in centuries past, but in light of contemporary knowledge, we have a responsibility to reject the continuation of its oppressive non-theology of sexuality.

Contemporary psychological, sociological, sexological knowledge and Biblical/theological scholarship supports the justice we seek as gay Christians. The debate concerning human sexuality in general and homosexuality in particular within the whole church, especially within the Protestant Tradition, is raging. It will be enriched by the full participation of gay (and bisexual) Christians who, with faith in the grace of God, are becoming more visible and are articulating the gay experience within the church.

Many gay Christians are today engaged in the process of growing toward a new understanding of ourselves as gay people and as Christians. Many are struggling with the problem of determining the nature of our involvement with the institutional church, evaluating whether or not such involvement does or would have meaning for our lives. Some gay Christians find they can celebrate and express their Christian faith apart from the institutional church and its accoutrements, ritual and nuclear-family-oriented congregational life. In personal relationships with others who affirm their dignity and share their faith, they experience the caring community Christ sought to foster.

Others of us identify with the institutional church for personal reasons known to each of us. Many of us believe the time has come for the church to confront its homophobic Tradition and change its narrow view of human sexuality. We know the Gospel is given to all persons. Perhaps we remain within the institutional structures because we are not without hope that the liberating spirit of Christ will make itself known through our insistence upon sharing fully in the life of the church as gay Christians.

We value the opportunity to know other gay Christians within the church that has been made possible by our willingness to become visible. Gay people have been organizing within religious structures since 1968 when the Reverend Troy Perry organized the Metropolitan Community Church of Los Angeles, a church specializing in ministry with gay persons. There now exists a Universal Fellowship of Metropolitan Community Churches with some 250 churches in the United States and at least six other countries.

Within Protestant denominations, gay persons have organized caucuses and specialized ministries. We have been joined in our efforts by many persons who are not gay but who honor our dignity and support our struggle for full human and civil rights within society and equality within the church. We are addressing a wide variety of concerns including official policy, theology, education, counseling ministries, mutual support (especially for gays employed by the church) and advocacy for civil rights protection.

Progress is slow—primarily because many gay persons fear taking the risk of becoming more visible—but it is certain. Official statements supporting civil rights legislation for gay people have been secured from the Governing Board of the National Council of Churches, the United Church of Christ, the Unitarian Universalist Association, the Society of Friends, The Presbyterian Church in the United States and the Disciples of Christ. Most Protestant denominations have declared opposition to laws which seek to proscribe consensual sexual expression between adults in private.

Recognizing the need for education among clergy and laity, several denominations have commissioned studies of human sexuality in general and homosexuality in particular. Most noteworthy is *Human Sexuality—A Preliminary Study*[6] commissioned by the United Church of Christ and completed in 1977. The United Presbyterian Church completed a study on homosexuality and ordination in 1978, but the affirmative conclusions were rejected by delegates to the Presbyterian General Assembly (May 1978). Studies in other denominations are currently underway at all levels of the church.

To date, only two openly gay persons have been ordained to the ministry: myself (June 1972) and Ellen Barrett, ordained an Episcopal priest in January 1976. Of course, there are thousands of gay persons, clergy and laity, in the professional leadership of the church. Given the prejudice that exists, and the threat of loss of employment, it is understandable that most church professionals who are gay have not openly affirmed their identity. It is to their credit that many are involved in gay caucuses and are furthering the education/advocacy process through their positions within the structures.

The various gay organizations listed at the end of this chapter seek to provide pastoral care for gay persons within the respective denominations, are facilitating education and offer understanding, support and opportunities for involvement in the gay movement within the church for gay Christians who are self-affirmed and visible as well as for those who, for whatever personal reasons, feel they cannot yet open the closet door. They offer the best hope for alleviating much of the isolation and sense of alienation experienced by persons who seek to give expression to their faith as gay Christians. In some areas ecumenical coalitions, especially for advocacy for civil rights legislation, have been formed in recognition of the importance of cooperative effort in countering the injustices created by 2000 years of sex-negative attitudes and doctrine.

As gay Christians we are called to fully accept ourselves and our sexuality as persons loved of God. We know our Christian faith is the foundation of our values in human relationships and our commitment to social justice. It inspires our vulnerability in loving. We recognize that our Christian faith is a vital part of the physical/spiritual pilgrimage that is our life.

Our ability, not disability, to relate to persons of our own gender is a blessing on this homophobic planet. The truth of God's love for us and in us has been distorted by the Judeo-Christian Tradition. Let us celebrate our faith and the ways in which we are able to give expression to it in our daily lives. No less than others, we stand within the circle of God's love and grace.

We are called as the persons we are to love one another. When we do so, we are being faithful to God and the revelation of the Christ, who personified the new humanity.

FOOTNOTES

1. Nelson, James B., *Embodiment*, Augsburg Publ. Co., St. Paul, MN., 1978.
2. Ibid, p. 48.
3. Ibid, p. 188.

4. Bailey, Derrick Sherwin, *Homosexuality and the Western Christian Tradition*, Longmans Green, Ltd., London, 1955, Republished: Archon-Shoestring Press, 1976.

5. Robert Treese quoted in Gearhart, Sally and Johnson, William R., *Loving Women/Loving Men: Gay Liberation and the Church*, New Glide Publ., San Francisco, 1974, p. 28.

6. United Church Board for Homeland Ministries, *Human Sexuality: A Preliminary Study*, United Church Press, New York, NY, 1977.

THE MOVEMENT IN THE CHURCH

American Baptists Concerned
198 Santa Clara Avenue
Oakland, CA 94610

Disciples of Christ
Rev. Robert Glover
Task Force on Human Sexuality
P.O. Box 1986
222 South Downey Avenue
Indianapolis, IN 46206

Brethren-Mennonite Gay Caucus
Martin Rock
Box 582
Lancaster, PA 17604

Friends Committee for Gay Concerns
Box 222
Sumneytown, PA 18084

Kindred (Seventh-Day Adventists)
Box 1233-A
Los Angeles, CA 90028

Integrity (Protestant Episcopal)
Mr. John Lawrence
10 Mercier Avenue
Dorchester, MA 02124

Lutherans Concerned
(LCA, ALC, MO. SYNOD)
Ms. Diane Fraser/
Mr. Howard Erickson
Box 19114A
Los Angeles, CA 90019

Moravians Concerned
Rev. James A. Kennedy
632 North 4th Street
Philadelphia, PA 19123

Presbyterians for Gay Concerns
Mr. Chris Glaser
P.O. Box 46412
Los Angeles, CA 90046

Unitarian Office for Gay Concerns
Mr. Robert Wheatley
Unitarian Universalist Assoc.
25 Beacon Street
Boston, MA 02108

United Church of Christ
Dr. William R. Johnson
c/o Maranatha at Riverside Church
490 Riverside Drive
New York, NY 10027

United Methodists for Gay Concerns
Rev. Michael Collins
P.O. Box 775
New York, NY 10011

Universal Fellowship of Metropolitan Community Churches
5300 Santa Monica Blvd. No. 304
Los Angeles, CA 90029

Evangelicals Concerned
Dr. Ralph Blair
30 East 60th Street, Rm. 708
New York, NY 10022

Affirmation (Gay Mormon Underground)
P.O. Box 9638
Denver, CO 80209

Judaism in the Gay Community

Barrett L. Brick

We gay Jews are witnessing a uniquely personal moment in history. Although the gay Jewish community as such is barely seven years old, the entire Jewish community is awakening to our voices and is beginning to face the challenge we pose: that we will no longer live a lie to our people. We are both Jewish and gay; we will not sacrifice one for the other.

Obviously, this will be a long moment. Perhaps this is the ultimate challenge we gay Jews pose to our people. It is one thing to understand Biblical passages more fully—and reinterpret them if necessary. It is quite another thing to bring about a major shift in attitudes, securing full acceptance within Judaism for gay women and men, socially as well as theologically.

And yet homophobia, whether actual bigotry or mere lack of knowledge, is hardly an attitude that Judaism can foster, morally or otherwise. The libel and slander that has been written and spoken of us by Jews and non-Jews alike must be repudiated, being direct violations of Torah. As Jews, commanded to seek and pursue justice, laws proscribing consensual homosexual acts must be opposed by our community. At the same time, the Jewish community will be expected to continue to rise to the call to eliminate discrimination. Many have already done so, organizations as well as individuals. Resolutions of support for gay rights have already been adopted by the American Jewish Committee, the North American Jewish Students Network, the Philadelphia B'nai B'rith Anti-Defamation League, the Central Conference of American Rabbis, and the Union of American Hebrew Congregations. The UAHC has, in fact, accepted the Los Angeles gay temple, Beth Chayim Chadashim, into its membership. Judaism's strong commitment to human rights should not be tarnished by those who insist on granting legitimacy to discrimination.

Here is where opposition seems to be greatest. "All right," we are told.
"You are gay and that's fine. We know stereotypes are wrong. We know
that most child molesters are heterosexual. You have a right to a home
and a job. But not where you can influence children. And you certainly
can't have custody of children, not even your own." What should
Judaism say about this?

Very simply, it must be said that all of us, nonparents and parents
alike, want only the best for children, our own and those of others, now
and in the future. Despite all the studies made of sexual orientation over
the years, we are sure of only one thing: throughout history, homosexuals
have existed, do exist, and will continue to exist, and that—despite the
prayers of fundamentalists, the death camps of tyrants, the empty promises of medical "faith healers" and the self-torture of many of us—is the
way of the world. Gays are among the children of Israel. The choice is
not between encouraging or discouraging people from being gay. The
choice is between creating a healthy or unhealthy environment for both
our gay and nongay children to grow up in, between enabling them to
achieve their full potential or holding them back through bigotry and
misunderstanding. Take away the lies of child molestation (a predominantly heterosexual phenomenon), remove the smokescreen of role
models (one's sexual orientation is not so easily malleable), and that is
the real question.

We are still, of course, working to create such a harmonious world.
While we do so, the Jewish gay woman or man need not feel isolated
from the Jewish community. A growing, thriving and enthusiastically
active gay Jewish community exists around the world, as the list of organizations at the end of the chapter shows. During the past six years
synagogues and groups have formed across the United States, as well as
in Canada, England, Australia, France and Israel, beginning with the
two of longest standing, Beth Chayim Chadashim in Los Angeles and
Beth Simchat Torah in New York. Most of the organizations have pros-
pered and become very active in both the gay and Jewish communities,
making major contributions to both, as well as providing valuable foci
for people seeking to explore what it means to be gay and Jewish.

Perhaps the most important contribution that these groups have made
and continue to make is that they have created a community for many
who felt anchored nowhere, who felt rejected by or uncomfortable with
other Jewish settings. The gay Jewish community is following the time-
honored tradition of forming synagogues and other entities based on
common origins or cultural patterns. Moreoever, through involvement
in the gay Jewish community, many gay Jewish women and men are becoming more involved with the larger Jewish community in their neighborhoods and elsewhere.

For example, shortly after its founding in February 1973, Beth Simchat Torah (New York) established an educational program for its members, offering classes in a wide range of subjects. Those that have evoked continued interest are classes in Hebrew, Yiddish, Bible Study and Talmud, but classes have also been offered at various times in Kabbalah, Jewish Concepts and Jewish Homemaking. Educational programs have also been developed at Beth Chayim Chadashim (Los Angeles), Or Chadash (Chicago), MCT-Mishpucheh (Washington), and the Society for the Protection of Personal Rights (Tel Aviv). This is just one of the ways in which a close-knit community is formed and strengthened. Of course, education is not confined to the classroom. Shabbat evening programs on aspects of Jewish or gay or gay Jewish life are part of communal education, as are Jewish film festivals, excursions to Jewish museums, creating and performing theatrical works, discussions with writers and scholars and many similar events sponsored by the various gay Jewish groups.

The members of many synagogues are active not only in their own congregations, but also in the larger Jewish community. A shining example of this is provided by Beth Chayim Chadashim's activities with the Israel Levin Center and the Jefferson Convalescent Home. The congregation's members have been actively involved with both organizations, donating time and money to help serve the food provided by the Israel Levin Center to elderly members of the Jewish Community, and providing Shabbat and holiday services (including Passover seders) and sorely needed social contact for the residents of the Jefferson Convalescent Home through Project Caring. Beth Chayim Chadashim's members have also helped sponsor Vietnamese refugees; holiday gifts for underprivileged children in Children's Hospital; and needed supplies and money for Fountain House, which provides temporary shelter for gays on probation and parole, as well as indigents. In New York, Beth Simchat Torah has been involved with fundraising and service efforts for various community service organizations, including Project Ezra, aiding the elderly Jews of the lower east side; and NYANA, the New York Association for New Americans, aiding our sisters and brothers of all ages who have come to our shores fleeing oppression.

Many congregations and other groups are involved in combatting the oppression of Jews and gays at home and around the world. The Society for the Protection of Personal Rights has been fighting for reform of the laws affecting gay women and men in Israel, and has aided in the preparation of Israeli television programs on homosexuality. When the Soviet Union imprisoned film director Sergei Paradzhanov on charges of homosexuality, Beth Simchat Torah sent formal letters of protest to the Soviet Union's ambassadors to the United States and the United Nations, and also to the United Nations Division of Human Rights. Similar letter-writing campaigns have been spearheaded with regard to the Soviet Union's (and other nations') brutal treatment of their Jewish citizens. Beth Simchat Torah participates annually in the Solidarity Sunday March for Soviet Jewry and in other demonstrations of solidarity with our oppressed sisters and brothers, with the welcome appreciation of the Greater New York Conference on Soviet Jewry.

Community involvement is an important function of any gay Jewish group. For example, after a vicious attack on several men in a gay area of New York's Central Park, members of Beth Simchat Torah's community relations committee were instrumental in setting up a meeting between police officials, city officials and gay community leaders to discuss park safety and attitudes of gays and the police toward each other. Community involvement leads to community recognition. After a member of the New York City Human Rights Commission, a Satmar Hasidic rabbi, announced his opposition to gay rights and his refusal to enforce the Mayor's executive order barring antigay discrimination, a spokesperson for Beth Simchat Torah was asked by various television stations to respond to this announcement. Both Beth Simchat Torah and Beth Chayim Chadashim have active speakers bureaus whose members do an extraordinary amount of outreach work throughout their communities.

The Zionist Hug of Beth Simchat Torah has rallied and focused involvement of the membership of the New York group and other groups with Israel. In New York the Hug has sponsored Jewish book fairs and Israeli brunches, as well as meetings with representatives of the Israeli government and organizations closely affiliated with Israel. The Hug also led the drive at Beth Simchat Torah to plant a grove of 1000 trees in the American Bicentennial National Park in Israel, which was formally dedicated in 1977 "in honor of all the gay men and women who worked and fought to create and maintain a Jewish homeland in Eretz Israel." That same year, a project involving all the gay Jewish organizations around the world was begun to plant a woodland of 2500 trees in Israel by 1980.

The international tree project is just one outgrowth of the affiliation of the many synagogues and other organizations of the gay Jewish community. Formal affiliation was first proposed at an emergency conference sponsored by the Social Action and Jewish Committees (now the Community Relations Committee and the Zionist Hug) of Beth Simchat Torah in December 1975, in response to the shameful United Nations resolution declaring Zionism a form of racism. This led to meetings in Washington, D. C., in February and August of 1976, at which the first major International Conference of Gay Jews was planned. This conference was hosted in New York by Beth Simchat Torah April 22–24, 1977, and was attended by over 200 people from across the United States and around the world. (This and future international conferences are actually two conferences: the International Conference of Gay and Lesbian Jews and the International Conference of Gay and Lesbian Jewish Organizations. The difference is primarily for voting purposes, between matters of general community concern and matters affecting formal conference organization.) Words cannot adequately describe the breadth and depth of feelings felt by the participants. Workshops covered a wide variety of topics of gay, Jewish and gay Jewish interest. Shabbat services were attended by over 400 people. Participants enjoyed Shabbat meals in hosts' homes. Even such painful issues as Judaism's attitudes toward women were openly, if not conclusively, discussed. Every conferee, whether an individual or an organizational representative, brought to the conference and came away with the commitment to work together to build a strong gay Jewish community, which will be an active part of the greater gay and Jewish communities everywhere.

The International Conference of Gay and Lesbian Jews (the word lesbian was added in 1978) is now an annual event. In 1978 it was held May 19–21 in Los Angeles, hosted by Beth Chayim Chadashim. It was attended by 170 participants from 12 organizations and other communities. As in New York in 1977, a wide range of workshops was offered, some participated in by very knowledgeable outside speakers. The 1978 Conference also, however, showed the potential divisiveness of the question of sexism in the community. By a vote of 6 to 5, the organizational representatives to the 1978 Conference voted to accept the invitation of the Society for the Protection of Personal Rights to host the 1979 Conference in Israel. Opposition to the motion focused on the charge of Israel's oppression of women.

Sexism and homophobia are closely linked, both stemming from society's attitudes toward accepted roles for men and women, denigrating anyone who would play what is seen as the traditional woman's role. Every gay synagogue has involved women in their services at every level, be it reading a passage from the siddur or being a rabbinic intern. Women have served on the governing bodies of many gay Jewish organizations and are active in all of them. As with homophobia, however, sexist attitudes do not change overnight. Just as a homophobic strain developed within Judaism, so did a sexist strain, and this has unfortunately been adopted by many in the gay Jewish community. If the Jewish community—gay and nongay—is to survive as a full community, it must recall that women as well as men are created in God's image. Sexism is as unworthy of our community as is homophobia. Community organizations lose something when they are overwhelmingly of a single sex. There are no magic answers to a problem that is based on attitudes, but the problem of sexism within the Jewish community must be faced and solved. To some extent, the gay Jewish community is pointing the way.

The relationship between gay Jews and the rest of the Jewish community should not, however, be looked on as a one-way street, with gay Jews
educating the greater Jewish community to the need for humane treatment of gays. It is true that gay Jews will have to do this (and are doing
this). They will also have to remind Judaism that individuals must lead a
fulfilling life of their own and not expect to do so through their children.
At the same time, there is much that Judaism can teach gays, both Jews
and non-Jews alike. For example, it is one of the marvels of history that
the Jewish people, brutally uprooted more than once from their homeland, neither lost their identity nor died out, but rather survived, not only keeping but also enriching their identity. Blending time-honored traditions with contemporary realities, the children of Israel created rich and
vibrant cultures in exile from their homeland. While other cultures
perished around them or mutated into cultures completely different
from their roots, the Jewish people have maintained their basic identity
for thousands of years, back to the day that Abram left the dusty streets
of Haran. Neither the threats and cruelties of persecution nor the tempta-
tions of assimilation have been able to destroy the Jews as a people—due
in no small part to the conception of peoplehood and community that
the Jews hold. This is an example from which the gay community, as it
stands today, can well learn. (That learning process has indeed begun.
The gay community has adopted the concept of community service
centers from the Jewish community. Virtually every gay Jewish group is
a community center.) A stateless people can survive, but it must possess
an identity and a culture. We cannot, as gays, let our identity and
culture be taken from us nor dictated to us. We must preserve it and also
affirm it. In some cases, this may seem to ask more of us than we are
ready to do, especially if it means coming out publicly and ceasing to
live a lie by denying our being. Is this what Judaism would have us do?

Consider the following. After Abram and Sarai left Haran and entered
Canaan, a famine occurred in Canaan, forcing them to go to Egypt.
Abram, fearing for his life if Pharaoh knew that Sarai was his wife, in-
troduced Sarai as his sister, and she went along with the subterfuge.
Abram's life was spared. Yet Sarai, his wife, was still taken into
Pharaoh's house. Of course, Abram was rewarded with goods for his
"sister." Pharaoh and his house were plagued, however, and the truth
came out. Pharaoh, indignant, sent Abram and Sarai on their way.

What was Abram to do? Stories of husbands being murdered for their
beautiful wives were known to him. Should he tell the truth and die, or
lie and live, yet at the expense of losing his spouse? It is true that Pharaoh
was in large part to blame for Abram's fears. Obviously, Abram felt
himself to be in mortal danger. The Torah itself makes no immediate

comment regarding Abram's lie. Yet this lie is regarded by Nachmanides as a great sin. How often have we modern gay Jews told similar lies for fear of losing less than our lives? Perhaps we, like Abram, felt ourselves to be in an impossible situation, in which a lie would be easier than the truth. As Abram, we are only human. Yet Judaism does set us goals to strive for, even if at times we fall short. One of these goals is to live openly and proudly, without fear.

But centuries-old beliefs do not change overnight. It must be acknowledged that, whatever the original attitude of the ancient Hebrews was toward homosexual acts, the tradition as it has developed within Judaism until today has been that such acts are abominations. Certainly, many religious leaders when asked about Judaism and homosexuality merely cite certain scriptural and *halakhic* texts to close the case. Yet part of Judaism's vitality is that it is a dynamic religion, one that refuses to be frozen in the past. Many religious and community leaders realize this and are responding accordingly. Much, however, remains to be done before the gay Jew is fully accepted within *k'lal Yisrael.*

It can hardly be denied that Jewish tradition as it developed from at least 2300 years ago looked upon male homosexual acts of any sort as prohibited in general. This does not mean that Jewish tradition must remain homophobic. Let us not deceive ourselves: the commands of the Torah do not change on a whim. Yet, historically, when the need has been shown to reach a better understanding of the words of the Torah so that they may better reflect the humane spirit of Judaism, such an understanding has been reached.

It is not enough, though, merely to examine certain biblical passages that specifically mention certain homosexual acts. Within Judaism there exists not only the scriptural view of homosexuality but also the cultural concept of marriage and procreation, which also must be understood. Marriage and procreation are *mitzvot* (religious precepts) in Judaism, and the tendency of many if not most gay Jews to fulfill neither *mitzvah* has often been a stumbling block in the path of our acceptance within the larger Jewish community.

Unlike Christianity which came to enthrone celibacy as an ideal, regarding marriage as a concession to human weakness, Judaism always viewed marriage as a basic *mitzvah*, for "It is not good that . . . man should be alone; I will make him a help meet for him." (Genesis 2:18). Furthermore, not only are Adam and Eve blessed by the words *p'ru ur'vu* ("be fruitful and multiply") but so were the sons of Noah commanded, and also Jacob. (Genesis 1:28; 9:1; 7; 35:11) Procreation, marriage, family life—these imperatives are bound up within Judaism and have continually been cited as prime reasons why homosexuality has no place within Judaism. After all, the argument usually goes, gays don't procreate, therefore what have they to do with family life? How then can Judaism accept homosexuality?

What is marriage in the eyes of Judaism—is it merely a vehicle for channeling procreation and child rearing, or is there another facet to it? It is true that the Bible shows instances of men taking second wives for procreative purposes when the first marriage had proved childless. The Talmud states that if a marriage has proven childless for ten years, the man may not "neglect further the duty of procreation." (Y'vamot 64a) From this, either bigamy or divorce is implied. But the tradition and experience of several centuries by the Talmudic period frowned on bigamy, expressly considering the wishes and feelings of the original wife. Neither was divorce against the wife's will seen as desirable or ethical by most commentators, and this feeling eventually became universal. Marriage in and of itself was viewed as something that should be sustained, childlessness notwithstanding. *Sh'lom bayit*, the peace of the home, was seen as an ideal to be preserved. The pity of unwanted divorce was a major factor considered in the Responsa literature. Additionally *iggun*, an "anchorage" to nowhere, as in the case of a wife whose husband was missing or any forcibly separated wife, was to be avoided if possible. For all these reasons, stemming from the source reason of the love and feeling the married couple have for each other, even the childless marriage is to be sustained. Companionship and fulfillment are reasons enough.

Within Judaism, not only is marriage independent of procreation, but so is sexual intercourse seen as independent of procreation. Within marriage, the wife has the right of *onah* (sexual rights) as a basic necessity of life (together with food and clothes). (Exodus 21:10) Such intercourse may be procreative or nonprocreative—and not necessarily in the "missionary position." Sexuality within Judaism is not seen as solely procreative in function, but is equally valid as an expression of love in and of itself. If this is the case for nongay Jews, this must also be the case for gay Jews. Once the procreative imperative is removed from sexuality, there is no barrier to a proper understanding of homosexuality within Judaism save for centuries-old interpretations of two passages in Leviticus. These interpretations are probably erroneous and are certainly harmful to the emotional, physical and spiritual well-being of a significant portion of the children of Israel. Once Judaism resolves this situation as it resolved similar situations in the past, the way will be clear for Judaism's full and open acceptance of its gay children.

GAY JEWISH ORGANIZATIONS

AUSTRALIA
Beth Simcha of Sydney
11/75 O'Brien St.
Bondi, N.S.W. 2026
CANADA
Ontario
Congregation B'nai Kehillah
66 Gloucester St.
Toronto, Ontario M4Y 1L5

Quebec
Naches
P.O. Box 298, Station H
Montreal, Quebec H3G 2K8
FRANCE
Beit Haverim
3 bis, rue Clairaut
75017 Paris
ISRAEL
Society for the Protection of
Personal Rights
P.O. Box 16151
Tel Aviv 61160
UNITED KINGDOM
Jewish Gay Group
c/o Norman Goldner
5 St. Mary's Avenue
London N3 1SN
England
UNITED STATES
California
Congregation Beth Chayim
Chadashim
600 West Pico Blvd.
Los Angeles, CA 90035

Sha'ar Zahav
P.O. Box 5640
San Francisco, CA 94101
District of Columbia
MCT-Mishpucheh
P. O. Box 24103
Washington, DC 20024

Florida
Congregation Etz Chaim
P.O. Box 330132
Miami, FL 33133
Illinois
Congregation Or Chadash
656 West Barry Street
Chicago, IL 60657
Iowa
B'nai Chorin
c/o Ruth Cohen
7085 S.E. Bloomfield Rd.
Des Moines, IA 50320
Massachusetts
Am Tikva
P.O. Box CY601
Boston, MA 02116
Michigan
Lambda Chai
P.O. Box 351
Farmington, MI 48024
Minnesota
Etz Chaim Fellowship
P.O. Box 3585
Minneapolis, MN 55403
New York
Congregation Beth Simchat Torah
P.O. Box 1270, G.P.O.
New York, NY 10001
Pennsylvania
Congregation Beth Ahavah
P.O. Box 7566
Philadelphia, PA 19107

Havarim
P.O. Box 59104
Pittsburgh, PA 15210

Telling the Family You're Gay

Betty Berzon, Ph.D.

On September 22, 1975, in San Francisco's Union Square, a woman moved out of the crowd, raised her arm, leveled a chrome-plated gun, and pulled the trigger. A man standing nearby saw the movement and pushed down on the gun barrel. The bullet missed its target by five feet. Oliver Sipple had just saved the life of the President of the United States. His quick action made him an instant hero. The President wrote him a letter thanking him. Over 1000 other people wrote to him praising him. It should have been a moment of triumph for Oliver. Instead it was a nightmare. "Within 24 hours, reporters had also learned that the ex-Marine was involved in the San Francisco gay community, and the story became page-one—and wire service—copy." (The Advocate, Oct. 22, 1975) The Chicago Sun-Times called him a "Homosexual Hero" in a headline. The Denver Post referred to him as a "Gay Vet." Oliver went into seclusion to avoid the media. He was so distressed at the prospect of his mother in Detroit reading about him as a gay hero that he all but declined to take credit for saving the life of the President of the United States![1]

This story poignantly illustrates the enormous apprehension so many people feel regarding the disclosure of gayness to family. It is for many an immobilizing fear that clouds judgment and prevents the kind of decision-making and planning about disclosure that could enhance family relationships. Because so much of the gay person's thinking about disclosure is conditioned by fear, it is important to understand better why this fear is so pervasive and what might be done to alleviate it.

Nearly every gay person with a family is concerned about this issue. It doesn't matter who the person is, what age, what socioeconomic status, what education, what occupation, there is a fear of disclosure and a pressure to disclose. Sometimes the pressure is just at the level of "I know I can't but I wish I could." More often it is stronger, and so is the fear. Stalemate.

Why is this such a problem to so many people? We live in a family-oriented culture. Given the prolonged period of dependency on family in our society, the family becomes a highly influential force in our lives, from the cradle to the grave. We are trained to look to the family for sustenance. We are trained to *need* our families. We are also trained to take on the values and attitudes of our families because it is more than the species the family is supposed to perpetuate, it is the value system of the culture supporting the nuclear family arrangement. So, the family is seen not only as the main source of sustenance but as the source of the values we live by.

Our families also give us a link with our past. They knew us when we were forming as the people we have become. Much of our identity is rooted in the family's expectations of us. These expectations get built into our hopes and dreams for ourselves, in either a positive or a negative way. I am drawn to a particular field of endeavor because it is one that is valued in my family. Or, I avoid same because I am rebelling against the values and attitudes of my family. In either instance I am acting in response to my family's expectations of me. Even when I reach adulthood and have developed my own ideas about how to live my life, the internalized values and attitudes of my family operate in me and must be contended with in one way or another. Families are hard to get away from.

In one crucial way gay people do not fit family expectations. I believe the initial turmoil young gay people go through is in response to the internalized expectations from family training. From early on, being gay is associated with going against the family.

It is not surprising then that fear of confronting the family with the news of one's gayness is so strong in the minds of so many gay people. The fear is especially strong if the person has not adequately worked through the process of individuation from the family, carrying over into adult life too many feelings of childhood dependency. Then the fear of abandonment by the "needed" parents is a strong motivator in concealing from them anything that might displease them. Sacrifices are made in the person's own life to avoid giving parents any reason to remove their approval. But when the sacrifices are as destructive to one's emotional life as concealing one's basic orientation to love and affection, the details of one's lifestyle, the true nature of one's primary relationships, reassessment of the situation is in order.

FAMILIES, WHO NEEDS THEM?

As an adult, what do you really want from your family? In light of the drastic compromises with life many people make to spare their relatives the knowledge of their gayness, this is a question that all gay people should ask themselves. I think most would answer that they want the family's love and support, validation for accomplishments, comfort in the face of failure, and attention to their struggles with life's dilemmas.

I have two questions to ask at this point: (1) are you getting these wants met enough to warrant concealing your true self from them? and (2) do they care enough about you to not withdraw their interest and support, not punish you, not abandon you because of any difficulty they might have in accepting your gayness? If the answer to the first question is yes, and you are quite sure about it, you may not want to read further. If the answer is no, I hope you *will* read further. If the answer to question two is no, there's nothing to lose in disclosing to them, is there? If the answer is yes, there's everything to gain, isn't there? Not that simple, you say? Of course not, and then again, it really is.

WHY DISCLOSE?

As a gay person and a therapist I hear over and over the reasons people give for not disclosing their gayness to their families, especially parents. "They're too old, they won't understand." "They're in ill health, it might kill them." "Everything is going so well for them, I don't want to spoil it." The basic themes, with many variations, are that being gay is not understandable and is so heinous a truth that it might be lethal, at least toxic, in its effect. Such protestations are, of course, impossible to check out without making the actual disclosure. Fear thrives in an information vacuum. The unknown is unnerving. I have found, however, that in the majority of instances the fears are either unfounded or exaggerated, and that which was feared is taken care of by careful preparation for and judicious handling of the disclosure experience.

Let's look at the positive side. Why disclose? What constructive purpose does it serve?

For the Discloser

Disclosure can serve to bring the family into your life in a more real way. It opens up communication. It makes subterfuge and pretense unnecessary. It makes it possible for the family to be there for you to cushion whatever hurts and setbacks you might experience because of your gayness. If they don't know about them they can't extend help in relation to them. Disclosure can strengthen the family bond. It can deepen love. It can help you become a homophobia fighter rather than a homophobia victim.

For the Disclosee

Disclosure can clear up the mysteries that are so typical of communication customized to conceal the fact of gayness. It can bring children and parents closer, providing opportunities for mutual support and caring. Parents often need validation from their children, though offspring have a way of neglecting this. The open communication that disclosure makes possible enhances the opportunities for parents to get the attention they might need from their children. In an emotional climate in which children are holding themselves back from their parents for fear of loss of approval it is less likely that either is benefiting as much as they might from the relationship.

So, there are reasons for disclosure and reasons against. Only you can balance the equation for yourself. Assuming you decide to disclose, there are some things you should know.

GUIDELINES FOR DISCLOSURE

Basically, you are creating a learning situation for whomever you are disclosing to. As in any learning situation you can set up the conditions for learning but you can't learn *for* the person. You will want to set up conditions to facilitate learning about your gayness in the best possible way. When, where, how, what to say, to whom, what to say about a lover if you have one, whether to include your lover—these are all things it is best to think through beforehand. In the following suggestions I will emphasize disclosure to parents since that is the situation gay people usually worry about the most.

Before You Disclose

It is important to spend some time with yourself doing two things. Examine your own attitudes about being gay. If you have mixed feelings, talk about them to someone you trust. If you have strong negative feelings, they will be conveyed and the disclosure will probably be a bad experience. Read some of the excellent gay-affirming books now on the market. Try to get straight about being gay before you talk about it to family.

Clarify why you are disclosing at this particular time. If, for instance, you are angry with your parents, try to deal with that anger somewhere else before you talk to them. If you bring anger into the disclosure you are likely to obscure the main message you are there to deliver and the occasion will be remembered as a negative one for everyone. Try to get in touch with the positive reasons for your disclosure and keep those in focus.

When to Disclose

The time to disclose is as soon as you are ready, taking into account whatever else is going on in the family situation. If possible, don't make your disclosure when other events are likely to co-opt the attention and emotions of the people you are disclosing to: your brother's wedding (tempting though it may be), your grandmother's funeral (you wish you'd been able to tell her because she had more sense and sensitivity than anyone else in the family), your parent's 25th wedding anniversary (you want to thank them for teaching you to love as beautifully as they do). Your disclosure is an important occasion for you and it deserves all the attention it can get.

Where to Disclose

I suggest that gayness be disclosed in a quiet, private place where you are unlikely to be disturbed or distracted, so that plenty of time is available to adequately deal with questions, discussion and reactions.

How to Disclose

Prepare the persons you are disclosing to by stating beforehand that you want to have a serious conversation about something that is very important to you both. Present your information in the most positive light possible. For instance, you would *not* want to begin by saying, "I have something terrible I want to tell you" or "You're not going to like this, but . . ." A better beginning would be, "There is something about me I want to tell you because I care about you and I want to be able to share more of myself with you."

What to Say

You've said you're gay and you've survived the moment. Now what? You might tell how you feel about being gay and how you hope they will feel about it and about you. And be prepared for the many questions parents usually ask, though they may not ask them directly at this time. You may want to bring them up yourself:

1. How long have you been gay?
2. Are you sure you are gay?
3. When did you first know you were gay?
4. Have you tried to change?
5. Have you tried being involved with (a person of the opposite sex)? What happened?
6. Does this mean you hate (are afraid of) men/women?
7. Don't you want children of your own?
8. Are you happy?
9. Do you think you'll always be gay?
10. What is your gay life like?
11. Have you told anyone else?
12. Who else do you plan to tell?

At this time or later you may want to get into more abstract explanations regarding such questions as the following, which parents usually think about.

1. *What does being homosexual mean?* It means being predisposed to seek out same-gender persons as love and sex partners.

2. *What causes homosexuality?* It happens through the same complex process that causes heterosexuality. It isn't known yet what goes into that process or how it operates to result in one person being gay while another isn't. Most experts agree that people's basic sexual orientation, as well as their sense of being a female or a male, is established by the age of five and is not a matter of choice.

3. *Can homosexuality be cured?* According to research studies and to the official positions of the American Psychiatric Association and the American Psychological Association, homosexuality is not an illness, therefore it is not meaningful to talk about curing it.

4. *Can a person who is homosexual become heterosexual?* Most experts agree that basic sexual orientation is unchangeable. A person may choose to suppress behavior that is expressive of a homosexual orientation. Sometimes that can be done successfully, sometimes it can't. Nearly always suppression seriously inhibits a person's ability to be emotionally spontaneous, since there must be constant watchfulness over homosexual feelings being experienced too strongly.

5. *Why do you use the word gay?* About 50 years ago *gay* was a code word to disguise references to being homosexual. Gay people have long since adopted the word *gay* as a self-descriptive term replacing the more clinical *homosexual*.

SPECIAL ISSUES

Following are some special issues to think about in relation to disclosure. They are generalizations and do not apply to everyone. You know your own family and you are the best judge of how to use these suggestions for yourself.

Is It Better to Tell Parents Together or Separately?

Use what you know of your parents, the way each relates to you and how they relate to each other, to decide on this issue. If they tend to support and comfort each other, it might be best to enable them to share this experience. If you have reason to believe that one will be more supportive of you, tell that parent alone first and have that good experience behind you when you tell the parent you are more doubtful of. If your parents tend to compete with one another, you may create a problem by telling one before the other. Try not to get into playing one parent against the other in any way. Tapping into your parents' anger at each other might seriously distract from the very important message you have to deliver. This is especially important if your parents are divorced and you have no choice but to tell them separately.

Don't Make the Other Person Say It for You

"There's something I have to tell you. You know what it is, don't you? It's . . . you know, don't you . . . ?" Ashamed to say the words? If so, you are not ready to make this disclosure. What counts here is the *affirming experience* of saying with your own voice, in your own words, to the face of someone important to you, that you are gay. If you have to force someone else to say the words for you, the impression you give might well be, "I can't say these awful words myself," which certainly is not the kind of tone you want to give to the disclosure of your gayness.

Should Your Lover Accompany You?

The presence of a nonfamily member could make it more difficult for those to whom you are disclosing to be as free to ask questions and comment as they might be with you alone. If you feel you need your lover present for support, weigh the advantages of that against the difficulty it might pose for your family. It may be easier, particularly for parents, to deal with your gayness in the abstract, before confronting them with your real-life lover. This might be true even if the family already knows and likes your "friend," who has now been significantly redefined for them.

"You're Gay Because of Your Lover"

Sometimes, in an effort to comprehend something that feels alien and disturbing at the outset, parents will attempt to explain their child's gayness by blaming it on a lover. "It's _____. If it weren't for her/him, this would never have happened to you." It's important to establish that your gayness is not something someone *did* to you, but something that expresses your basic nature, that you would be gay even if you were not in this relationship.

Parental Guilt

"Where did I (we) go wrong?" This question is often heard from parents struggling to understand the news of a child's gayness. You are, of course, much of what you are because your parents directly or indirectly created the circumstances in which you grew up. Therefore it is not surprising that they would be concerned about what they did to make you gay. No matter how good a job you do in presenting your gayness in a positive context they might initially relate to it in terms of their own homophobic conditioning. In response to this question, first reassure your parents that there is no wrong involved, that it is unnecessarily self-punishing to think of your being gay as a failure in their parenting. It is also inaccurate since the determinants of one kind of sexual orientation versus another are as yet unknown. What is important is that good parenting does produce the ability to love others and if you have that capacity you should be grateful to your parents for making it possible. Let them know.

Counterpersonal Family Culture

In some families it is the custom to avoid dealing with anything of an intimate nature, especially if it is sexual. To introduce information about yourself that tells family members more than they want to know about your personal life is going against family "culture." As much as anything it is often this countercultural behavior that brings a negative reaction. If this is the case with your family, recognize this and take it into account when you are making your disclosure. The fear that they are going to hear something sexual about their children is very strong with some parents. In the face of this kind of obstacle to communication it is best to reassure in some way that you are not going to expose them to the graphic details of your sex life in discussing your gayness with them. Not doing this effectively could make it impossible for them to listen to you at all.

Disclosure to Children

Sometimes the family members you want to disclose to are children, your own or nieces and nephews with whom you want to have as honest a relationship as possible. Many would disagree with me, but I advocate open discussion with young people about being gay. With the coverage homosexuality is being given in the media, it is unlikely that any youngster who can see, hear and read is going to escape knowing that gay people exist and that a lot of attention is being paid to them these days. In the absence of accurate information, the young person may well get inaccurate information from homophobic sources and develop the same antigay attitudes that prevail in much of the rest of society. If that young person is in your own family it is in your best interests to make sure, if possible, that his/her attitudes toward gay people are enlightened ones. Listening to your 12-year-old nephew tell queer jokes and mince around in parody of effeminate men is not likely to brighten up the family occasion you've been looking forward to. It is likely to create tension between you and him and he won't even know why. In the meantime he goes right on thinking of gay people as strange creatures out there somewhere who have nothing to do with him or his family. It does not serve you, him, the family, other gay people or society to perpetuate his antagonistic and punishing attitudes by remaining silent about them.

How do you talk to children about being gay?

First, the youngster's age should determine the level at which you talk. Obviously you aren't going to talk about sexual behavior to a very young child. If you talk about it at all to a teenager, do so with sensitivity to the struggles that young person may be having to understand and feel comfortable about his/her own budding sexuality. In the latter instance, ask questions as you go to determine how much the young person knows already and how comfortable he/she is with what you are saying. The best approach, I believe, is to talk about being gay as loving and caring for and having a close, important relationship, like marriage, with a person of the same sex. Talk about familiar concepts such as marriage, and personalize what you are saying as much as possible. Bring the idea of being gay closer in so that it can be associated with that which is already known and related to as part of a familiar emotional landscape.

Sometimes adults are reticent to discuss homosexuality with youngsters because they don't want to unduly influence the sexual orientation of the young person. While we don't know exactly what determines sexual orientation, we do know that one does not become gay by hearing about it, or by being in the same family or by talking about it with someone who is gay. On the other hand, young people do become honest, courageous, open and direct in their relationships with others by seeing it happening around them..[1]

Seeking Professional Help

Sometimes the family will try to push you to seek professional help in order not to be gay. You, of course, will gently let them know that you do not need or want such help. However, if they are having particular difficulty accepting your gayness, you might think about referring *them* for help. If you should decide to do this, take time to find gay-oriented professionals who are understanding and supportive of gay people and who are unlikely to reinforce whatever homophobic ideas your family already has. If you live in or near a large city, consult local gay organizations for the names of counselors. The Association of Gay Psychologists publishes a directory of gay-oriented therapists around the country.[2] If you do not have access to the kind of professional described above, talk with your family's minister, priest, rabbi or doctor to assure yourself that such a referral would be helpful. Since most medical doctors and religious counselors tend to be conservative in their attitudes toward sexual minorities, be sure yours is enlightened enough to not compound the problem that already exists.

PREPARING FOR DISCLOSURE

I believe disclosure works best when it is prepared for well. There are several things you can do to prepare yourself. First, read gay-affirming literature for information about homosexuality and gay life you might need to answer questions and talk knowledgeably about the topic. Second, use the "Letter of Affirmation" below to work out what you want to say in the disclosure. Third, get one or more friends to role-play the disclosure experience with you so you can try out different approaches and explore solutions to problems that might arise.

Letter of Affirmation

Dear_____

There's something I want to tell you. It's difficult for me to tell you this, but it's important to our relationship that you know.

I'm gay. I have been for _____

The way I feel about being gay is:

The way I want *you* to feel about it is:

The way I want you to feel about *me* is:

Before closing, I want to say to you:

AFTER THE INITIAL DISCLOSURE

If your family did not know you were gay, you have told them something that is probably very unsettling. If they did know but weren't facing it, you have broken the contract of silence and changed the rules for the way you all relate to this important fact. In either case they'll probably need some time to adjust. And different people adjust in different ways. Some do it silently, some noisily. Some do it in a thoughtful and reasoned way, some go crazy. Some will blame you excessively, some will blame themselves excessively. Some will be sad, some angry, some punishing. Some will badger, some will withdraw. Some will be hungry for more information, some will not want to hear another word.

Give them time and understanding. Be available but not pushy. Keep your perspective. You have done this to improve family relations. Disclosure is a courageous act and it is an expression of your willingness for your family to be an important part of your life. You are offering them an opportunity to deal with you as the person you are, not the person they imagine you to be. Don't lose that focus.

When the opportunity comes, begin to normalize the topic of your gayness. Don't harp, but talk about it naturally, as a part of your life. For those involved in gay community activities, that subject is often an easy vehicle for talking about being gay. If it is feasible, invite your family to meet your friends. Recommend reading, and try to bring them the books yourself. Let them know when there is going to be a gay-affirmative film or TV show or magazine story. Encourage them to talk to other relatives and to friends about your gayness. You'll probably meet with a lot of resistance to this initially. It is important that they have someone to talk to. The more they keep their feelings to themselves, the less chance there is of the normalizing process happening.

Remember, though, it is a very hot potato you've handed them. The gay family member often hears, "It's okay that you've told me (us) but don't tell your father/mother/Uncle Joe/Aunt Ida." Be prepared for this reaction. It may anger you at first because it seems to be saying, "Don't tell anybody else this terrible thing." In a sense it is saying that, but it is saying more about the person speaking than about you. Very often the notion that father/mother/Uncle Joe/Aunt Ida won't be able to handle your news is inaccurate. The real issue is usually a fear of guilt by association. "What will they think of *me?*" Your disclosee has not had time yet to work through, or even work on, this issue. Be understanding. Don't argue the point, but don't make promises for the future either. Helping your relative (especially a parent) learn to handle the hot potato comfortably and gracefully is one of the most important things you can do as a part of your coming out. The disclosure for you probably has been the culmination of a lengthy process of preparation. It's a relief to have it over with. The people you are disclosing to are just beginning the process. Help them. Keep communications open. Don't let a mood of secrecy develop around your gayness. Use your creativity to find ways of introducing discussion of it in ways that will inform and enlighten.

Actually, one hardly has to make a special effort to introduce the topic to the American living room with grandstanding pop vocalists and minor politicians mounting media campaigns to save the world from homosexuality. Gay people I know who were determined never to bring the topic of their gayness into family discussion find themselves in the midst of God-and-Anita-against-the-heathen arguments at the family dinner table whether they are ready for it or not. It is a subtle irony, the spotlighting of our lives in so many ways, and in so many places by the people who would stamp us out. If nothing else, the Anita Bryant and John Briggs campaigns have made homosexuality a prime-time issue for American families who might otherwise have never knowingly seen a real live homosexual.

Another way to help your family adjust to having a gay member involves participation in a peer support group, if one is available. If your family lives in or near a large city, there might be a Parents of Gays (POG) organization they can participate in. Or they might be willing to talk on the phone to a POG member nearby. (See the listing of POG groups at the end of the Fairchild chapter in this volume.) Typically, these groups have "hotlines" which a parent can call anonymously.

Remember, both you and your family are common victims of antigay prejudice. You can help one another.

IF THEY DON'T ACCEPT YOUR GAYNESS

It happens. Some parents refuse to deal with what they have learned about their children and it doesn't get any better over time. That is the chance one takes in deciding to make the disclosure. Actually, it is not as chancy as most choose to believe it is. There are, after all, clues from past behavior as to how parents are likely to deal with the disclosure. Parents who have always been loving will, perhaps with time out for a period of adjustment, continue to be loving parents. Parents who are rigid, demanding and punishing do not deal well with any news that does not fit their agenda for their children. They probably won't be any more accepting of this than of anything else that conflicts with their fictionalized version of who their children are.

Sometimes it is necessary to let go of a family who simply don't or won't try to understand. It is sad. It is extremely frustrating. It is angering. But it is the best course of action for your own growth, when the passage of time has not mellowed the angry response or softened the rejecting attitude. Gay people who allow such a rejection to color their own self-image or burden their spirit are ignoring one of the most impressive truths there is regarding human growth: it is possible to grow beyond your own parents' capacity for dealing effectively with life. You've somehow learned to do it better than they can. Even in the saddest of times this is a phenomenon to celebrate and be thankful for.

FINALLY . . .

Recently I heard a woman member of Parents and Friends of Gays in Los Angeles talk to a group of lesbians about her experience of learning that her teenage daughter is gay. After a period of feeling upset and then coming to terms with the news, she began to chauffeur her daughter to the Gay Community Services Center to attend lesbian rap groups. As she described driving her daughter to the Center and waiting for her while she participated in the raps, most of the women in the group she was addressing sat open mouthed. The image of this pleasant-looking woman sitting in the lobby of a gay community center while her child was inside learning to feel better about herself as a lesbian was obviously mind boggling. There was a silence and then someone said, "I can't believe this. You sat and waited for your daughter while she went to lesbian raps?" The woman smiled and said, "Well she wanted to go there and she couldn't drive, so what else was I to do?"

I thought of the painful years I'd spent, so alone, trying to understand what my strange and disturbing feelings were all about. It was unimaginable to speak to my parents about them. Unimaginable to have a place to go to learn what it all meant and that it was okay. Unimaginable to be taken there by my parent.

How things have changed for some, and will for many more, as we learn to open our lives to those around us, those who are perhaps waiting to know us better and love us harder if only we can give them the chance.

FOOTNOTES

1. For specific suggestions to gay parents on talking to their own children about being gay, see my chapter, "Sharing Your Lesbian Identity with Your Children: A Case for Openness," in Ginny Vida's *Our Right to Love.* Prentice-Hall, 1978.

2. Association of Gay Psychologists, P.O. Box 172, Ansonia Station, 1990 Broadway, New York, N.Y. 10023.

For Parents of Gays:
A Fresh Perspective

Betty Fairchild

Along with the gay rights movement, which has finally received public attention, a related endeavor has emerged across the country. Since 1972, independent groups and individuals have started working with parents of gay daughters and sons to help them understand their child's sexuality, and homosexuality in general. Indeed, it is time to eradicate the grief and pain, the guilt feelings and the fear, hostility and anger that have been the lot of parents—and consequently of their gay offspring. The prime movers in this endeavor are parents themselves, backed up by their children, other gay women and men, and occasional professional advisers. Their goal is to remove the isolation of such parents from each other and to help them understand what being gay means to their children and to others.

I myself am one of those parents. When my son told me he was gay several years ago, I was as isolated and as uninformed as most parents are. Fortunately, over the following years I experienced a complete re-education and gained a new and positive outlook on my son's life. I would like to share this viewpoint with those of you who are in similar circumstances.

THE PROBLEM: HOMOPHOBIA

In Western society, we are all victims of false and destructive stereotypes about homosexuality, most of them so well known I need not itemize them. However, many of us are freeing ourselves of these beliefs and atti-

101

tudes as we come to understand human sexuality in a new light. In so doing, we draw closer to our gay sons and daughters; we learn to know and
care about our children's friends and lovers; and we find our own lives
immeasurably enriched in the process. I am convinced that the same joys
are possible for you.

Few of us respond easily to the revelation that one of our children is
gay. Some of us react in ways that are less than helpful to our children or
ourselves. But even as sincerely concerned parents, we find ourselves
beset with questions and anxieties about this new phenomenon in our
family: What does this mean to our child? to us? How can we deal with
our feelings about it? What should we *do* about it, if anything? Where do
we turn for help?

Until recently, it was almost impossible to find information that did
not add to our fears and worries. Today, the number of excellent books
and other material and of well-informed advisers proliferates rapidly
and it is easier to find accurate and reassuring information. (A list of current sources appears at the end of this chapter.)

Homosexuality is not terrible and disastrous. Nor are you, as a family
and as parents, destined to face it in utter isolation. When you know that
at least 10 percent of our population is primarily homosexual in affectional and sexual preference, you will realize that many thousands of
mothers and fathers are dealing with the same issues as you. At present,
you may not know any other such parents; you may think you don't even
know any gay people. As a matter of fact, however, we all do; most of us
are simply not aware of the homosexuality of some of our most respected
associates, friends and perhaps relatives.

The truth is that gay people exist, function well and lead normal and
rewarding lives. Gay men and women contribute to every profession and
occupation, at every economic and social level—in fact, there is no
group in this country (or elsewhere) without homosexual women and
men.And this has always been true, although we hear about it more these
days. The problem is not homosexuality but *homophobia:* society's irrational *fear* of homosexual persons.

PARENTS' RESPONSE—AND RESPONSIBILITY

Once we overcome the fear of homosexuality and realize that it has existed throughout history as a variant of human sexuality, we can view it
rationally and go on to understand its place in the lives of our children.
And it has a place. It is *not* the only thing to know about a person, only
one facet. When we learn that someone—particularly our own child—is
gay, we may forget everything else we ever knew about that individual
or we may believe that there is nothing more to know. How many young

people have said, in hope and despair, "I am the same person I was before you knew. You loved me then; I hope you still love me now."

Indeed, *reassurance of your love is the initial and primary need of your child.* For most gay people, the decision to tell their parents was a long and agonizing one to make. Based on their wish and need to share this part of their lives with their families, it is yet a tremendously difficult decision because of their anxiety about their parents' response. Rather than being faced, as many young people are, with accusations, threats, anger and rejection after this revelation, how much better if you immediately affirm your continuing love and concern. Since many of us feel *responsible*, in some unknown way, for making our child homosexual, our reaction to the news may be guilt or shame. But as Ruth Simpson has put it in *From the Closets to the Courts:*

> The larger part of the burden of providing security, comfort, and love in a parent-child relationship logically should rest with the parent. That a child is homosexual does not make the parent retroactively "unfit"; a parent of a homosexual child becomes unfit, in the true sense of the word, only if ignorance and prejudice drive the parent to ignore or degrade the homosexual child.

When you have affirmed your love for your child, it is vital to keep open the lines of communication. Ask questions and really listen to what your child has to say. Be honest about your need to learn. Too many of us start out by providing answers on a topic about which we know virtually nothing.

How much information your child can provide will vary. Some very young women and men are not yet familiar with the larger issues of homosexuality, but they *do* know how they *feel*. If your daughter says, "I'm very happy in my relationship with Gini," believe her. When your son says, "I've known for years that I'm attracted to other men," don't dismiss this statement (although some parents do). An older child may be better informed, particularly one with a background of activism, one who may have worked (unbeknownst to you) for months or years for gay rights and equality. But along with a continuing interchange of feelings and experiences with your gay child, you will probably want to seek other information, to get a more complete picture of what it's all about, for your child will not have all the answers.

BEING GAY: IT IS NOT YOUR FAULT! IT IS NOT A CHOICE!

If you are like most parents, you have assumed a heavy load of guilt and shame. "Where did we go wrong?" you ask. "If only we had known sooner, perhaps we could have done something." "*Why* is my child gay?" "We really tried to bring our kids up right but somehow, with Barbara (or Jack), we must have failed." There are some good answers to these questions, although they may not be the ones you expect.

First, regardless of what "causes" homosexuality, a lot of energy is wasted in agonizing about the past. If you focus on *why* and *if we had only known*, you will have little energy left for more constructive questions: "Where do we go from here? What can we do *now*—for ourselves (to learn more) and for our son or daughter (to support that child helpfully)?" Second, when you begin to view homosexuality as a natural variation of sexuality, you will see that there is no blame and your feelings of guilt will probably disappear.

From studies of the lives and backgrounds of thousands of healthy homosexuals there derive no facile answers as to why one person in a family develops a homosexual orientation and another a heterosexual one. It is not known to what degree the family situation contributes to a child's development of sexual preference, but the time-worn reference to such characteristics as "dominant mother/weak father" does not hold up, since it is clear that gay women and men come from all kinds of home situations, including warm, loving, close-knit families. When you no longer regard being gay as bad, the causes, while they may be of some scientific interest, are of much less importance to you and your family.

I have known a parent to ask: "How can you bear to live this way?" as if the child had deliberately *selected* a homosexual way of life. Another says: "Since you've chosen this lifestyle, please don't bring your friends here." or "If you choose to live this way, I suppose there's nothing I can do." Whether we attribute our child's gayness to our own failing or to choice, many of us start out, as I did myself, with the assumption—and great hope—that our gay children can change if they want to.

The reality is quite different. (Ask yourself if you could change your sexual preference on request.) By the time our young people come out as gay, they have undoubtedly experienced feelings of attraction to the same sex. Although they may have denied this to themselves at first, they know they feel closer to their own gender than to the opposite. With the tremendous societal pressures to be heterosexual, our children may have found that coming to terms with their *own* sexuality was difficult and troubling, but ultimately unavoidable. (How many of us would *choose* to encounter the scorn with which our white, male-dominated, heterosexual society greets anyone who dares not to conform?) So we can be sure that by the time they are ready to confront us, our children are pretty clear in their own minds about their sexual orientation. Therefore, our expectation, demand or hope for change is simply unrealistic. The sooner we recognize this, the sooner we move toward understanding. The important question is not "Why can't they change?" but "What do I need to know about my daughter as she sees herself right now?" "How can I better understand my son and what being gay means to him?"

THOSE WRETCHED STEREOTYPES!

How well we know the stereotypes of homosexuals—and how they distress us: the effeminate man (who wants to be a woman); the tough, muscular woman (who wants to be a man); the ineffectual, sick weaklings who couldn't hold down a job—or shouldn't be allowed to. Our fears that homosexuals are out to *get* heterosexuals, that they attack children, that they will somehow contaminate us if they are allowed to work or live among us (which, of course, they already do), that they should not be allowed to become ministers or teachers—not to mention the interesting argument that our future world population is in jeopardy if we permit homosexuality.

Many of us fear that our own gay children will never have a good home, a family life or children; that they will never know real love, that they will automatically be excluded from a successful career or that they will be outcasts and misfits, harassed and looked down on all their lives, ending up lonely and unhappy. The irony is that if those projections do come true, it less likely to be because the individual is gay than that society's oppressive attitudes and behavior toward homosexual persons cause them to happen!

The majority of gay people do not fit these stereotypes, although it is possible to point out individuals who do. (In my experience, apart from transsexuals, who are not gay but are often confused with gays, I have never heard from a gay woman who wants to be a man, or vice versa.) In fact, you will find far fewer differences than you imagine between your gay son or daughter and your other children. (Review our "fears" in an earlier paragraph and reflect on how often young people today, of whatever inclination, decline to live out such parental standards and expectations.) Furthermore, there are many encouraging, even exemplary, aspects to the gay person's life.

RELATIONSHIPS

It is usually a great source of comfort to learn that our gay child has found a loving relationship with another person. To most nongay people, unfortunately, homosexuality equates only with sex, and we commonly believe that at least male homosexuals are doomed to—or deliberately seek out—a life of promiscuity, fleeting contacts and degradation.

I remember how I first became aware of *love* as part of my son's life when he broke up with Seth, a man I knew and liked. His obvious and genuine heartbreak was distressing to me, but I also realized that his feelings of loss were identical to those his sister had felt when a love relationship was ended. I was somehow comforted as I thought, with a kind of sympathetic shock, "Why, he really *loved* Seth!" and this opened up for me a whole new dimension of gay relationships. I have found that gay people are often surprised to learn that their parents are not aware that love is possible between two men or two women. "But we are no different from anyone else," they reiterate, "except in whom we love." Recent writings by women indicate that the pleasure and rewards of lesbian associations and relationships are far more complex than simply "loving other women."

Like many other parents, I have had the privilege of becoming close friends with many gay people, and have time and again seen deep, caring relationships between two women or two men. I have seen for myself the scope of concern and love shared by these couples, which often includes a genuine enjoyment of each other's company and a sense of *fun* that seems to be missing from many nongay relationships. There is frequently a remarkable absence of traditional role-playing within a gay relationship. The rather insulting question "Which one is the woman and which the man?" is meaningless to many gay lovers. With the force of heterosexual impact in our culture and the lack of visible and strong homosexual role models, some gay couples do assume a pattern of dominant/submissive relationships. This may well change as their awareness of egalitarian potential develops.

In any case, although a pattern of fleeting sexual encounters is apparent among some gay people (sometimes consciously chosen by those who refuse to conform to heterosexual patterns), there is certainly a strong potential for a loving, supportive relationship for the gay woman or man. If it does not last forever (although we know of couples who have been together 50 years), this is not so different from the marriage/divorce condition of straight society.

A word more about relationships: Too many parents deprive themselves and their children of great happiness, by refusing to acknowledge that their daughter or son has a lover. Instead of showing interest in the person who is so important to their child, these parents simply ignore that person's existence.

Perhaps these parents are in the minority. There are many of us who do let ourselves get to know our child's lover, and we often come to care deeply for that person, who may become virtually a member of the family. And even if we find little to like in our child's choice of lover, as sometimes happens, it is not much different and certainly no worse than the negative feelings we may have for another child's spouse.

When you welcome your child's lover into your home and your lives, you may at first resist accepting their expressions of affection. I have known parents to insist they will always be extremely uncomfortable with their child's even most casual interaction with a lover—an embrace of greeting, a loving arm around the other's shoulder as they chat with the family, hands held at parting—and God forbid two men should kiss! While the nongay world's aversion to men's affectionate gestures is probably greater than to women's, there is still the mother who says: "It's okay for Linda to visit, but I can't bear to see her touch Jan."

I contend that, aside from our general sexual uptightness, much of this distress is based on our *unfamiliarity* with affectionate behavior between members of the same sex. Our eyes are not used to it, our minds are not used to it, and our emotional response to it is deeply ingrained (but not ineradicably) by outmoded taboos against same-sex affection. Since as a parent you are trying to understand what it means to your child to be gay, an open attitude toward reasonable expressions of affection is a part of the process. Few of us are comfortable in the presence of heavy love-making between any two people, but once you see simple affection for what it is, it no longer matters whether it is between Don and Bill or Tom and Sue. When that happens, you may find, as I did long ago, that Don and Bill's (or Jan and Linda's) tender embrace, and even their quick kiss, is very endearing.

As parents, we must see that it's a matter of adjusting our viewpoint, not of insisting that others restrict their spontaneous behavior to our rigid standards. Life itself can be a continuing growth process for us, to our enhanced pleasure and enrichment, or it can be a narrow confinement that keeps us critical and discontented (perhaps because other people seem to have more fun than we do).

HOME AND CAREER

Many of us believe our gay children will never have the good things of life. I have not found that to be true. With or without monogamous relationships, comfortable, attractive, even luxurious home surroundings are common among gay people.

If a successful career is what your gay child wants, she or he can no doubt achieve it. True, there are more employment hassles for gay people, especially for those women and men no longer willing to pretend to be something they are not. This refusal to pretend does not mean wearing a sign saying "I am gay." It means refusing to leave a lover at home during office social functions; it means a refusal to talk vaguely of "dates" or to refer to one's lover as a roommate, or to live in fear that one's participation in gay counseling services will become known at the office. But for those willing to pay whatever price is demanded, their options are open. As we have noted, gay men and women presently work at all levels of every occupational and professional field.

GAYS AND CHILDREN

If you have reacted to your child's confession of gayness with the thought "No grandchildren!" you have lots of company. But keep in mind that these days, your heterosexual child may also choose not to have children. While this may not comfort you as a wishful grandparent, it does emphasize again that your gay child is not so very different. Besides which, gay people can be, and are, parents. Both men and women have married and had children before coming to grips with their homosexual orientation. And when the good word comes that adoptions by responsible gay people have been legally approved, many potentially excellent parents who happen to be gay will be able to bring children into their lives, and perhaps into yours.

NOT AN END BUT A BEGINNING

These are some of the reassuring aspects of a homosexual lifestyle. There is much more to know. You will need to give yourself time to absorb these ideas; none of us achieve with instant understanding a new way of looking at life. And if you do experience distress and anxiety about your gay child, take care not to *stop* with those feelings. I was able to overcome my negative feelings (which were fairly intense) by talking with my son and his friends, by reading widely, through conversations with other parents, both in and out of parent groups, and perhaps as much as anything, through getting to know scores of gay women and men.

I hope that you will find others to talk to who will share your concerns and help you—friends, relatives, counselors and certainly other parents. (This isn't always easy to do; check the Parents of Gays list for group locations.) I hope, too, that you will start reading and will try to meet gay people whenever you can. But most of all, be open with your own gay child. All our children are precious to us, I know, and surely we are willing to work toward knowing each of them as honestly as possible. If at times this seems difficult, look forward to the rewards of deeper, more loving relationships with your daughter or your son, of a family more closely united. It will be more than worth the effort. Just you wait and see.

PARENTS OF GAYS — INTERNATIONAL

Some of this list, where no POG group exists at present, are parents who will talk with other parents and gay people. Some groups have just formed. Starred names (*) indicate nonparent working to get a group started or simply acting as POG contact.

ARIZONA
- Faith and Ed Parker
  4217 E. Hazelwood
  Phoenix AZ 85018
  (602) 957-1738

CALIFORNIA
Long Beach
- Parents and Friends of Gays
  of Long Beach
  700 E. Roosevelt Rd.
  Long Beach CA 90807
  (213) 427-4347
     or
  Dorothy Johnson
  5149 Anaheim Rd.
  Long Beach CA 90815
  (213) 495-2951

Los Angeles
- Parents and Friends of Gays
  P.O. Box 24528
  Los Angeles CA 90024
  (213) 472-8952

San Diego
- Al Johnson*
  Gay Center for Social Svcs.
  2250 - B St.
  San Diego CA 92102
  (714) 232-7528

San Francisco
- Scott Wirth, Coord.*
  Parents of Gay People
  c/o Operation Concern
  Pacific Medical Center
  P.O. Box 7999
  San Francisco CA 94120
  (415) 563-0202
     or
  Ms. Frances Neer
  (415) 387-7902

San Jose
- Steve Century, Coord.-POG*
  c/o Lambda Assoc./Santa Clara Co.
  P.O. Box 26126
  San Jose CA 95159
  (408) 264-1880 (o)
       241-0542 (h)

COLORADO
Boulder
- Rosemary Browder
  1920 - 19th St. #4
  Boulder CO 80302
  (303) 449-1950

Denver
- Betty Fairchild
  700 Emerson St.
  Denver CO 80218
  (303) 831-8576

FLORIDA
Jacksonville
- Parents of Gays, c/o MCC
  P.O. Box 291
  Jacksonville FL 32201
  (904) 354-1318

Miami
- Ireen Mickenberg
  1300 Lincoln Rd. #602
  Miami Beach FL 33135
  (305) 672-8846

Pensacola
- Jean Smith
  Parents of Gays
  P.O. Box 4479
  Pensacola FL 32507
  (904) 453-1923

GEORGIA
- Jake Shipp*
  816 Piedmont Ave., N.E.
  Atlanta GA 30308
  (404) 876-5177

HAWAII
- Millie Penkava
 Nulah Harrington
 95-2056 Waikalani Pl. #A103
 Wahiawa HI 96786
 (808) 623-2492

ILLINOIS
- Guy Warner*
 Parents of Gays
 P.O. Box 924
 Chicago IL 60690
 (312) 929-8650

INDIANA
Indianapolis
- Stacy and Ethel Wesner
 120 First St. N.E.
 Carmel, IN 46032
 (317) 844-8771

 Terre Haute
- Duane and Ginny Sinn
 Parents of Gay People
 337 S. Fruitridge Ave.
 Terre Haute IN
 (812) 234-3977
  238-1454

IOWA
- Bill and Lois Miller
 3428 Brandywine Rd.
 Mason City IO 50401
 (515) 423-5911

KENTUCKY
- Barbra Maynor
 418 Marret Ave.
 Louisville KY 40208
 (502) 636-0649

LOUISIANA
- Michael Thurber* (temp)
 POG
 P.O. Box 52364
 New Orleans LA 70152
 (504) 568-0647

MAINE (summer only)
- Evelyn and Floyd Bull
 RFD #2 CP80
 Kennebunkport. ME 04046
 (207) 967-4837

MARYLAND
- Parents of Gays, Baltimore

 (301) 235-HELP, 366-1415
  or
 Jane Durham
 5434 Relcrest Rd., Apt. A
 Baltimore MD 21206
 (301) 483-4042
  or
 Nancy Gross
 (301) 366-7274

MASSACHUSETTS
- David Griffith, Coord.*
 Parents of Gays
 80 Boylston St., Ste. 855
 Boston MA 02116
 (617) 542-5188

MICHIGAN
- Parents of Gays
 MCC-Detroit
 c/o Trinity Methodist Church
 13100 Woodward Ave.
 Highland Park MI 48203
  or
 call: (313) 534-9314

MINNESOTA
- Families of Gays
 c/o Neighborhood Counseling Ctr.
 1801 Nicollet Ave., So.
 Minneapolis MN 55403
 (612) 874-5369
  or
 Sylvia Rudolph
 4645 18th St., So.
 Minneapolis MN 55407
 (612) 722-8416

MISSOURI
 Kansas City
- Phyllis Shafer
 1838 E. 49th St.
 Kansas City MO 64130
 (816) 921-7779

 St. Louis
- Arthur and Marian Wirth
 7443 Cromwell Drive
 St. Louis. MO 63105
 (314) 863-2748

NEW JERSEY
- Evelyn and Floyd Bull
 Princeton Arms North, Apt. 150
 Cranbury NJ 08512
 (609) 488-4537

NEW YORK
  New York City
• Parents of Gays and Lesbians
  Metropolitan Duane Methodist
    Church
  201 W. 13th St. at 7th Ave.
  New York NY 10011
        or
  Jules and Jeanne Manford
  33-23 171 St.
  Flushing NY 11358
  (212) 353-4044

  Rochester
• Howard F. Wood
  35 Wellesley St.
  Rochester NY 14607

OHIO
• Liselotte Sherwood
  1177 Northwest Blvd.
  Columbus OH 43212
  (614) 294-9082

OREGON
  Portland
• Parents of Gays
  Ann Shepherd
  2438 S.W. Hamilton St.
  Portland, OR 97201
  (503) 244-3225

  Springfield
• R. Flynn
  P.O. Box 467
  Springfield OR 97477

PENNSYLVANIA
  Pittsburgh
• Parents of Gays
  c/o Persad Center, Inc.
  Shadyside Center Bldg.
  5100 Centre Ave.
  Pittsburgh, PA 15232
  (412) 681-5330
        or
  Dottie Lou and Lamon Forrester
  (412) 366-0226

  Philadelphia
• POG-Philadelphia
  Gay Community Center
  326 Kater St.
  Philadelphia PA 19147

TEXAS
• Rosemary Zule
  603 Roy
  Houston TX 77007
  (713) 869-8061

VERMONT
• Ruth and Hank Abrams
  Highgate Apts.
  Barre VT 05641
  (802) 476-5002

WASHINGTON D.C. AREA
• Parents of Gays-D.C.
  c/o Ilse Mollet
  263 Congressional Lane #407
  Rockville MD 20852
  (301) 468-0091

WISCONSIN
  Milwaukee
• A. Schwerbel
  (414) 475-6862

  Whitewater
  Dorothy and Floyd Froemming
  928 W. Peck St.
  Whitewater WI 53190
  (414) 473-3491

CANADA
  Edmonton
• Cecillia McCormick
  P.O. Box 2918
  Postal Station A
  Edmonton, Alberta T5J OWO
  (403) 464-5500
  Pager #1873 - 24 hours.

  Montreal
• David G. Cassidy*
  POG-Montreal
  5311 Sherbrooke W. #916
  Montreal, P.Q. H4A 1U3
  (514) 288-1101

ENGLAND
• Parents Enquiry
  Rose Robertson
  16 Honley Road
  Catford, London
  England SE6 2HZ

Being A Gay Father

Don Clark, Ph.D.

When I was asked to write this chapter, I paled at the prospect. What generalizations could I find that would have meaning for most gay fathers? (I did not even try for *all* gay fathers.) I expressed my trepidation to my old friend Betty Berzon and she sanely reminded me that I could only share my own experience and hope that it would have some meaning for other people. I can do that, I thought. And then I remembered laboring to write an open letter to my children three years earlier as my part of a panel presentation entitled "Gay Parents and Parents of Gays" at the 1974 meeting of the Association of Humanistic Psychology. It had been a much more difficult writing assignment than usual because I had to write to my children and to the world at the same time. Focusing on the children made me stay as honest as possible and that made me feel uncomfortably vulnerable when talking to the world.

But it worked. So I decided that I could best fulfill this assignment by publishing that open letter of three years ago and then adding to it an open letter of today, showing the changes *and* the constancies. It represents a record of my progress as a gay father over a period of years. It does not speak for all gay fathers but it does speak for me and I hope it will have meaning for others.

August 1974

Dear Vicki and Andy:

This letter is for you but I am writing it in more grown-up language than I would use with you today when you are seven and

112

nine years old. The reason is that I have a special purpose for writing it. Many grown-ups are curious about what it is like to be gay and to be a father. Some of them have a hard time understanding that it is possible to be both gay and a father. So this letter is written to share some of my thoughts, feelings and experiences with them; it is to be saved for you to read when you are older because I think that then you, too, will find it interesting.

The world is filled with fear of people who are different. The nice word for such people is *nonconformist*, the not-so-nice word is *deviant*. That *deviant* has an unpleasant ring tells the story. The word indicates a deviation from the norm, statistical mean, or average. We are uncomfortable about events and people when they are not average. This fear of the *different* cheats us of the richness that would be available in our world if we were to encourage differences. It also leads to atrocities that more open civilizations would view with distaste.

There was a time when the fairest youths were given by their parents to be thrown into the fiery depths of an active volcano in pious fear of the god who supposedly lived there. They hoped that the sacrifice of their children would appease the god and save lives and crops in the community.

Our cruel god today is not a volcano, it is the god of conformity. We sacrifice our fairest, wisest and most gifted to it. Parents sometimes disown a daughter or son who is gay. When the fear of nonconformity becomes hysteria, whole groups are sacrificed, as when Americans of Japanese ancestry were rounded up, stripped of their life's possessions and their human rights and put in barbed-wire-enclosed concentration camps in this country.

At any time, a talented priest of the God of Conformity, someone like our once-revered Senator Joseph McCarthy, can point the accusing finger of nonconformity by calling someone a name like *communist* or *homosexual* and strip that person of community respect, livelihood, freedom and possibly even life itself.

I know that these things can happen. This is the kind of fearful thought that I am withholding from you, Vicki and Andy. Homosexuals provide an easy target group for persecution. The high priests of conformity like to use us to whip public fear into hysteria because we are not visible. If gay people do not speak or behave their truth, they cannot be identified. Priests of conformity love to trade on this idea that the criminal could be anyone—a neighbor, a friend or even a relative, and use it as a device to divert the attention of the public. Traditionally, for instance, big city politicians produce a publicized crackdown on homosexuals just before a major election. It fills the front pages of newspapers and diverts attention from seemingly less urgent items such as how these politicians have been using public funds and public trust.

It could happen one day that our priests might whip up a wave of profound hysteria and, explaining the regrettable danger of having subversive homosexuals loose in the community, fill concentration camps with identified and supposed gay people. If this were to happen, I would do my best to escape detention but I would, almost surely, be separated from you. I will try my best not to let this happen. My visibility as a gay person, my writing, my public speaking and this open letter are an attempt to make it less likely that it will ever happen.

You two, Vicki and Andy, are more important to me than my own life. It is a flat sounding statement, but true. Remember the last summer vacation that we spent on Long Beach Island? I am thinking of the time when the three of us went to the beach and you two went into the water. The tide began to carry you out before anyone realized what was happening. You were too frightened at the time to notice, but I was only a little surprised to find that my instinct was to preserve your lives at all cost. I had already gotten you into shallow water, Andy, and had gone back for you, Vicki, when I felt myself going under, pulled by the tide. My one impulse was to find enough footing to keep your head above water and somehow keep pushing you toward the shore.

I carry half the responsibility for having given you each a start at life and I continue to carry the responsibility for helping you to build your own lives. I believe, as your father, that I owe you the truth. I have told you that I will never knowingly lie to you and I mean it. It is my job to tell you the truth, as I understand it, and respect your attempts to find your own truth.

Part of my motivation in being openly gay is to further my own growth. Another part is to provide a model for you. I want each of you to see that you have the right to be yourself and to speak your own truth aloud.

It is not an accident that I began to be more open about my gayness after you were born. It was partly the flavor of the times. Black people were teaching us how to throw off oppression with nonviolent dignity and many of us were marching in the streets to protest the immorality of war. Those things helped. But it was holding you in the June sunlight, Vicki, and watching you delight in the beginning of each new day, Andy, that made me look into your open, trusting eyes and wonder what sort of lives the world would permit you to have.

Such thinking helped me to understand that oppression and restriction thrive on the cooperation of the victim. I began to understand that if I wanted a wide world of possibilities for you, I had better start doing what I could to build such a world. The first, and most urgent, personal step was to become truthful and visible in my gayness.

As you grow up, people may tell you that I am sick or immoral, or that I use you kids and Mom as a shield to hide behind. I know that hearing these things may hurt you. I hope that you will not be bullied. I hope that in thinking about these things your understanding will grow and you will become stronger.

I believe the charge that homosexuality is a sickness is a lie. I have read everything that I can about homosexuality and gayness. I have read as a trained social scientist. I have also read with an understanding based on my own life experiences. This lie is based on the naive assumptions that normality equals mental health and that the true norm of human behavior is synonymous with the *current mode* to which the masses are encouraged to conform.

Nor do I believe that I am immoral. I am speaking my truth even when it is uncomfortable or dangerous. I believe that is being moral. Being gay means that I can view other men as possible loved ones. I am capable of sexual, emotional and spiritual attraction to another man. This means that I reject my culture's training to compete and kill other men in commerce and war so as to support the power of my masters. In rejecting the prescribed masculine role and accepting myself as a potential lover of another man, I believe that I am moral. I offer my hand to build rather than to destroy.

As to using the two of you and Mom for a shield, your experience is sufficient to show the untruth of that. You've heard Mom and I reminisce about our years together since we met at age 17. Our nine years of friendship before we married helped us to get to know one another well. It provided the truth and mutual respect that are the foundations of our profound love for one another. You have shared many of our sorrows, joys, anger, frustrations and moments of quiet appreciation. If, from your own experience, you wonder why someone would imply that there is dishonesty in my love for the three of you, consider once more the fear that is generated by nonconformity.

Many people, both gay and nongay, have accepted the notion that there are two kinds of people. They believe that you must choose from Column A or Column B. They ignore the truth that life, like a great restaurant, offers its best delights to the discriminating who dare order a la carte. All the data from respectable social science research supports the view that human nature is a matter of continua rather than categories. But the myth of gay vs. straight continues.

Since I have chosen a satisfying straight lifestyle and yet am admittedly gay, I do not conform to the myth of categories. As a non-conformist, I am anxiety provoking and therefore viewed with distrust by some people. When people are fearful, they are apt to strike out. By now you know that this is what provokes most of the teasing on the playground.

If people strike out at you by saying nasty things about me, try to remember that they are afraid. Their fear makes them irrational and as with anyone irrational, be wary not to provoke them. But also understand that what they are saying is not of any importance. The time to engage in dialog with them is when they are back in their right senses. Meanwhile, treat them with tolerance and patience, but do not permit them to molest or harm you in any way. If necessary, use the superior strength of your sober truth and rational sense to hold them at arm's length or leave them to their own ugliness for the time being and come back to them another day, when security has sobered them once more.

I hope that both of you choose carefully the individuals you love. I hope that you permit yourselves to enjoy the widest range of attractions possible. I hope that you are not restricted in taste by skin color, politics, gender or language. But I hope that while permitting yourselves the widest possible range of attractions, you become selective in finding the individuals with whom you choose to share love and friendship. Look for the persons with whom you can share in ways that help both of you to grow in understanding, depth of feeling, appreciation and respect. Beware the programming of our culture that would lead you to believe visual appearance equals beauty. Waistline, age, teeth, and eyelashes have little to do with the beauty of love or even with the possible shared fun of recreational sex.

I hope that each of you will find the courage to speak your truth aloud, as you find it. I hope that you will never strike out to hurt anyone whose truth is different from yours. Destroying property and lives can call attention to your cause but ultimately it generates more fear. If you find the courage to speak your truth aloud consistently, and if you let those with opposing truths speak theirs aloud, while refusing to support the oppression of yourself or others, then the decades and centuries will decide the ultimate truths. It takes the courage of the child who said the Emperor was naked. It takes remembering that striking out against the truth of someone else can rob our world of someone like Martin Luther King.

I am gay. I am your father. I hope to be permitted to watch your lives unfold. If this imperfect world should somehow separate me from you, know that I will have lost the most precious gift that life has granted me. Know also that I am aware of your love for me and Mom's love for me. I know that I will be with you always because I am built into your flesh and we have had wonderful years together. Thank you for being yourselves. And thank you for helping me to find myself.

October 1977

Dear Vicki and Andy:

It is now three years and two months later. Some things have changed and some remain the same. Perhaps this is one way to trace truth, seeing what remains true through time.

You are twelve and eleven years old now. Your mother and I separated 21 months ago and you live half-time with me and half-time with her. We have all weathered the worst of that trauma in our lives, though the death of the marriage and the snug nuclear family will be mourned, the way any important death is mourned, for years to come.

Do you know what gave me the courage to say the words aloud and acknowledge that I truly did not want to be married any more? I took a long walk on the beach one day when we were all there together and I sat and looked into the ocean for a long time. I admitted to myself that I was done with marriage (not done with your mother or with you), and that I was hanging on to the *form* of marriage in the most pleasant ways possible because I wanted you to have that kind of storybook family during your growing-up years.

I knew better. As a psychologist I had for years pointed out the error of that kind of thinking to other people. It usually leads to resentment all around, hidden lies and deep unhappiness for parents and children. I imagined how it would hurt the two of you to have the words spoken aloud and the pain that would come with the actual separation of your parents.

And then another truth descended on me with the timeless certainty the ocean seems to witness with such serenity. I remembered that the most precious gift that I can give you is to have you see me live my life openly so that you can see options that are open to you as you grow older. I realized that to stay in a marriage that had died for me would too easily be seen as the insecurity of middle age—hanging in there for fear of taking those risks that provide opportunity to grow but also provide the chance for hurt, disappointment and pain.

I knew then, as I know today, that the law of life is "grow or die." I knew I wanted to keep growing. And I realized that I wanted to *show* you rather than just *tell* you that it is possible to take growth risks even in middle age, to survive the pain and to grow more into the person you can become. Within a week of that realization I plunged into the turmoil that accompanies such a major change in life.

I know that today you miss some of the times we had together as a family. So do I. But I also know, because you have told me and because I can see it, that all four of us are freer of tension and all four of us are much more clearly developing our individual lives. It has had a price but we are growing.

And that brings me to a major point that did not ring true as I read the letter I wrote to you three years ago. I made a point then of telling you that your lives were more important to me than my own. These past three years have taught me a subtle shift of that truth. Your lives are very important to me *and* so is my own. The big thing that I have learned is that unless I live my own life the best way I know how, getting as much out of it as possible, growing every year until I die, tending my life like a garden and bringing out its beauty, I cannot complete the parental responsibility of giving you your own individual lives.

If I stay locked into presumed responsibilities to you or other people and use those presumed responsibilities to divert my energy and retard my growth, I will be resentful and I will have demonstrated beyond any words I may speak to the contrary, that the true purpose of life is to serve others through self-denial. If I ever believed that, I no longer do. I do not want to see the two of you grow up to follow a cultural script that says you must play out certain responsible and respectable roles at the cost of your own flowering.

This leads us into complex areas of philosophy. I know you and trust you as I do myself. I know you would not willingly harm another person. I know that you will honor your love relationships and do what you can to help those you love. But you do not help those you love by sacrificing your own identity.

I am not sure I would have been able to work my way to this truth had I not been gay. I see so many nongay friends locked into roles that are unsatisfying. Rather than dare to break the mold of these roles, they struggle to carry the burden. Day by day I see the beauty of their individuality and spontaneity die. But I had to face it. The day I admitted to myself and others that my truth was different, I no longer fit exactly into any culturally prescribed role. I admitted that I was gay—a man capable of sharing sexual, emotional and intellectual love with other males. I could still compete against other men but not with the abandon of a man who is unaware of that kind of love potential within himself.

I never had cared for the mandate to compete and to kill that I received in this society, presented nakedly in the Army. Once an admitted gay, I had to find slightly different ways of relating to other males. And I had to find new ways of relating to women. I was impelled to see them as more than sexual objects or housewives, before such altered perceptions were fashionable.

Perhaps most pertinent, because I was gay I had to find new ways of being a father. Many gay fathers feel they must hide their truth, but I knew you and that I would be better off in the long run if we had no lies (covert or overt) between us. I wanted to find ways of being that would make you proud of me, but I knew they would have to be different ways.

I have seen that struggle come to fruition in the past few years. I have seen the pride in your eyes when you introduce me or my gay friends to friends of yours. I have heard the pride with which you are able to speak with your friends in an easy and natural tone of voice about my being gay, while they are tempted to whisper or be embarrassed.

When my book was published earlier this year, you went with me to the first TV taping of an interview and also to the first newspaper interview, and I could see the pride in your eyes. And the day the man and his child from Jehovah's Witnesses came to the door, I looked the man in the eye and you, Andy, looked his child in the eye as I told them that their church had a damaging and unacceptable attitude toward gay people and I would not discuss it with them until they and their church had taken on the responsibility for better educating themselves in this area. You, Andy, saw the confusion in their eyes, the unsureness, and you said you felt sorry for them. I was heartened by your compassion and I was heartened by the sureness in your own eyes.

Among the characteristics of both of you that I value deeply are your sensitivity to other people and your capacity for compassion. We often have talks around the dinner table about public figures, neighbors or friends at school. You are wonderfully perceptive in seeing how negative behavior is often related to a person's hidden pain or unhappiness. I know that the hours spent in those talks have helped to build your understanding. I have tried hard to facilitate this kind of understanding because I knew it would help you to understand gay people and the people who strike out at them.

Perhaps the most difficult person for us to understand together this year was Anita Bryant. At first you were thrown off balance, bewildered that a seemingly nice woman would want to deny some basic rights of citizenship to people like the many gay people you know personally. It would have been easy to see her as insane or as a simple villain. But we had to go deeper than that. We had to work toward understanding how the world keeps changing in reaction to social change. We had to see how social change has been accelerating in the past few decades and how people are now more easily frightened than ever. It was more difficult, but better for growth, to understand Anita Bryant as the willing pawn of those in our society who stand to profit from certain groups of people being held down and kept relatively powerless. It made her actions no less evil but more understandable. It made her negative drama something that we could learn from.

There will be more of this kind of thing coming along. You can already see what too many voting adults cannot see, that the issue is not simply whether gay people are entitled like any other citizen to be credentialed teachers, but rather whether group after group of citizens can be stripped of their civil rights so that the group in power can become stronger and stronger.

You already understand what a basic threat it is to the foundations of democracy. And you are helping to see to it that these issues are discussed in your classrooms. I wonder if this could have happened if I were not gay? I want to believe and I do believe that my gay identity has forced all of us to stretch and put more effort into discussion and into understanding so that we would not knuckle under in unnecessary shame. It has made me terribly proud of both of you and proud of myself.

I was really touched when I returned from San Francisco's gay parade this year, full of the enormity of it, touched by the quarter of a million visible gay people, moved beyond words by the flowers carried by individual marchers that became the gigantic memorial to a gay gardener who was murdered just because he was gay. What touched me when I told you about it and as we looked at pictures on TV and in news accounts was your feeling of having been left out and your strong demand that you be included in the parade next year. I have never taken you to a gay parade because it felt like my cause, not yours, and because I still carry in my mind commandments not to involve you in such matters when we have no idea whether you will grow up to be gay or not. Your sureness of wanting to be there, marching in the gay parents group, and the feeling of hurt that you had been left out made me pay more attention to your rights as people who happen still to be children. I invite you now for next year.

I stopped writing just now and looked around the room to gather my thoughts. I was thinking about how you, Vicki, are moving into adolescence and how much effort both of us are devoting to gracefully building our individuality. You must follow your path and I must follow mine and we must keep alive the love and mutual caring that make us so eager to follow one another's progress along these paths.

You, Andy, are on the verge of the same process. I wonder if we would be so mutually respectful of the need for individuality if I were not gay and we had not had to come to terms with that difference all these years. I think not.

What caught my eye as I thought this, are the books that you have out of the library now. One is about Martin Luther King, Jr., one about Annie Sullivan, and one about Helen Keller. What sort of youngsters borrow such books and read them along with the Hardy boys and Teen Miss? The answer is that they are the kind of young people I want to have in my life always. You are full of life and searching, keeping up with what is popular among your schoolmates and thoughtful enough to want to learn about people who are different.

If I have learned anything, it is that I cannot predict the future. You know that my lover and I have had serious talks about sharing a home. You know we would like to do that. You know that he and I are concerned about how it would influence your lives and the lives of his children. We know our living together would be another of those actions-speak-louder-than-words examples about taking charge of your own lives and following the path of love.

It is mostly logistics that stop us now, since his children and their mother have a half-time home fifty miles away from the half-time home you two have with your mother. It may end up that commuting will be necessary, if annoying. I have faith that if that happens we'll find ways to get something extra out of it. Maybe we'll live in the city and get to do the city exploring we never have time for now. Maybe we'll all learn from the pros and cons of living in a bigger family. We'll just have to wait and see. But whatever comes, I now know we'll do it together and learn from it.

There is a gay fathers group in San Francisco that periodically has pot luck dinners with fathers and their children. We'll have to try one of those one day soon. It's another adventure, another membership open to us because I am gay and because you are glad to have a gay father. I see many such opportunities opening to us in the future.

That's the gift we have given to one another. You made it necessary and possible for me to be openly and proudly gay. My being openly and proudly gay made it necessary and possible for you to learn early the benefits of exercising your unique individuality rather than hiding it in mock conformity. It has seemed hard sometimes but today it seems lucky all around. I feel sad for those parents who try to force their children into a mold so that they will look like "respectable" citizens. They never will know what individuals they could have enjoyed for a lifetime within their own family.

So that's it. Maybe I should write you a letter like this every few years. It certainly does help me to see clearly how lucky I am to be a gay father.

Being A Lesbian Mother

Diane Abbitt and Bobbie Bennett

Once we were just mothers. We concerned ourselves with the typical problems of child rearing—what diaper to buy, when to toilet train, which school would best suit our children's needs—and nobody noticed. We were just two out of millions of concerned women doing our best to make the right decisions in raising our children. Then five years ago everything changed—and nothing changed. Now we are still just two concerned women raising our children, but our child-rearing practices are of great interest to other people. Why? What wrought this miracle? What has brought us to the attention of those we meet? What has given us the honor of having these words published? The answer is one simple seven-letter word that precedes the word *mother: Lesbian.*

We are two women, ages 35 and 34, living in a typical middle-class neighborhood with our four children—two boys and two girls, ages seven, eight, nine and ten—two dogs, three cats, two parakeets and a fish. The only thing that sets us apart from the families of our middle-class neighbors is that our family has no father and one spare mother.

Five years ago we combined our respective families. The decision to do so was easy. Carrying it out has proven to be the most difficult yet most rewarding undertaking of our lives. It's hard to trust another person to help raise your children and the transition to "our" children has been a very slow process.

The hardest concept for our children to accept was our definition of *family*. Over and over they would ask, "How can we be a family?" And time and again we would answer, "A family is people who live together and love and take care of each other." We knew we were winning when the children started teasing strangers about their being siblings. A few months out of every year our two oldest children are the same age. They would put people on by saying they were twins (they look nothing alike) and then confuse people further by giving their birth dates (five months apart). With humor came acceptance. For instance, one of the most touching moments we have shared was when our oldest boy, who calls his mother "mom" and his spare mother "aunt," handed us a picture he had drawn in school. On the bottom was lettered, "To mom and mom."

Like most lesbian mothers there is a small part of us that worries and has doubts about what effect our lifestyle will have on our children. At the same time, intellectually, we realize that our children will turn out just as good or just as rotten as children being raised in a traditional family. But for that small part of us that does doubt and have fears, a well-documented study on lesbian mothers would be much appreciated. At least if we ever found ourselves in court fighting for our children, we would be armed with something substantial that the court would have to examine.

We find ourselves, individually and as a couple, spending an inordinate amount of time discussing our children. We have been told that we are overconcerned, too strict, too permissive, too rigid, too loose, overprotective, underprotective, etc., all of which is probably true at one time or another. What distinguishes our neurotic fixation on our children's development from that of our nongay sisters is our ever-present awareness of the future. Should we succeed in our effort to raise four fantastic, productive, responsible, contented human beings, it will be a statement to those who condemn the lesbian mother as unfit, solely on the basis of her lesbianism, that they are wrong. In reality, we know there are those who would say that our success had occurred in spite of our lesbianism. We most certainly know that if we fail it will be blamed on our lesbianism.

One fear surely shared by almost every lesbian mother is that of losing her children in a custody battle. Such a court battle not only risks the loss of her children, but adds a humiliating debasement of her person when insensitive, uneducated judges order her, over the objections of her attorney, to describe the intimate details of her sex life with her same-sex lover. It is impossible to adequately describe the effect of this degradation on women who have experienced it. For the individual mother who anticipates this "Armageddon" the question becomes one of how to handle her fear of it and how to best prepare for it.

The manifestation of this fear can often be seen in the aforementioned perfect mother/perfect child syndrome. After all, a little voice inside says, "The more perfect my children, the more perfect I am as a mother, the better my chances in court."

The best advice for a lesbian mother anticipating a custody fight is to stay out of court if possible. Custody is decided in the "best interest of the child," which the judge usually equates with "better" or "normal." Since judges are most often white, older, middle aged, straight men enforcing their own value system, a lesbian goes into court with two strikes against her before anyone says a word.

There are a wide variety of "bargains" that can be arranged with your spouse so that you can get custody of your children and not go into court. For example, you may be willing to take less in the way of a property settlement or you may grant extensive visitation rights to your spouse. Child custody arrangements are a complex area of the law and we have touched on it only briefly and superficially. If you have problems in this area, consult an experienced, sympathetic attorney and follow her advice.

All people struggle with the question of how much of their private life they are willing to expose to the world. The lesbian mother knows that her decisions will have far-reaching repercussions for her children as well as herself. The decision to tell or not to tell her children of her lesbianism usually determines how much she is willing to tell the rest of the world. Some lesbian mothers never tell their children; others are completely open about their lifestyle, and the rest fall somewhere in between.

The lesbian mother who chooses not to reveal her lesbianism is usually motivated by fear—of psychological damage to her child, of her child's rejection of her, of losing her child. Or she might be concerned about her child's telling others. This could result in job loss for her and/or rejection by her family, friends or neighbors. She might also fear her child's being hurt by her/his peers upon disclosure to them. These women lead a double life, a particularly difficult arrangement for the woman who lives with her lover.

Our approach, from the beginning, has been to be completely open with our children, to encourage discussion and to answer their questions as honestly as possible. We decided to do this after a careful discussion in which we weighed the pros and cons of remaining in the closet. The key word was *honesty*. We pride ourselves on being totally honest with our children and encourage telling the truth to the point where severe punishment is handed down for lying. What would hiding our lesbianism do to our family's value system? We decided that when the children found out (as surely they must), two things would happen. One, they would lose all belief in us and in everything we had attempted to teach them, and two, they would think that we were ashamed of who we are and they might buy into that shame.

We believe that if we have a positive attitude about our lesbianism and impart it to our children before they reach the age where peer pressure molds their thinking, that they too will have positive attitudes and will be better equipped to handle some of the problems that may lie ahead.

This doesn't mean that we will be surprised if at some point in the future one or more of our children withdraw from us emotionally and think that we are awful. Looking back at our own adolescence and speaking with others has made us realize that most children have to find fault with their parents at some level so that they can become separate individuals in their own right. As teenagers most of us "hated" our parents because they were poor or rich or ugly or fat or Jewish or black or Republican. We fully expect to go through this with our own children. It's a part of growing up and children have an uncanny way of seeking out their parents' most sensitive spot and exploiting it. Our children aren't going to have to do a lot of searching to find our spot. We only hope that when our time comes we can be as objective as we are now. It will still hurt, we know that; just because you expect something doesn't necessarily make it easier to deal with when it happens. However, knowing that if there weren't lesbianism, there would be some other "spot," should make it a little easier. Perhaps one of the most difficult aspects of motherhood is the fight to keep a sane perspective and reasonable expectations of one's children.

Right now, the children being of "tender years," it's hard to know exactly what they think of our lesbianism. They can all verbalize a proper definition of the word: "A lesbian is a woman who loves another woman." What this means to them still is not quite clear.

It appears that the word *love* is the key. On our way home from a conference once, our oldest son expressed it well. We were all tired and cranky, being stuck in traffic at the end of a long day, when our eight-year-old daughter popped up with the comment that she was a lesbian. Our oldest son, not to be outdone, looked at her and said, "I'm a lesbian too." Scornfully she replied, "You can't be a lesbian! A lesbian is a woman who loves another woman." Said he, "I love my Daddy." With that the other two joined in and within 30 seconds, we were busy giving a lecture on different types of love and where lesbianism fits into the broad spectrum of things.

We encourage these types of discussions, no matter how they arise, and answer specifically and as fully as possible the questions asked—no more, no less. Their questions tell us how much they are ready to learn and we are anxious that they grow at their own pace.

We have tried to explain to the children that some people think that the way we live is wrong. We discuss prejeduce, using blacks, Jews and other minorities to illustrate our points. We have never told the children not to tell anyone about our lesbianism. We have left this decision up to them, reminding them of the possible repercussions such as ostracism and teasing.

So far we have only one child, our eight-year-old, who has come out of the closet. She accomplished this feat in a most unusual way; coming out in her classroom during "Show and Tell." She announced that she was being raised in a lesbian family, that her Mommy was "chief" of the lesbians (we do a lot of movement work) and that she got to go to a lot of lesbian conferences. Now mind you, this was a first grade class. One of her peers told her it was "inappropriate" for women to kiss each other. We found out about the incident one day when we were kissing good morning in the kitchen while the children were having breakfast. She turned to us and said, "That's inappropriate," and then told us the whole story. The teacher's reaction? "We have got to learn to respect the differences of others."

Three of our four children have had this first grade teacher, an older woman with a reputation for being a conservative, tough, no-nonsense person. We wanted our children to be in her class because we felt that they would get a better education, even though we suspected that she would not understand or approve our lifestyle. We have never talked with this woman about our lifestyle, even though over the last three years we have met with her fairly regularly. She has always been warm, kind, interested and concerned when we discussed the children, their problems or our problems with them. She expects and accepts that we will both show up for parent/teacher conferences or that one of us will pop into her room to ask about our nonbiological child.

We hope that in some way we have been instrumental in raising her consciousness about lesbian families. We know she has raised ours. We no longer automatically pigeon-hole any nongay person we meet as having nothing in common with us or as a nonsympathetic bigot to be avoided. We now show up together at all teacher/parent conferences and we haven't had one bad experience yet.

In keeping with our attitude of openness and honesty with the children, we are also openly affectionate. Affection is a very important part of loving and we want our children to know not only how much we love them but how much we love each other. Many people have disagreed with us, telling us that we should reserve our expresssions of affection with each other for the bedroom and not expose the children to a sexual contact between two same-sex adults. We feel that it is essential to differentiate between affection and sex. This isn't done in many heterosexual households. Who knows how many people who have grown up without seeing their parents kiss? We believe that what is important is growing up with affection, not the sex of the people expressing it. It is only by seeing and being involved in warmth and loving that children grow into giving, loving adults. We agree—keep sex in the bedroom, but affection, never!

Many people ask if one of us is considered the daddy by the children. The answer is an emphatic *no*. We have divided child rearing much the same way we have divided the other chores of maintaining a home and family. Each does what is most comfortable. One of us gets physically ill when a child vomits, so the other takes care of the children when they are sick. One of us used to be a primary-school teacher, so she's in charge of homework time. One enjoys bathing the children, the other drying their hair. This has worked out pretty well. A problem arises only when neither of us enjoys or wants to do a necessary task, for example, chauffering the children around—to school, from school, to and from friends, and so on. In this example we split the load. Of course, natural talents and abilities enter as well: The mechanically inclined one usually fixes the toys; one cooks and other does the dishes; and so on.

We are both strong disciplinarians and for the most part run a tight ship. We have found that this is necessary for survival with a family of six. It helps when everyone knows what is expected of them and this includes the children.

An interesting problem arises from this discipline: each set of children fears and respects their stepmother more than their mother. This presents an interesting problem. We both acknowledge that our own children "have our number" and we are thankful that the other is there to step in when the situation gets rough. On the other hand, there seems to be an inevitable resentment by the biological parent of the disciplining nonbiological parent, even when we both agree that the discipline is appropriate.

Working within the gay, lesbian and nongay communities to change attitudes and to achieve equality and full civil rights for gay people is very important to us. To this end we are active in many organizations, we lead workshops, we give lectures, we do radio shows and speak with legislators, counselors, therapists and attorneys. Having children affects the way we handle our activism. We do not give magazine interviews as lesbians nor do we appear as lesbians on TV. We adopted this policy to encourage the children to decide for themselves when and whom to tell of our lifestyle. Sometimes this is not easy to follow, and there have been times when the policy has been slightly bent, but overall we feel it has worked. When the children are older and capable of fully understanding why it is important for us or people like us to give interviews and to be on TV, and if we *all* agree that this is important and something we want and are willing to do, then we'll do it.

In the gay community, children and parenting are not common phenomena. We have found people who just plain don't like kids, as in the heterosexual community. However, most of our gay friends enjoy being around our children and talking with them. For many of our lesbian and gay male friends, our children provide the only real opportunity they have to relate to the world of children. We are surprised at how often our children are included in gatherings with our friends and how genuinely disappointed our friends are when we don't bring them. Of course, the other side of the coin is our friends' distress when they don't want the kids and we can't find a babysitter.

Friends often volunteer to take the children for a day or a weekend, which provides immense enjoyment for us and them. We think our gay male friends have a particularly interesting reaction when we share our children with them. It's as if some part of these men have bought into the myth that they can't be trusted with children and they are touched that we would share and trust our children with them. We have watched them talk with the children, rough house with them, calm them when they're scared and pick them up and soothe them when they are crying. We love the caring and warmth our male friends display around the children.

We like men and so do our children. We feel it's very important for men to be around for the children to interact with; just as important for our girls as for our boys. We feel fortunate in that the majority of the men our children relate to have a feminist consciouness and we hope, despite peer and social pressures, that we will end up with four fine feminists. (Right now we think the odds are 50/50.)

We are often asked how we would feel if one or more of our children were homosexual. We believe the scientists who tell us that our children's sexual preference was already decided before we got together. However, we're not sure that this is something we could have consciously influenced even if we had wanted to. After all, most parents raise their children assuming they will be heterosexual, yet it is estimated that between 10 and 20% of the U.S. population is gay.

We want our children to be happy and to accept themselves. If this means being gay, then that's fine. We have discussed the societal pressures our children will have to endure if they are gay. It's not easy in our country to be a member of a minority, and like all mothers, we don't like envisioning our children in any kind of pain. We hope that the next generation of gay men and lesbians will have less pressure to deal with and be even better equipped to handle it.

What you have just read is our truth. Mothering is a very personal experience, a very individual experience, and nothing in this chapter is meant to reflect on mothering in general, lesbian or otherwise. We must all learn to trust ourselves, our abilities and our insights. While the experts can give us advice and help us use our own skills and wisdom more effectively, it is up to us, ultimately, to do the job of raising our children. We hope sharing some of our thoughts and experiences is helpful to you. You are not alone. Good luck!

Gay + Art = Renaissance

Loretta Lotman

> **GAY** keenly alive and exuberant.
>
> **ART** the conscious use of skill and creative imagination, especially in the production of aesthetic objects; also, works so produced.
>
> **RENAISSANCE** a movement or period of vigorous artistic and intellectual activity.

"You gay people are all so artistic!"

Yes—and we sho' can dance.

Dictionaries often miss the essence of a meaning. "Just the facts, Ma'am" is a monolithic way to approach the artistic urge. The drive to write, compose, sing, dance, paint, sculpt, act or otherwise encapsulate the spirit of life is a complex personal and emotional experience. It is more than the simple decision to ally skill with imagination.

> **ART** a compulsive inversion of personal pain, ripped from the soul into an external medium where it can be shared with others.

Artists are people who have survived society long enough to see it and state it. The world inflicts pain upon those who are different, forcing them to conform to the mainstream or step more completely outside it. Outsiders have the choice of swallowing their difference in order to buy into a societal system and fit, or standing outside that system and exploiting their difference and their pain.

Gay people are an artificially created group of outsiders. From the time we recognize our sexuality, the straight world takes on many of the characteristics of the Gestapo. There are real penalties to be inflicted if our reality is known, so we learn to hide our difference and conform to our "appropriate" role. Thus, we hold onto our emotions tightly and secretly, and try not to let our artifice show. But nothing emotional can be completely buried; feelings not dealt with directly come out sideways. The energy of hiding takes its toll on gay women and men. We are all familiar with the litany of escapes: alcohol and other drugs, the obsession for constant diversion, suicide. Avoidance of core feelings leads to negation of the self. It leads to a heightening of emotional pain, not a release from it.

One option to all this negativity is in art. The personal act of creation allows creators a positive chance to vent their feelings and get them *out*. This is not to say, however, that their art is necessarily gay or political. Gay artists have learned through the ages to mask their most personal vision and to work to attract patronage, sales and personal autonomy. The works from these artists have been an emotional code, wherein the individuals could work out passions and frustrations, yet never have their inner thoughts guessed. Only now is the veil slowly being raised on our cultural past so that we can begin to discover our gay artistic ancestors and how their homosexuality affected their art.

Most modern artists who are also gay have risen to prominence through their ability to define and encapsulate "acceptable" aspects of life. "It's OK to be artistic; just don't be a queer about it" has been a double bind gay artists have had to live with. Once a successful career has been built upon illusion—or at least selective information—few artists would dare to risk their status to come out with an open statement. Self-induced repression is habit forming. Our artistic brethren and sistren generally choose to content themselves with covert statements, if they try to say anything at all. Overt forms of self-exploration are not yet their style. Old survival mechanisms die hard.

ART   daring where you're not and no one ever has been.

We as gay people are at a unique point in our history. We have never before had the freedom to define ourselves, for ourselves, free from a history of misconceptions. The silence surrounding our lives has been broached and the world is learning that, yes, we do exist. As stereotypes are forced to fall, something must take their place as images of possibility. Politics dictates; art explores. While politics has made our future possible, it is up to the artists to help us define our personal options.

But established artists are not willing to take chances with their creative reputations by making political statements. Thus, it is time for us to develop a new generation of artists from within the community. We need people bred on equal parts creative obsessiveness and political consciousness. There is a completely new genre of art to be explored: that which results from gay artists putting *gay* and *art* together to speak the Truth. As the first few trickles of self-expression build to a vortex of creativity, we will be reinterpreting the world from a new point of view. This will be the new Renaissance.

Who will shape this fine new epoch? Anyone who puts forth an artistic vision without first censoring the gay part of their identity. Anyone who hones their art so as to feed the roots of an emerging People. Anyone who is willing to take the next step into honest exploration of gay life, love and pain. Brilliance springs from unexpected places. Maybe, if given half a chance, it will come from you.

ART   the purest way two minds can touch.

All of us, gay or not, are raised in a society that discredits emotions (*see:* maudlin, sentimental, soppy). Yet few things are as honest as an emotion clearly expressed and released. We are raised to discredit our feelings; nevertheless they sneak out in unexpected ways. One common, though quiet, release is poetry. A poem is the essence of an emotional thought, in completion and repose. Most people I know, regardless of their sexual or creative identity, have written poetry at some time in their life. They hide their emotions in words, then hide those words in drawers and dare not tell a soul what they really have to say.

Time for a little reader participation—no cheating allowed: Have you, the reader, ever written poetry related to your gayness? I don't ask for creative judgments on the merit of your writing, the relative importance of rhyming couplets versus free verse, or the need for limericks in our life and time. I simply want to know if you've written words, emotionally and honestly, that stem from the fact that you are gay.

Now that you have looked over your shoulder (even though no one knows what it is that you're reading), shrugged an embarrassed shrug, squirmed and then reluctantly admitted, "Ummm, yeah, I guess I have"—there's something else I want to know. Have you ever shared this poetry? Have you shown it to more than just a lover or close friend? Have you read it to a group? Submitted it to a gay publication? Tried to get it published by yourself?

No, huh? Congratulations. You are in the majority. Most of us, used to discrediting the validity of our thoughts and emotions, let alone our existence, have stuck our writing in drawers with a sigh and a "No one is really interested," then left for drink or disco.

But you're wrong. I'm interested. So are many others. Your silence holds our legacy. Gay culture, gay art is not something created by someone else, "those people . . . over there." It is something alive, vital, real that must be created on a daily basis by all of us. I need to know the contents of that drawer, of your mind. I need the strength that comes from our corroborating each others' mind and vision. You rob me when you withhold your thoughts. You rob other gay people who desperately need to know that they are not the only one—not just sexually, but emotionally and intellectually. You are the new gay culture and the new renaissance—but only if you bother to share.

> **ART**   the living record of the spirit of civilization, created by
> an individual as a statement on life and times.

What we call history is a record of battles, politics and elections—the fight for power. The history of our civilization resides in art. When there was time, peace and inspiration enough, individuals found ways to record, ornament and somehow glorify the life they lived. The spirit and emotions of an age were encoded in the moments of personal creation. Music, words, visual enhancement—these were formed when the world was quiet, when the abrasions of humanity did not intrude and individual Truth could be recorded.

It is time for We, the Gay People, to take advantage of this respite in our persecution and raise liberation beyond any hollow ring of rhetoric. The best thing the political movement can do now is create time and space for our incipient artists to share their creations. Few things in life are as vulnerable as the fledgling artist, especially when s/he first opens the artistic closet door to offer work and ask, "Is anybody interested?" Supportive environments are easy to create: open poetry readings, especially for people who have never read before; performance sessions at conferences; art displays and hootenannys in community centers or coffeehouses. We can create the time and space to nurture our new, emerging talent, if only we try.

And we must try. Society doesn't like to be contradicted, unless that contradiction is placed firmly in artistic expression. Only then are new ideals allowed to live as images to us all. It will take all the power and perfection of artistic expression that we can muster to create a new reality, to truly change our world instead of temporarily denting it. *We* know that gay is good, but most people would like to take that knowledge from us, destroy it for all time. We cannot allow that to happen.

Right now, we should be building among us a Voice that will be heard through succeeding generations of gay people. Without a legacy of understanding, we could easily lapse back into an era of fear, hate and bigotry. This must not be allowed. It is time for us to show the world that, yes, we *are* that artistic when we take the pains to show it. That we have reached a point in our history when we will record, explain, ornament and, yes, damn it, glorify our lives as a bequest to the future. That gay is so good we want to sing, perform, write, paint, sculpt and otherwise rejoice about it.

The only way this will happen is if you and I, my artistic sistren and brethren, get off our asses and do it. We must create and share without fear. You see, we have a world to change.

And just wait 'til they see us dance!

The Older Lesbian

Del Martin and Phyllis Lyon

We first became aware that we were aging when Jess Stearn published his book *The Grapevine* in the early '60s. It came as a jolt. In it we found ourselves described as two *middle-aged* women who had founded the Daughters of Bilitis, the first national lesbian organization. Now, more than 15 years later, we are experiencing another reminder that we are getting on in years. No longer are we asked just to put older lesbians in touch with each other. Now we are asked to write and to speak on the subject—presumably from our own perspective as "older lesbians."

We admit to a certain slowing down. The body doesn't always keep pace with the mind. We haven't slowed down in our activities, but we do require more rest. We remember the days when we could outlast women 10 to 15 years our junior. Nowadays we may opt out, not feeling up to partying but preferring a quiet evening at home. Probably the biggest generation gap we feel, however, is with the music—its ear-piercing loudness. We enjoy the nostalgic music of the '40s and the camaraderie found in straight bars that appeal to the "older" set. In one sense we feel comfortable with this peer group, yet we are alienated by their heterosexual presumption. We have braved it a time or two to dance together. Since there are more older women than men, we found no raised eyebrows, and by being so daring, we actually freed other women, who had no male partners, to dance with each other.

What we describe here appears to be a reversal of what we have seen among other lesbians of our age (Del is 57 and Phyllis 54). Many of them have spent their entire lives in the closet and are desperate to find others in their peer group of the same sexual persuasion. As activists in the gay and women's movements since 1955, we have made countless friends and acquaintances in the gay community—female and male, young and old. But we have always tried to remain connected to the larger community and so have many straight friends as well.

Admittedly, we are reluctant to use the term *old*. Age is relative. It is used to compare people and it has a lot more to do with mind-set than wrinkles or gray hair. Turning 50—the half century mark—does give one pause, however; the years left are definitely fewer. Death takes on a reality it never had before—not necessarily ominous or fearsome. We believe in everlasting universal consciousness and we believe that death is relative. But we are now much more aware of our time left on earth, of financing our retirement, of protecting the other financially when one dies, of the many things we still wish to accomplish, of the joys of leisure time.

SENIOR POWER AND GAYS

Senior Power became a political force in the '70s with the advent of the Gray Panthers and the organizing of older people to voice their needs and demand their rights. Legislators and government bureaucrats were forced to concern themselves with the economic and health issues that face retired citizens on fixed incomes. Although the condition of the elderly is less than ideal, some improvements have been brought about: establishment of senior centers, Medicare, food stamps, allowances for working beyond age 65, regulation and monitoring of convalescent homes, discounts on municipal transportation and consumer goods.

Not surprisingly, the needs of older gay people have been virtually ignored. While elderly gays face many of the same problems as other senior citizens, they suffer in addition from the consequences of being gay in a homophobic society.

In his article "In Search of Old Friends," Rick Goldberg says, "Gay people are less likely to have children, who could be of support financially and emotionally. Gay people are subject to the isolation of being gay in a straight society, which becomes increasingly acute as they grow older. And gay people are particularly subject to the pressures, both internal and external, which can make it so hard to sustain relationships that will last into old age."[1]

That any survive to old age is a miracle in itself, considering all the personal and social obstacles that have plagued them all their lives. Generally speaking, gays of advanced age today are likely to have been closeted throughout their lives. They grew up in a time when sexuality was never discusssed—let alone homosexuality. In isolation, thinking "I am the only one," they struggled with their sexual identity. Then once their homosexuality was acknowledged, they struggled with self-acceptance. It wasn't easy to have a positive sense of self when all the literature available described "perverts," who were supposed to be like you but with whom you couldn't possibly identify. While there were never any laws against homosexuality per se, there were laws against its sexual expression. In addition, the church said you were immoral and psychiatrists said you had a personality disorder. With these three strikes against you, there was seemingly no choice but to burrow underground, pretend to be heterosexual, lie about having lovers of the opposite sex, meet furtively in gay bars or hope that some one you cared about would surreptitiously convey that the feeling was mutual. If you were exposed as gay, you might lose your firends and family, your job or career. There was also the ever-present threat of blackmail.

The oppression of such a way of life—the isolation and the loneliness—is most evident among today's gay seniors. Although there is a growing sense of community among gays, the oldsters do not readily avail themselves of alternative support services and social outlets that are now provided for and by gays. Many are still afraid to come out, even though they may be retired and need no longer fear the loss of a job. They still worry about prestige and protection of the family image. They cannot break out of the closet because they see it as a place of safety—a protection from ridicule and derision. They refuse to recognize it as the source of their imprisonment—or cannot bear to. For couples who practice self-denial the break-up of the relationship or the death of a partner can be devastating. The pain, difficult at best for any of us, is even more excruciating because there is no one to turn to for support and comfort, no one who understands the depth of a relationship between two "friends."

What gay seniors suffer from is invisibility. Too many of them have made invisibility a way of life. Their unique needs as older gays will not be met—cannot be met—until they make them known and become as assertive as their heterosexual counterparts. Under the umbrella of Senior Power and within the gay community, people must be made aware of the special needs and services required by gay seniors.

RESEARCH AND OLDER GAYS

Little data is available on older homosexual women and men. So much of the research on homosexuality has concentrated on sexual activity and etiology—presumably with the goal of stamping it out. Even *Homosexualities*, the latest book of the Kinsey Institute, admits to failure in addressing the psychological, social and emotional aspects of gay life.

Chris Almvig recently conducted a survey of aging gay people as part of her masters program in gerontological administration at the New

York School for Social Research. Finding subjects for the survey was not easy. Almvig advertised in gay publications and sought the help of gay organizations. Out of 2500 questionnaires distributed, she received a little over 300 responses—only about a quarter of them from lesbians. Almvig surmises that the reason there has been less response from lesbians is that a lot of women move out of the city or get in such a close monogamous relationship they don't participate in gay activities. She adds, "A lot of them have made it in a career, and want to stay away from anything that might attract attention. For example, a lot of older lesbians won't even use the word *Ms.* because they feel it might raise some suspicion."

Almvig also points out another problem that is probably almost non-existent among men—the problem of women refusing to see their homosexuality for what it is. "I know a lesbian couple who have been together ten years who know only two other lesbians. They don't call themselves lesbians. They hate the word *gay.* They think they're in some special category, and they think it's just really unusual that they found a very special woman in their life. They're in love with each other, and it has nothing to do with being gay. There are a lot of older lesbians in this category—that's how much oppression has affected them."[2] We used to call such women *lace curtain lesbians,* a way of saying they were too nice to be lesbians and had thus drawn the curtain of secrecy that separated them from their selves, their would-be friends and a support group.

An overwhelming majority in Almvig's survey felt "positive" to "very positive" about being gay. Many felt, however, that younger gay people discriminate against them; they expressed concern about their diminishing sexual attractiveness. A large number of men said they were looking for younger sexual partners; the women were more interested in someone of their own age. Both groups had a comparable number of significant relationships, many that lasted over 20 years or into old age.

The response to the question of roles in the relationship was surprising to Almvig. She had expected that gays who predated the gay and women's liberation movements were into playing male and female roles in their relationships. But the survey showed this kind of behavior to be very much the exception. From our own experience in the '50s, butch – femme role playing was practiced among lesbians, particularly those who frequented gay bars. Since these bars were the only place we had in which to socialize, many of us acted out such roles because it appeared to be expected, but we did not necessarily practice them in the privacy of our homes.

Probably the most interesting result of Almvig's survey is the strengths exhibited by older homosexuals, often overlooked when we examine their isolation and loneliness. Many gays believe that they suffer less from the traumas of growing old than heterosexuals do because they have planned more for old age, both financially and physically. They know that they will have to take care of themselves and do not expect family support. They are far more likely to know how to perform both the tasks associated with women and the tasks associated with men and are less likely to be completely helpless upon the death of a spouse. Many have been cut off or separated from their families at an early age, have lived alone for long periods of time and have built up ego strength, which heterosexuals have not had to do. Many gays have also invested a good deal of time in building a tight, stable and secure circle of friends. The strengths of older gays in Almvig's survey have been substantiated by other studies conducted by Jim Kelly of Brandeis University and Douglas Kimmel of City University of New York.

The survey also gathered information about the needs of older gay people. Most respondents were not interested in a gay retirement village. Among those who were, the overwhelming majority preferred one that included both women and men. When the subject of nursing homes was broached, interest in a gay environment increased greatly. This is not surprising, since patients in a nursing home, no longer able to care for themselves, are completely dependent. In the totally heterosexist environment of most nursing homes, a gay person would feel extremely vulnerable and isolated.

The Center for Homosexual Education, Evaluation and Research (CHEER) at San Francisco State University is conducting a major research project, funded by the National Institutes of Mental Health, to study the adaptations and problems of homosexual women and men 60 years of age and older. [2] The pilot study included in-depth interviews with six homosexual men from 61 to 77 years old (mean age, 68) and five lesbians from 60 to 69 years old (mean age, 63.6). Five of the men lived alone; one lived with a former lover with whom he had been living for 15 years. Four of the women lived alone; the other had been living with her lover for 27 years. Heterosexual male and female subjects were matched on age and living status. Respondents were largely from middle-middle- and upper-middle-class backgrounds, but the homosexuals tended to be more highly educated than their heterosexual counterparts.

Homosexual men perceived the loss of youth and the changes in physical appearance that accompanies aging more negatively than any other group. Asked if they considered themselves to be "young, middle-aged or old," homosexual men and heterosexuals of both sexes generally viewed themselves as "middle-aged." Lesbians were more varied in their response. A 69-year-old considered herself "old," but had never considered herself "middle-aged." She had become "old" five years earlier when she began to experience health problems. Another lesbian considered herself

"60 years young." She added, "Once I caught myself acting old. I was so surprised. But I won't be old till after I die."

Homosexual men frequently viewed their homosexuality in terms of sexual activity, whereas lesbians viewed their homosexuality in terms of interpersonal relationships. But gays of both sexes indicated that gaining self-acceptance and self-esteem had been long, sometimes life-long struggles. Isolation and loneliness were experienced more frequently by older homosexuals than by the heterosexuals. All respondents reported diminishing sexual activity, but homosexual men reported greater sexual activity than any other group. The men, regardless of sexual orientation, gave sex a higher priority than did the women. Two of the homosexual men and all of the lesbians indicated the need to integrate sexual with affectional and emotional needs or attachments.

Regardless of sexual orientation, men gave work higher priority than the women did. This is not surprising, since women's work is not valued by society. Lesbians gave work higher priority than heterosexual women, presumably because they had to support themselves. More women than men were employed. Three of the six homosexual males had lost a job, or jobs, because of disclosure of their homosexuality. None of the lesbians in the sample had experienced this discrimination.

Attitudes toward retirement, especially among the men, were generally positive. The positive attitude by gay men was frequently accompanied by a sense of relief at not having to hide any more. Homosexual respondents of both sexes reported more social service and personal–spiritual growth activities in their leisure time than did the heterosexuals.

When asked how homosexuality had influenced their lives, one man admitted that it created a narrower horizon for him; "I have been, in a sense, not crippled, but cramped because of it." A 69-year-old woman said that for her it had meant a diversity she would never have known had she been stuck in a conventional suburban community where bridge, golf and the country club became the way of life.

These are preliminary surveys with small samples. They may prove to be more the exception than the rule, since most older gays do not identify with gay organizations. There is need for in-depth studies of the lives of homosexual persons in both urban and rural settings—their adulthood, not just their childhood; their relationships, not just their sexual activity; the way they view themselves, not just the ways heterosexuals view them.

One such study might be a comparison of the way in which lesbians and heterosexual women view and come through menopause. In *Our Right to Love*,[3] a lesbian resource book produced in cooperation with women of the National Gay Task Force, Bataya suggests that gay women age more gracefully than straight women and have fewer problems when going through menopause. Lesbian women, being more outside the culture, are less influenced by old wives' tales and are more independent of cultural expectations.

ISOLATION AND LONELINESS

Among lesbians there is not the same accent on youth and looks as there is among male homosexuals. Older women are welcomed into rap groups or organizations. Younger women with a growing sense of the history of the gay movement and of women in general are eager to learn what it was like in "the old days." They are often in awe of long-lasting relationships and constantly ask for tips on how to cope with parents and society, how to stay together despite the pressures against them.

Gay men have always found it easy to meet their peers in bars and bath houses, but lesbians, who are not just looking for sexual encounters, experience difficulty in finding each other. Although many more lesbians have come out with the support of the women's movement, they are mostly in their twenties or thirties. When a lonely older woman gathers her courage and makes the effort to attend a lesbian gathering, she usually retreats when she finds that most of the women are so young. Then she isn't there to meet her when another older lesbian turns up at the next meeting.

In response to our book *Lesbian/Woman* we received hundreds of letters from isolated and lonely older lesbians who rejoiced in their new knowledge that there were others like themselves who understood. Some were lesbians who had rejected the gay life for the more respected and accepted heterosexual family life—women who found that as the years went by their longing for a close lesbian relationship seemed almost unbearable. Many of these wives were waiting until the children finished high school or left home in order to fulfill their own needs and desires. Two grandmothers who had met years before at a church camp had become fast friends—their husbands, too. They sent us photos of the 25th anniversary celebration of one of the couples and confessed they were awaiting the time when their husbands would die so they could be together. Other women who had been in a lesbian relationship of long standing poured out their grief over the death of a lover. These couples had no gay friends, and the surviving partner felt bereft and alone. True, some of them had straight friends or relatives who knew, but it had never been discussed. These women needed to vent their pent-up feelings to someone of their own kind.

A couple in Utah wrote: "We are in our fifties, have been together for 18 years, but have never declared our love for each other in front of a third party. When we shut our doors at night we shut the world out. We have no gay friends that we know of. We are looking for companions, friendship and support, but in the lesbian organizations we've contacted we find only badge-wearing, drum-beating, foot-stomping social reformers. They consider our conservative life 'oppressed,' and we think of their way of life as 'flagrant.' There must be more like us, but how do we meet them?"

There are, of course, countless numbers of women like "them." But, like them, they are in the closet or are a part of a very small and tight lesbian clique that is very difficult to break into. The invisibility of closeted lesbians prevents their meeting each other except in ways which they find forbidding.

Some women who have never identified as lesbians decide in their later years that they would like to have a relationship with another woman. One in a small town in Kansas said, "I am tired of the constant male emphasis on sex and have always been attracted to women. I would like to know how to go about finding a congenial woman companion at my age. I am over 50, twice divorced, living alone and quietly going crazy. Does one put an ad under the Personal column in a lesbian paper or magazine? Or just how does one make contact with others for the first time?"

The likelihood of this woman finding a lesbian companion in a small town is remote. But there are probably other divorced or widowed women where she lives who are also lonely. How simple it would be for them to team up. It's a widely known fact that women outlive their husbands and often spend many years alone. Furthermore, the diminishing sex life of the elderly does not necessarily mean a diminishing sex urge, but the lack of opportunity. A less homophobic and more humane society would encourage women of advanced age to get together. Why should these spouseless women be denied the pleasures of companionship and sexual fulfillment? If they could shed their inhibitions, they could live out their days in an enriching lesbian relationship.

DEATH AND DYING

Upon the death of a gay partner, the survivor faces many problems. First, the survivor is not regarded as next of kin and becomes virtually nonexistent when the deceased's family swoops in and takes over. Oh, yes, there is that "peculiar friend" of Mary's whom the family may take into consideration or dismiss, depending upon the openness of the relationship and the family's acceptance of it.

We learned of the sudden death of Gerry, a friend of ours, when someone sent us a clipping from the small-town Arkansas newspaper that carried her obituary. The article listed her mother as the only survivor. We couldn't help feeling outraged that there was no mention of Doris, the woman she had lived with and loved for more than 15 years.

Gerry and Doris had moved from California to Arkansas, had bought a modest farm and gone into the business of raising rabbits. In the isolation of this remote rural area people are dependent upon the few neighbors they have, and Gerry and Doris had never dared to reveal the true nature of their relationship. Nor had they come to an understanding with Gerry's mother, their only living parent. The depth of Doris' grief for Gerry left no doubt that the two were more than just friends. The neighbors responded with warmth and sympathy. And the two women who survived Gerry—mother and lover—wound up consoling each other.

Because Gerry had served honorably in the WACs she was to receive a military funeral. Her mother, knowing that the flag that covered her daughter's coffin would be presented to the next of kin, asked that it be presented to Doris. The WACs refused. When the time came and the flag was, indeed, presented to the mother, she rose to the occasion and handed it, in turn, to Doris.

This example is, of course, exceptional. All too many families are extremely callous and insensitive. They come and bury their dead and they lay claim as kin to the worldly possessions of the deceased—no matter the sentimental value to the surviving partner. Gay couples do not have the same community property rights as married couples. The "family" has prior claim, and few gays are in the position, or have the stomach, to contest that claim.

Medical personnel in hospitals are equally insensitive when one's gay partner is ill or dying. No matter how long two women may have been together they are still not related. When a lesbian is seriously ill and in intensive care, hospital rules limit visitation to family and her partner may thus be barred at a time when she needs her most.

Imagine being in pain and under sedation and having a sister or brother you haven't seen in years take over, simply by virtue of blood ties. If you are unable to make life-saving or life-taking decisions for yourself, you want someone who is close to you and who knows your personal wishes to make them for you, not some stranger, who may lay claim as kin but who has frowned upon your spinsterhood and has little use for "that person" you live with. The torture of the intrusion and separation from the loved one can devastate the patient, who has little energy left to fight for her rights and the dignity of her personal relationship. The partner, caught in an awkward situation, feels helpless and full of remorse because her hands are tied legally and socially. A straight friend suggested that gays might be protected by a "living will"—that is, giving power of attorney to one's partner in case of incapacitating illness.

Doris told Phyllis that she panics at the thought of being confined to a nursing home—she would feel so alone. All she would have left then would be her memories, and there would be no one to share them with. One circle of lesbian friends in the Midwest planned ahead to avoid that eventuality. They found through an aunt's experience an excellent home and applied in advance of retirement, planning to end their days together there. One of the group is already in the home; two others have bought a house nearby and take her out twice a week. In the absence of nursing homes for gays, others might well profit from this example.

The need to plan ahead may be even more crucial for gay women and men than for heterosexuals who have built-in societal protections and support services. Because gay pairings are not recognized, even when a member of the clergy performs a covenant or wedding service for the couple, it is highly important that they obtain legal advice before buying' property. It is also important to have wills drawn up so that either partner will be protected. In some instances gays have formed legal partnerships or corporations to safeguard their mutual holdings.

RESOURCES FOR GAY SENIORS

Chris Almvig is taking steps to establish a center for older lesbians and gay men in New York City. A primary goal of the new group will be to provide assistance to homebound elderly gays, those whose other support systems have been decimated by death or disability. Eventually, the group hopes to set up a multipurpose center, perhaps even including residential facilities.

Discussion groups for older gays have been started in a few gay centers across the country. Women's centers also are addressing the role of older women and would probably be a source of support for older lesbians who are free enough to be open about their personal relationships. In some areas gay women have started up SOL groups for Slightly Older Lesbians, a means of meeting and socializing with women of their age group. Some women have found each other by advertising in *The Wishing Well*, a publication dedicated to helping gay women find others with similar interests, needs and objectives. Some bars, like Bacchanal, in Albany, California, have older lesbian nights.

The Gay Nurses Alliance, a national organization, acts as advocates not only for gay nurses, but also for gay patients. GNA has an effective slide show which vividly portrays the plight of the gay patient for presentation at workshops and conferences. The group also lobbies for relevant legislation and provides referrals for counseling.

San Francisco has a group social outlet for older gay people called

Gays Over Forty (G40+). We were invited to an early meeting and found about seven or eight seniors trying to establish a means of meeting their peers. They also hoped to start a support network for those who are bedridden or confined to their homes. None of these women and men had been active in the city's gay community. They had been closeted all of their lives. Most were retired and reasonably comfortable financially. Though relieved of the pressure to be circumspect in order to maintain jobs, they were nonetheless reluctant to mix with those they perceived to be too militant or outspoken or young. They wanted to make contact with older gays who had backgrounds and tastes similar to their own.

We suggested that the best way to reach other older gays would be through publicity in the straight press and that another way was to request that the Downtown Senior Center schedule regular meetings for gays and that they be publicized among all other senior centers and groups. A delegation from G40+ did approach the executive director of the Senior Center, but not unexpectedly he turned them down flat. Unfortunately they accepted this denial without protest. A practice of a lifetime is not easily overcome. The group refused to seek help from the gay community to put pressure on the Senior Center to deal with the unique problems of gay senior citizens. If they weren't willing to follow through, it seemed useless for us to push the issue.

But we are still angry. Why must the gay community always have to provide for their own without any help from the larger community? Federal, state and local governments do not hesitate to collect taxes from gay citizens, but seldom does any of that tax money fund projects that would benefit them. When the San Francisco Human Rights Commission's Gay Advisory Committee held public hearings sometime later, Del testified about the incident with the Senior Center and deplored the lack of sensitivity and city services for senior citizens who are gay. The situation remains the same. Perhaps that will be our new crusade, when we come to the full realization that we are, indeed, older lesbians.

FOOTNOTES

1. Rick Goldberg, "In Search of Old Friends." *Atlanta Gay News*, July 1977.

2. Fred A. Minnegerode and Marcy Adelman, "Adaptations of Aging Homosexual Men and Women." Paper presented at convention of the Gerontological Society, New York City, October 1976.

3. Bataya, "The Spectrum of Lesbian Experience—Age," in *Our Right to Love*, edited by Ginny Vida (Englewood Cliffs, New Jersey: Prentice-Hall, 1978) pp. 233–35.

RESOURCES FOR OLDER LESBIANS:

The Wishing Well, P.O. Box 1711, Santa Rosa, CA 95403. Quarterly, subscription $10.

Bacchanal, 1369 Solano Ave., Albany CA 94706. 415/527-1314. Older Lesʼban night on Thursdays.

Slightly Older Lesbians, 2329 San Pablo Ave, Berkeley CA 94701. Thursdays, 7:30 to 9:30 p.m.

Gay Nurses Alliance, P.O. Box 17593, San Diego CA 92117. Publishes *Signal* three times a year. Subscription by contribution of at least $5.

Gay Nurses Alliance, Box 5687, Philadelphia PA 19129. 215/849-1171.

The Other Side, P.O. Box 132, San Rafael CA 94902. Lesbian social organization with many older members.

Atlanta Lesbian Feminist Alliance, 1326 McLendon St., N.E., Atlanta GA 30307. Mailing address: Box 5502, Atlanta GA 30307. 404/523-7786. Membership primarily young but witnessed a special warmth between the young and older lesbians while visiting there.

Gay Nurses Alliance, P.O. Box 530, Back Bay Annex, Boston MA 02117. 617/266-5473.

All the Queens Women, 36-23 164th St., Flushing NY 11358. 212/359-9204. Open days. Rap groups for lesbians and older women. Publishes *Womanspace* $2 per year.

Women's Liberation Center, 243 W. 20th St. (8th Ave.), New York NY. 10011. 212/255-9802. Gay Older Women's Liberation raps, Monday, 8:30 p.m.

Babyface, 1235 Dorchester, Montreal, Quebec Canada. 510/861-0896. Bar for older lesbians.

Adjustments to Aging Among Gay Men[1]

Douglas C. Kimmel

Many gay people grow up without gay parent-figures or grandparent-figures. Unlike heterosexuals and persons in other minority groups, gay people can become adults without having had any significant contact with other gays who are middle-aged or elderly. As a result, gay people often may be uncertain about what to expect as they grow older, and without any positive role models, they may expect the worst. Indeed, the stereotypes about aging gay men and women in our society are very bleak. But are these stereotypes possibly one of those myths that have instilled a fear of being homosexual, a self-hatred if one is gay, and contempt for other (especially older) homosexuals? Perhaps these stereotypes are another manifestation of the general social stigma about homosexuality that has attempted to discourage gay people from living their lifestyle and developing solid feelings of self-acceptance and acceptance of other gay people, young or old.

If the estimate that 10% of the adult population is gay also applies to persons over 65, and only about 5% of persons over 65 are living in nursing homes, then there are perhaps twice as many gay men and women over the age of 65 than there are nursing home residents over 65. In absolute numbers, this would imply that approximately two million persons over 65 in the United States are gay. Yet until quite recently there has been almost no research on the characteristics and lifestyles of aging homosexual men and women.[2]

To begin an exploration of the patterns of aging among gay persons we interviewed 14 gay men between the ages of 55 and 81 in 1975 and 1976.[3] We located the respondents through organizations that attract an age-mix of gays, such as Dignity, Integrity and the West Side Discussion Group, and a seminar on gay counseling, all in New York City. One respondent was contacted through a personal newspaper ad in which he identified himself as gay and over 60. No respondents were obtained from bars or baths and no respondent provided the names of other respondents. Average age of the respondents was 64.9 years; half were over 63.

Since it is probably impossible to find a sample that is representative of all older gay men, our study does not necessarily reflect all of the lifestyles of aging gay men, nor the actual proportion of gay men over 55 who were living with lovers or had been married. These men are generally more educated and enjoy a higher standard of living than elderly men in general. (However, gay men may have more opportunities for education and financial success than men with families to support.) At best, this sample reflects some of the patterns of aging among 14 "gay grandfathers."

There was considerable variation among these men on nearly every dimension we studied. This, in itself, suggests that any stereotype about aging gay men is an oversimplification. Since these men were each so different one from another, the notion that all gay men grow older in the same way is simply invalid.

Three of the respondents had a long-term lover and a consistent pattern of stable relationships that spanned nearly their entire adult life. One had been with his lover for 30 years; although they did not share the same apartment, they lived near each other, shared dinner nearly every night and spent weekends together. Another had had a lover of 40 years who had died; he had been with his current lover for five years. The third had been with a lover for 25 years before the lover died, and had been with his present lover for 13 years. In one case, the two lovers were about the same age. In the other two, the lover was about 25 years younger than the respondent; both of these men had been the younger partner in a previous relationship that had ended with the lover's death. One respondent described his experience this way:

> When he first started getting ill he called me every five minutes at the office and I'd either have to run home and take an extra hour at lunch or something to keep him calmed down and quieted. . . . He could remember things that had happened years ago, but couldn't remember that he had called me five minutes before. . . . I didn't have any support during those months. . . . I was sure I was going to lose my job. . . . I couldn't go to the office and say, "I need time off, my wife is sick [like heterosexuals can]. . . . He died December first. So one cold January night I went out and went to the Yukon (bar). I just sat in the back and watched the dancing. It wasn't until several months later that somebody approached me and wanted to be friendly. And that's how it all began. . . . The way this fellow feels about it now, this is going to continue until the end—my end, I presume.

Four of the men had been married to women and two had children. One of these was a grandfather whose son found out he was gay and beat him up. Their relationship is very distant now. Three of the men were divorced and one was a widower. All of these men knew when they were young that they were gay and only one had married before his first gay experience. One had had a gay lover for eight years while in his twenties, but when the lover left for a distant job, he was very lonely and married about a year later. Only one formerly married man reported that he had been entirely heterosexual during his married life; he returned to homosexuality after his wife died.

Six of the men had lived alone nearly all of their adult lives, although four of them had experienced at least one homosexual affair. And one respondent was living with a roommate who had been his lover several years earlier. One of these men had had a series of extended relationships with young men over the years and wanted very much to meet another man in his twenties to continue this pattern. Another had adopted a heterosexual son many years ago; the son is now married and the respondent is a grandfather who enjoys a close relationship with the family. Another long-term loner had been so sexually repressed that his "first really close sexual experience with anybody" occurred just three months before the interview—at the age of 59; his first sexual experience of any kind was at age 56, although he had decided that he was homosexual many years earlier. He commented:

> I felt that by the time of 50 you dried up. And, in a way, sex grips me more than it did years ago. Somehow I managed to get by without tremendous urges in that respect. . . . My 72-year-old friend can do it two or three times a day and not be bothered.

All of the men indicated that they were sexually active and that sexuality continued to be an important part of their lives. Their comments included these three:

> Sex is better now, less accent on the genitals and more on the total person. . . . One, two, three times a week now; my erections are not as hard as they were five years ago, but it's just as enjoyable.

> It's never been as satisfying as it is now; I don't have sex as often as I did, but once a week at least.

> Not as important, but important; erections are not as easy and I can't ejaculate as often; there's not as much drive and urge; but I enjoy it more than I did when I was young because I repressed it then.

As with many other characteristics, there was considerable variation in the preferred age of the partner. Two respondents reported a distinct preference for younger men; two indicated that they strongly preferred men who were not young (*young* meaning approximately 18 to 30).

Because these men were born between 1895 and 1920, they had to deal with being homosexual during a very different time in history than young homosexuals today. Three examples of their comments make this point:

> I went to high school in the 1920s and that was a pretty lively time, too. There were all kinds of social revolutions going on around the world and one of them was sexual. People were being a lot more frank and honest about sex than they had been previously. But it was mainly heterosexual relationships that were being much more free. . . . I was aware of (homosexuality) in me when I was about 14 to 15 years old. But I didn't know what to do about it. There was nobody to go to get advice. I just sort of suffered along not knowing what to do.
>
> Of course, my lover and I didn't meet in a gay bar. There were no bars then. It was Prohibition. . . (Gay people) would meet at bath houses, on the beach and railway terminals, places where people could congregate and not be noticed; or motion picture theaters, or just eye contact on the street.
>
> It was like living in the underground. . .Everyone, when they came out, went into the closet, as the expression goes.

Not surprisingly, several of these men experienced considerable guilt about being homosexual. One had been in psychotherapy for most of his adult life in an attempt not to be gay. Another had tried to take his own life after his divorce. At least two had had a serious drinking problem a few years previous. Another had suffered a great deal of "religious guilt."

Most of them however, had overcome these serious problems and had found much greater self-acceptance in recent years. At the time of the interview, only three of the 14 seemed clearly depressed and lonely—primarily for reasons that had little to do with being gay. The other respondents ranged from this extreme of loneliness to the three who were living happy, contented, fulfilling lives.

The respondents noted some of the special challenges for gay men as they grow older, including: lack of social support when a long-term lover dies; adjusting to not being able to play the bar-cruising-game as when younger; feelings about not having children or being at the end of one's family line; and the tendency of some to withdraw into a circle of friends and to no longer have social contact with young persons. The stigma of being gay also, makes ordinary problems of aging more difficult, especially if combined with a belief in the stereotype that aging is a bleak experience for gay men.

The respondents also pointed out some of the advantages of aging as a gay person. There may be more awareness of responsibility for self, so that the preparation for aging does not rely on potentially unrealistic expectations of family or children. And there is a continuity of life for gay men who have not had to deal with children leaving home, who have not been confined to only male or female roles in performing the necessary tasks of living, and who may have already lived alone as adults. Also, gay men in their sixties often have a self-selected friendship network on which they can rely.

When asked what should be done to improve the quality of life for aging gay men, one respondent summed up the feelings of many:

> Make the gay world aware of the potentials and value of older gay men—just the opposite of the way it is now. Now men of great intellectual stature are called an "Old Auntie." There's a great deal of prejudice in the media—newspapers and magazines. The crux of the matter would be if young people could be educated that old age is not ugly. It's really a matter of tradition that this country doesn't have. . . . In this country straight people don't have it, and in gay life it's the worst.

How can we begin to lift the stigma that has too often been placed on older gay men and women? And how can we prepare ourselves and help those we care about who are growing older? Two general points seem to be especially important.

The first is that older gay people have many of the assets and problems of older people in general. In a sense, aging tends to be an equalizer of differences in terms of social class, race, sex, and sexual orientation. Even differences in religion, culture, education, income and occupation tend to become less important as individuals become very old. All of these factors, significant during most of adulthood, are eclipsed by the dominant issue associated with advancing age—health.

An old person in relatively good health is very different from a person of the same age who is in poor health; and those in poor health are more numerous among each successive age group in later life. Thus, older gay people are likely to have concerns similar to those of nongay elderly: health, income, housing, access to high-quality medical care, transportation, access to social and cultural activities, companionship, maintaining eating and household tasks, fear of crime (especially mugging) and maintaining a satisfying pattern of activities. All of these concerns can to some degree be prepared for, but advancing age typically brings increased vulnerability in each of these areas.

There is a growing difference between the young-old (between 70 and 80) and the old-old (over 80). Because of advances in medical technology, the young-old group enjoys better health and significantly less age-related impairment in all areas than was the case a decade or two ago. This trend is likely to continue so that we are really talking about the old-old group when we think of the physical problems that are so significant in their range of effects on the aged. Of course, there is a sex difference involved, since women typically live longer than men. But even for men, the decade of their seventies is probably more like that of their sixties than like the decade of their 80s (except they are more likely to be retired).

The second point that emerges from this study is that being gay seems to have important effects on older people, especially those in relatively good health and those who are not old-old. While the first generalization implies that older gay people are likely to need a similar range of services as nongay elderly persons, and face a similar range of problems, this second point suggests that there are in addition, particular concerns for gay people. It may be important that they be worked through before the problems of very late life take precedence. Let me suggest some of the unique issues that seem to be especially important for understanding the experience of older gays.

One significant issue seems to be vulnerability. All gay people are especially vulnerable, because being gay subjects them to special threats of exposure, loss of job, social stigma, arrest or physical violence. To a large degree, these threats exist primarily in gay persons' perceptions of their environment, and may be relatively unlikely in reality; but the sense of vulnerability is often very real, regardless of its source.

Because today's elderly men and women grew up in a more sexually repressive period, the fear of, and sense of vulnerability to, social oppression is often much stronger among older gays than among younger gays. In its least limiting forms, this may lead gay people to avoid revealing their lifestyle and sexual orientation even when it might be beneficial to do so. Close friends and confidants, one's family physician, lawyer, accountant and neighbors may know about the individual's homosexuality, but may never have discussed it, even though open support and professional assistance might reduce the gay person's vulnerability.

Self-imposed secrecy about one's lifestyle can likewise inhibit the development of deep and lasting relationships with a variety of gay and nongay persons. Some of these relationships could provide important support during periods of physical or emotional vulnerability. While most older gay persons have developed a friendship network that provides mutual support in times of need, those who have not are more vulnerable to the losses that often accompany aging. Thus, the fear of vulnerability can prevent the development of the very supports that might reduce actual vulnerability. This is the kind of self-fulfilling prophecy that results from the social oppression of gay people. Perhaps all gay people need to deal with their fears of vulnerability, especially so in the later years when these fears combine with the fears related to aging.

An issue closely related to vulnerability is the life-long pattern of secrecy, hiding, lying, covering-up, and leading a double life that characterizes some older gay persons. This involves not only the perception of vulnerability, but also an internalizing of the social stigma about homosexuals. For example, some men learned early in life (in the 1920s and 30s) how awful it is to be homosexual. As a result they pay great attention to reports of homosexuals who have been exposed or attacked. They hide their homosexuality, restrict sex to furtive forbidden encounters. They feel guilt and shame and end up leading a llife as demonstrably awful as they had learned to expect. Again, the vicious cycle of social oppression. Typically, these men have been loners all their lives, oppressing themselves through self-hatred, avoiding meaningful relationships with other gay persons because of the stigma they place on homosexuality, and hiding their lifestyle from even their few trusted friends.

Thomas Mann's *Death in Venice*, now a movie and opera, portrays this grim theme. An old homosexual goes to Venice and becomes very attracted to a young boy/man who is vacationing with his family. Despite threats of a plague in the city, he remains in Venice because of his one-sided involvement with the fantasy/reality of the boy. He is a caricature of an aging homosexual queen and catches the plague and dies after the boy and his family have left Venice.

The theme of this story is: Homosexual lives are grim and inevitably end tragically. Such a syndrome of tragedy can function as another self-fulfilling prophecy, depriving these older gay men of their sense of integrity and dignity, while also denying them any hope of fulfillment or satisfaction. Although my study indicates that this lifestyle is not prevalent among older gay men, it is not uncommon; and perhaps this "tragic syndrome" is present at least to some degree in the inner fears of many gay men. It rests on the more general misconception that homosexuals cannot escape punishment for leading their socially unacceptable lifestyle. As one of my therapy clients expressed it, "One day, I'll get my comeuppence." This misconception could be at the root of much of the fear of aging among gays. Whether phrased as "One day I'll no longer be attractive" or "No one loves you when you're old and gay," there seems to be a deep—and unfounded—fear of growing old as a gay man. Those who hold this misconception seem to notice only those older gay men who confirm it and ignore those who disconfirm it. In reality, the majority of older gay men disconfirm it.

These two themes—vulnerability and secrecy—apply to the distinction that is beginning to be recognized between the terms *gay* and *homosexual*. Stephen Morin, in a recent article in *The American Psychologist* stated it very well:

> The emerging definition of "gay" or "lesbian" is different from that
> of "homosexual." The term *gay*, like the terms *black*, *Chicano*, and
> *woman*, connotes a value system as well as designates group mem-
> bership. *Gay* is proud, angry, open, visible, political, healthy, and
> all the positive things that *homosexual* is not.[4]

Many older gays grew up thinking of themselves as homosexual and
tended to incorporate the negative, self-destructive connotations of that
term into their identity. Most have largely overcome the effects of the
social stigma attached to homosexuality through their own positive experiences; however, a few have so hidden their identity or struggled
against it that the stigma has remained largely intact. Future generations of older *gays* will, I hope, be quite different from today's older
homosexuals, but now an important task is to help all gay persons more
fully develop a positive gay identity, one that will liberate them from the
stigma of homosexuality.

A third theme for understanding the aging gay experience is this anger
at years of oppression. To be sure, many older gay people have channeled this anger in constructive directions. Some have worked hard for
success in their occupation, or created an outstanding home or two, or
built up a strong friendship network. Often this pursuit of success, prestige and personal comfort may be a partial attempt to reduce the vulnerability discussed earlier. Sometimes it may also reflect an attempt to
overcome or disprove the stigma of homosexuality. In many cases there
has been a very satisfying and meaningful use of talent and creative
energy and this has reduced their vulnerability to aging and provided
profound satisfaction, and self-esteem. For these persons, the anger at the
oppression of homosexuals has largely dissipated, and while they may
still be angry at the degree to which they have to hide their lifestyle, they
may also use the secure base they have established to support or be involved with the gay liberation movement.

For at least a few others, however, success has not brought relief from
their fears of vulnerability. Their lack of self-acceptance has stigmatized
both themselves and potential gay friends, while their anger has largely
turned inward leading to profound depression. The majority of older gay
persons are probably in between these two extremes—neither crippled
by, nor largely free of, the inner anger about a lifetime of oppression,
suppression, hiding and fear.

To develop a positive identity as a gay person, it is often necessary to
recognize this inner rage and to come to terms with it. Similar in many
ways to the rage of other oppressed minority groups, this "gay rage"
sometimes take self-destructive forms and at other times is expressed in
violence. Gay anger is not directed at heterosexuals per se, but at the

unfairness of oppression in general and at those institutions and groups who blatantly attack homosexuals. Adolescents who beat up "faggots" in gay cruising areas, spokespersons who repeat antihomosexual stereotypes and inaccurate myths, and religious or professional organizations that condemn gay people all provoke this inner anger that, for many, has built up over the years.

Every gay person deals with this anger in a different way. Occasionally, as in the Stonewall Riot of 1969, violence erupts. More typically, the energy is channeled into constructive projects or into gay political activities or community activities. Often, and perhaps ideally, this anger is also transformed into gay love. From holding hands in public to lovingly performing the sexual activities that are derisve epithets in other contexts, gay people can turn the oppression into self-fulfillment. By recognizing the anger inside, instead of turning it on themselves or other gay people, they can channel it to overcome the grim stigma of homosexuality through an affirmation of being gay.

These three themes—vulnerability, secrecy and anger—are important for all gay people but they seem especially significant for older gays, because older gay people have been oppressed longer and more severely than younger gays. However, the preparation for satisfaction as an aging gay person involves recognizing and struggling with these themes as early in life as possible (for some this means their sixties or seventies).

There are two additional issues that may have less to do with being gay than with growing old. The first of these is the "dirty old man" myth. Our society is not highly accepting of sex at any age. It is quite intolerant of sex among the aged. Whether the issue is remarriage among the widowed elderly or among old couples living together outside marriage (so that social security and inheritance are not affected) or among gay people seeking sex partners, the stereotypic attitude is "They are too old!" Although Masters and Johnson found that men and women are capable of having satisfying sexual relations at least into their seventies and eighties, an older gay person who desires sexual relations may feel abnormal, especially if cruising is involved and if the preferred partner is much younger. To be sure, some people are pursuing fantasies—of lost youth or lost innocence or beauty. This is normal in our youth-oriented society. Since sexuality potentially involves the whole person at all ages, this may be especially true in the later years, so let us explore this more deeply.

It seems that the competitive, conquest-oriented, orgasm-focused emphasis in sex for younger men gives way during the second half of life to more concern with communion, companionship and facilitation of the partner's mutual sexuality with one's own.[5] Studies have found that men also become more responsive to the feminine aspects of themselves and women become more responsive to their masculine impulses during the latter half of life.[6] Perhaps this process is less dramatic in gay than in nongay men and women since gay people may typically integrate their masculine and feminine aspects more fully than nongay people in our culture. However, it seems that sexuality in later years can be richer and more responsive to one's entire humanness than during early adulthood.

A second, closely related issue that also applies to both gay and nongay persons focuses on the meaning and satisfaction in life. During the first half of life, efforts to reach future goals provide much of the purpose and sense of accomplishment in life. During the second half, life's meaning seems to require, to some degree, a striving for something that will come after death.[7] For some, this involves a religious belief in an afterlife of some sort. For others, it involves the satisfaction of creative accomplishments that will live on after death, or the hope that one's children (biological or spiritual) will grow and flourish. Another major source of satisfaction, even later in life, is to look back with kindness and acceptance over one's life and find meaning in one's personal intersection with history.[8] For oppressed gay men and women whose lives have been filled with self-hate, this is not easy to attain. But for most gay people the range and depth of satisfaction during the second half of life appear to be a great as for nongay men and women.

With either theme, there is a danger of clinging to the style of the first half of life until very late in the second half, or that is, continuing to search for the sexual satisfactions or sources of meaning that were significant early in adulthood, when one is, in fact, well into the second half of life. Sexual satisfaction and meaning in life are, of course, as important during the second half of life, but it is likely that their sources differ from those of the first half. Pursuing the sources more important during early adulthood may be unsatisfying in later life, not because they are unattainable—they often *are* available (e.g., sexual conquest or goal achievement)—but because the second half of life has different sources of satisfaction for those needs. Thus, new potentials and opportunities are open to persons during later life, but the transition from early adulthood may be as major a change as the transition from adolescence to adulthood.

To conclude this chapter, I wish to call attention to some of the concerns of older gays.[10] One definition of *community* involves the extent to which its members care for other members who are in need. Therefore, it would seem that the full development of a gay community involves greater concern with elderly gays, especially those who are in poor health or are suffering the losses often associated with growing old in our society. In New York City there has recently been organized a service program called Senior Action in a Gay Environment, Inc. This program will seek to reach older gays who need help with shopping or trips to the doctor, or who could benefit from a friendly volunteer visitor who brings a gay newspaper or helps in correspondence with gay friends, or who needs a daily telephone reassurance call. This program also plans to develop a bereavement couseling program for gay persons who have lost a long-term lover. Other services will be provided by referral. Although in many neighborhoods, most of these services are already available to *all* older persons, the gay community has a special responsibility for older gays.

The concerns we expect to encounter among elderly gays include legal issues, problems associated with physical illness and disability, adaptation to bereavement, and general loneliness or isolation. Important legal issues include the obvious ones of wills, estates and general protection of inheritance in the manner desired by the client. In addition, there are the questions of legal custody of the person if there is a loss of mental functioning; visitation rights if the person has been placed by the family in a nursing home or institution, as well as related issues that may arise from family members stepping in to take control of an elderly gay person's life despite the wishes of the person and the person's lover or long-term friends. These issues will require referrals or participation of gay-oriented lawyers in the program.

Physical illness may bring either short-term or long-term need for care at home. In those cases where professional care is required, a friendly volunteer visitor from the program could provide added support; when appropriate, the program could coordinate the variety of services required. If professional care or a home-health aide are not needed, and family or friends are unavailable, the program volunteer could allow the person to remain at home, in cooperation with other programs such as those that provide hot meals to homebound elderly. Physical illness may also bring problematic relations with physicians, hospital staff members, nursing homes, social workers or the family. In these cases, the program may be able to facilitate communication, give support and provide referrals when appropriate.

Bereavement counseling will be an important and unique service of the program since the variety of problems that surround the loss of a long-term lover in the gay world have received almost no attention. Legal issues, problems with family members, the reactions of health-care and funerary professionals, and reactions of the bereaved's family or employer may all compound the disorientatioon and grief. Although counseling programs for nongay widows have recently come into existence, the complications of being gay make a bereavement counseling service mandatory for any program dealing with older gay men and women.

The general problems of isolation and loneliness, and all of the themes discussed earlier in this chapter, are likely to be common concerns among the elderly gay men and women this program hopes to reach. Because these people are also likely to be the most secretive about their sexual orientation, they will be especially difficult to locate. Like all lonely and isolated elderly persons they will have many needs, and although a gay presence may be helpful, physical, medical and housing needs will be more easily met than social and personal needs. Perhaps this program will provide an opportunity for these persons to identify themselves as gay in a nonsexual setting for the first time and this may begin the development of a positive gay identity for those who are most crippled by the social oppression of homosexuals. Eventually, the program may develop a senior center for gay men and women as one means of aiding the development of a gay identity and a network of social supports for the more isolated gay men and women in the community. It will not be known until the program actually begins, however, whether more than a few of these gay people will be reached, or whether they will be open enough to profit from such a center.

All of these areas are new and exploratory. Relatively little is known about gay people as they age; it is time this changed. While we all need to begin preparing for growing old many years before old age actually is upon us, time is especially crucial for those gay men and women who are now old. If we are a gay community, then we need to reach out to our gay grandparents not only for their sake, but also for ours. Perhaps older gays have important lessons to teach us about living as a gay person and perhaps we can help bring them the message of gay liberation.

FOOTNOTES

1. Special thanks to William M. Ralph who, as an undergraduate student at City College, conducted half of the interviews and contributed substantially to the study reported here. A portion of this chapter was published in *Christopher Street*, November, 1977, 2(5); it is reprinted here with permission.

2. Jim Kelly has reported on a study of the myths and realities of aging gay men in *The Gerontologist*, August 1977, *17*(4). Currently, a federally funded study of aging gay and nongay men and women is being conducted by Fred Minnigerode and Marcy Adelman at the Center for Homosexual Education, Evaluation and Research (CHEER) in the Department of Psychology at San Francisco State University.

3. Kimmel, D.C. Gay people grow old too: Life-history interviews of aging gay men. *International Journal of Aging and Human Development*, in press(b).

4. Morin, S.F. Heterosexual bias in psychological research on lesbianism and male homosexuality. *American Psychologist*, 1977, 32, 633.

5. David Bakan's book, *The Duality of Human Existence* (Chicago: Rand McNally, 1966) is a provocative analysis of the agency (e.g., competitive) and communal components in human life. Jung (see footnote 7) felt that older persons

ideally integrate these masculine and feminine components of personality; see also footnote 6.

6. See David Gutmann, "The Cross-Cultural Perspective: Notes Toward a Comparative Psychology of Aging," in J.E. Birren and K.W. Schaie (eds.), *Handbook of the Psychology of Aging* (New York: Van Nostrand Reinhold, 1977).

7. Carl G. Jung emphasized the difference between the psychology of the first and second halves of life; see "The Stages of Life" in J. Campbell, *The Portable Jung* (New York: Viking, 1971).

8. Erik H. Erikson labeled the last two stages of life "generativity versus stagnation" and "integrity versus despair"; see *Childhood and Society* (New York: W.W. Norton, 1963, 2nd ed.).

9. See Jung, *op. cit.*

10. For a discussion of gay adult development and older gay men, see Kimmel, D.C. Adult development and aging: A gay perspective. *Journal of Social Issues*, in press(a).

Becoming a Gay Professional

Martin Rochlin, Ph.D.

". . .a new breed. . .the gay professsional whose labor is as much one
of conscience as it is of career."
Randy Shilts, *The Advocate*, July 14, 1976

How does one become a gay professional person? There are two answers.
One is the way porcupines make love—very carefully. The other is the
way prizefighters maneuver a bout—with courage, determination and a
lot of fancy footwork. Either way, it's worth the effort.

ROUND ONE—THE TITLE BOUT

Before the events of gay liberation leading to the 1973 ruling of the
American Psychiatric Association that homosexuality was no longer to
be considered a pathological diagnostic entity, the mere conjunction of
the words *gay* and *professional*, so natural to me now, would have con-
stituted an inconceivable non sequitur. A professional, after all, was a respectable pillar of the community. A homosexual, in contrast, was a religious transgressor, a statutory outlaw, a psychopathic personality, a
social pariah. One could not hope for the status of membership in the
elite professional fraternity if one were spiritually impoverished, devel-
opmentally retarded, emotionally unstable, sexually perverted, socially
deviant—in sum, substandard and unacceptable by the criteria of any
major institutional value system.

Small wonder then, though hardly obvious to me at the time, that
completing a doctoral program in clinical psychology took on more of
the quality of intrapsychic warfare than of educational development. I

approached the content and process of graduate study with enthusiasm. However, when all that stood between me and the title "Doctor" was the final completion of a dissertation, I was startled and dismayed to find myself virtually immobilized every time I so much as considered approaching a typewriter. I experienced no depletion of creative energy. On the contrary, I resumed the challenge of the Chopin Etudes I'd neglected since my student days at the Juilliard School of Music. I took up life drawing, oil painting, gourmet cooking and even took an extended trip around the world for which I'd never been able to find the money or the time. I was blocked in only one very specific direction—taking the final step over the threshold of role identity from that of graduate student/working entertainer (with which being gay felt relatively congruent) to that of professional psychologist (with which being gay did not seem to jibe at all). It's not unusual for gay people, because of internalized socially conditioned feelings of unworthiness, to unconsciously sabotage careers, relationships, and the earning of titles or positions of respect. In my case, though initially I was unaware of the origins of my internal saboteur, the escalation of conflict on the battleground of my fragmented identity finally forced me to recognize what was going on. Mr. Hyde, the horrid homosexual I felt I was, was in mortal combat with Dr. Jekyll, the respectable Jewish doctor I was brazen enough to aspire to become.

Each of the adversaries of my divided self found allies in the outside world. One formidable antagonist was the chief psychologist of one of my internship training facilities, whose area of specialization happened to be the "psychopathology" of homosexuality. It was not helpful to hear this self-styled expert, in a seminar for mental health professionals, proclaim his straight-liberal position on civil rights for homosexuals and then launch into a lengthy discourse on the degeneracy and wretchedness of the homosexual "condition." He spoke, for example, of how heterosexual psychotics could, through severe self-hatred, develop homosexual feelings by choosing "the *worst aspects of our society*" with which to identify. In his description of what *"the* homosexual life" is like, he presented only stereotypes, such as the chaotic cruisers of John Rechy's *City of Night*, the self- destructive closet-queens of Laud Humphreys' *Tearoom Trade*, the physical and emotional mayhem of the S and M scene, and the despair of the pathetic old auntie. While bolstering his prestige as an expert by boasting of his personal acquaintance with Dr. Evelyn Hooker, he betrayed an ignorance of her work by citing "sick parental relationships" and "fear and hatred of the opposite sex" as etiological factors in the "pathology" of homosexuality. The horrid homosexual Mr. Hyde in me welcomed this ammunition for the vendetta with my gay and good Dr. Jekyll.

In the other corner are some of Dr. Jekyll's boosters, whom I remember with warm gratitude. My lover, with insightful humor, reassured me he'd still love me even if I changed from a "child star" into an "adult psychologist." One of the most supportive interventions offered by my therapist was the straight-liberal assertion that some of his best friends *and colleagues* were gay, although he was not free to divulge their identities. (How I wished it were possible to meet one of those gay psychologists—positive gay role-models were scarce in those days!) Once, when the chairwoman of my doctoral committee visted my home and met my lover, I admitted to her my apprehension and embarrassment about the exposure of my lifestyle. She bantered affectionately that I was "even crazier than she'd thought," and that she wished I'd appreciate rather than disparage my perfectly sound lifestyle. Somehow, with a lot of help from my friends, the "title" bout for my doctorate was finally won.

ROUND TWO—BECOMING A PROFESSIONAL PERSON

The process of securing both my first staff appointment (a county position requiring fingerprinting) and a psychologist's license from the state, which would ensure my professional status, required the exposure of a long-guarded secret. I had to answer "yes" to the inevitable question of whether I had ever been arrested for an offense involving moral turpitude. Twelve long years before, when the idea of studying psychology had not yet materialized, I'd been arrested on a charge of "lewd vagrancy." Having recently arrived in California, my male companion and I were parked high in the Hollywood Hills enjoying each other affectionately, though not sexually, while admiring the wonder of the city lights below, when we were intruded upon by two police officers. The behavior resulting in the arrest had been quite natural and harmless, neither criminal nor immoral. The arrest undoubtedly would not have occurred if my companion had been female. The charges were ultimately dismissed, and the unconstitutional registration as a sex offender expunged after a year of summary probation. Nonetheless it was still on record that I had indeed been appreheded for a crime of moral *turpitude*, defined by Webster as "vileness," "*inherent* baseness," and "depravity."

This skeleton in my homosexual closet was now revealed to all those who held the power to decide my professional status, for without a job or a license my degree would amount to little more than a pretentious bit of wallpaper. A full-scale investigation instituted by the Board of Medical Examiners resulted in their eventual permission to take the state board exams. And, after extensive questioning by the oral examiners regarding ethical issues that might be involved in dealing professionally and personally with matters of sexual deviance, a license finally was granted.

My next discovery was the depth and range of my powers of homophobic self-deception. By that time, my affectional/sexual proclivities were already well known, and apparently somewhat tolerable to those in the key positions of deciding my professional credentials and competence. I had both the job and the license. Still I found myself continuing the popular homophobic game of "I-know-they-know-and-they-know-I-know-they-know-but-let's-all-pretend-nobody-knows." I used neuter pronouns in discussing extra-professional functions. I sensed (probably accurately) that being gay might be okay if it was attended by sufficient penitential guilt, kept quiet and not flaunted. That was still in the days before "the love that dared not speak its name wouldn't shut up" (as it is sometimes said about the developments of gay liberation). It was also before I'd developed sufficient gay consciousness and self-esteem to challenge the inequity of straight people having carte blanche to flaunt their heterosexuality with impunity whenever they wished.

I now suggest to other incipient gay professionals, in dread of those questionnaires on moral turpitude, that they consider the possibility that an arrest record could turn out to have some positive value, as it did for me when it nudged me to venture a big toe out of the closet of my internalized homophobia. I considered Round Two a significant victory, hollow as it came to feel in some of the following rounds.

ROUND THREE—BECOMING A GAY PERSON

The dark depression of grief when one is confronted with the death of a loved one is often followed by a sharp illumination of life. My own life had been relatively spared from significant loss until the deaths of my brother Dan in 1967, my lover Vic in 1968, and my father in 1970—the three men who'd been closest to me. It was a harrowing period of emotional upheaval, in which my own physical survival and sanity often felt alarmingly tenuous, but from which I somehow managed to emerge with gradually increasing strength and wisdom.

Dan had been the only person in my family who'd simply asked about, and with whom I'd shared, the reality of my homosexuality and the true nature of my relationship with Vic. Years later, during the nine months in which the agony of terminal cancer ravaged his body but miraculously enriched his spirit, he implored me and Vic to stop concerning ourselves with how others might view our homosexuality, and to better appreciate the beauty of our love for each other. In the process of dying, he shared with me the basic human values which had become poignantly crystallized for him in his 46th and last year of life. It was a precious legacy.

Vic and I lived and loved together for almost 19 years when a sudden heart attack ended his 43 years of life. We'd never exchanged the "til death do us part" vows traditionally forced upon straight couples. On the contrary, because we'd both been heavily brainwashed by the popular myth that homosexual men are too emotionally unstable and sexually promiscuous by nature to sustain love relationships, each of our 18 anniversaries came to us as a kind of pleasant surprise. I view with skepticism the romantic cliche that love conquers all, and yet our love did indeed seem to conquer the homophobic oppression of the '50s and '60s, internal as well as external, that militated against our relationship. Without the vows, death itself turned out to be our only invincible opponent.

It is an enduring source of sadness to me that Vic's death preceded by only seven months the birth of the new gay movement and that he so narrowly missed experiencing some of the exciting consequences of the Stonewall revolution of June 27, 1969. When we met in Washington, D.C., in 1950, we were both successful in our respective fields, Vic as an attorney and I as a cafe entertainer. We resisted our growing involvement with each other for fear of endangering his career, not yet realizing that our love would rescue us from the even greater danger of sabotaging our gay potential. My regret that he missed out on gay liberation is balanced by an enduring pride and joy that, at least in the private world of our pre-Stonewall closet, we were as fully gay and as fully human as we could be. We managed to create a union that enabled each of us to be more fully ourselves, more sane and more silly, more placid and more passionate, more angry and more affectionate than either of us had thought possible. The warmth of our relationship did not destroy our careers, but rather provided a benign climate in which Vic's professional career flourished and mine was born.

Gay rage, channeled into assertive action, is an essential ingredient of gay liberation and gay pride. After Vic's death, some angry recognitions emerged amid the myriad feelings I experienced. At that point, rage was still obscured by despair, but the seeds of indignation were sprouting and the anger proved to be a continuing source of the strength I needed for survival and further growth. This was a radically different kind of grief than I'd experienced with the loss of my brother. My *right to grieve* the loss of a brother was even granted official sanction, e.g., I received a paid leave-of-absence from my job at the hospital. In contrast, my *right to grieve* the loss of my lover was curtailed by the same social disapprobation that had attended our *right to love* in the first place. The privileges and comforts accorded the bereaved widow(er) in our society are reserved for heteorosexuals. If the loved one is not of the opposite gender, secret love may well end in solitary pain.

Although death was no longer a stranger to me when I lost my father, I had yet another painful revelation regarding the prohibitive cost of my protective closet. How could I bear saying goodbye to dad before I ever had a chance for the full hello I might have experienced if I'd been as completely myself with him as he'd been with me? It was only after his death that the full impact of his influence on my life became clear. He was a man of great dignity and integrity, who tenaciously maintained his convictions against every personal and societal pressure brought to bear upon him throughout his lifetime. During World War II, he seemed to be the only grocer in New York City who steadfastly refused to exploit the food rationing and shortages for black market profiteering. As a proud atheist, when told he had only a year to live, 20 years before his actual death, he assured those who'd argued "there are no atheists in foxholes" that he'd never once been even tempted to cover his bets with prayer. As a loving humanist, he supported the individual differences of his sons and helped me to resist rather than strive for conformity. He might have been, in his life, a powerful ally in my struggle for gay selfhood, if I'd been able to let him in on that struggle. Even in death, however, it's not too late for the parts of his spirit that survive in me to continue to fortify and warm me.

The harsh blows of loss shook me into taking a closer look at the pieces of life I was trying to pick up, so I could put them back together in a more meaningful way. I knew in my gut what we all know in our heads. We have only one life to live. If I didn't live mine my own way—the gay way—the legacies of courage, love, and truth bestowed upon me would be demeaned and my own human potential wasted.

ROUND FOUR—BECOMING A PROFESSIONAL GAY

I'd been knocked down in Round Three, but I was saved by the bell of a new gay liberation movement, a bell set ringing by the Stonewall riots. At first, I was too stunned by those knockout blows to hear it very clearly. But the brave, beautiful new gay activists began to reach and revive me.

In Zen wisdom it is said that when the student is ready, the teacher appears. On June 21, 1972, I was ready to venture into the Leo Baeck Temple in West Los Angeles to attend a program entitled "The Homosexual in America." Lo and behold, the teacher did indeed appear in the person of Betty Berzon, director of the program, a woman who has continued to be a loving and beloved fellow pilgrim in the joyous struggle for gay growth, freedom and dignity. At the conclusion of the workshop, it was easy for me to congratulate her on her fine work, but it took all the courage I could muster to introduce myself to her, not as a gay psychologist, but as a psychologist who was, by the way, gay—a seemingly simple expository statement, but the very first time I'd been that open and direct with a colleague in juxtaposing those two aspects of my identity.

Betty's companionship and encouragement helped me begin to explore some new territories. It could not have occurred to me that first time I entered the strange counter-culture world of the Los Angeles Gay Community Services Center, that I was not really straying further into an alien wilderness, but just beginning to find my way home. I came to know and love some of the radical visionaries involved in the new gay activism. Their questions, challenges and reformulations of the sociology, politics and psychology of homosexuality were like spiritual aperitifs, awakening and sharpening the hunger of my starved consciousness. At last, "homosexual" was becoming less linked with "horrid." "Straight" was becoming more associated with "up*tight*" than with "up*right*," as in "straight and *narrow*."

That period of accelerated gay consciousness raising swung the pendulum of my social posture from that of "Uncle Bruce," who *knew his place* and tried to survive by keeping a low profile, to that of "Militant Martin," who wouldn't go anywhere without his literal and figurative button: "How dare you presume I'm heterosexual?" I learned the exhilaration of protest through activism. I joined my gay sisters and brothers in rallies, gay pride parades and demonstrations, planning sessions for "zaps," and endless philosophical raps on sexism, heterosexism and homophobia. I spent nights on the hot line, offering support, advice, or just a sympathetic ear to gay brothers and sisters isolated by fear, geography or both. Long-distance calls came from towns I'd never heard of and my heart went out to those with no access to the kind of gay support group I was enjoying.

Once, during a convention of the American Psychological Association, while enjoying the personal as well as political gratification of dancing with another man in the ballroom of the super-straight convention hotel, a gay colleague suggested I really ought to *lower* my consciousness a bit. As valid as that observation may have been on the surface, I wasn't quite ready for moderation. I'd trudged the long way from homosexual to gay, then leapt from gay to exuberant. The exuberance was nourishment for a long-starved spirit. It was the magic key that could open the doors to authentic selfhood. It was a rechanneling of misdirected rage, the elusive ingredient my therapist and I sensed was missing from my years of psychotherapy, but that neither of us had been able to identify correctly in those pre-Stonewall days. I was eventually to "lower my consciousness" in moving from the position of *professional gay* to the more integrated one of *gay professional*, but I look upon that period of heightened awareness and involvement, insistent irreverence and deliberately outrageous insolence with joy, gratitude and love for those with whom I shared it, those who are still to discover it and those experiencing its sweet intoxication at this very moment.

I believe each of us has a set of internal self-regulating mechanisms that, despite occasional malfunctioning, can usually get us back on course if we but learn to trust them. My own inclinations toward the pure idealism of my father, for example, have always been tempered with the tough-minded, chicken-soup, practical common sense of my mother. I've come to value and rely on each of these tendencies to step in just in the nick of time to rescue me from going over the brink. Even in the full-flowering ebullience of my zapping gay militancy, I both feared and hoped for the loss of innocence and consequent synthesis I knew was coming.

Some particularly disturbing experiences triggered my self-regulating mechanisms toward the end of Round Four. The most potent of these experiences was the distressing paradox of thinking and speaking like a radical therapist intent on changing "the system," while selling services for fees as a Beverly Hills therapist who was a fully franchised and functioning part of the very mental health *industry* he was attacking.

Round Four ended with the discovery that there was as much danger of losing the integrity of my individual identity in conforming to the radical gay partyline as in conforming to establishment values. The real enemy was unmasked as *orthodoxy of any kind.* Liberation does not lie in the direction of seeking the right set of rules to govern one's life. On the contrary, individual identity and freedom require the relinquishment of all dogma. In my own case, the actualization of the *professional gay* was beginning to pass over into the Hegelian opposite of the *gay professional,* in which it was not to be lost, but rather preserved and fulfilled.

ROUND FIVE—PUTTING IT TOGETHER

As I began to weave the threads of my life into a more harmonious fabric, and the former Horrid Homosexual Hyde evolved into a healthier and happier Gay Marty, loving took on new textures. Similarly, as the former respectable, polarized Dr. Jekyll developed into the integrated Gay Professional Dr. Rochlin, the practice of psychotherapy became a more meaningful enterprise. Relieved of the burden of traditional role considerations, I found more energy for the growth of insights and skills. The once unbridgeable chasm between the personal and professional sides of my life was reduced to an easily traversed, duty-free border enhancing the quality of both loving and working.

The kinship I've always experienced with my mother, my remaining brother and other family members, has been strengthened by the comfortable candor of my present gay lifestyle. The regrets I experienced at having excluded my father from a crucial part of myself provided a forceful lesson. Too much of my life was lived in self-imposed exile, guarded with the rationalization of protecting others from what I perceived as the painful truth about myself. As the reality of my gay orientation has become a more positive part of my identity, that rationalization has become untenable. It has become clear that the only alternative to gay *disclosure* is gay *enclosure*. As my family and I have come to recognize each other as common victims of conventionality and homophobic bigotry, we've become better able to help one another toward greater freedom from fear and deceit. As a Jewish family, it is obvious to all of us that the problems of anti-Semitism cannot be solved by attempts either to convert ourselves to Christianity or to pass as gentiles. That kind of submission to social prejudice, at the cost of personal integrity, is clearly as tragic and as futile for gay people as it is for Jews. Learning to listen more to our hearts than to our prejudices has deepened our respect and our love for one another.

Just as the texture of familial affection has been enhanced by the growth of a more positive gay identity, so has the quality of romantic attachment. The relationship I enjoy with Paul, my lover of the past five years, is like a phoenix risen from the ashes of a homophobic past. We live and love, not in the shadows of shame, but in the sunlight of joy. Paul is much younger than I, but his encounters with his own capacities for grief and vulnerability, as well as cheer and vigor, gave him a crash course in the understanding and reverence of life that came more slowly to me. We never promised each other the rose garden we've made together. It seems to just grow naturally from cultivating the seeds of sexual attraction with mutual respect, affection, kindness, honesty and sharing. The existential basis of our partnership leaves little room for fantasies of past regrets and future promises, but more room for discovering the real, enduring romance of the ongoing process of life and love. With few demands, and just a few negotiated ground rules, we've developed a profound trust in one another. What we expect from each other is based solely on what we know about each other, and we like what we know.

Professionally, the benefits of an integrated positive gay identity are as rewarding as in the personal sphere. My decision to become the first totally up-front, fully accredited gay male psychologist in Los Angeles elicited some admiration, some concern and some criticism from colleagues. An announcement of my Gay Community Services Center board membership in the L.A. County Psychological Association Newsletter brought a variety of responses. Some notes of congratulation for my "courage," "integrity," and the "social value" of my openness came as delightful surprises from unexpected straight supporters. A frightened homosexual psychologist, on the other hand, wrote: "Many professionals share with me the belief that our colleagues and our communities are not ready to accept the openness necessary to become active in the GCSC program or others of similar philosophies. . .it may have negative repercussions, as it has in my case." A nongay psychologist responded to a letter of mine published in the American Psychological Association Monitor with the admonition: "I am repelled by the term *gay psychologist*. If you flaunt your gaiety. . .you will be judged for it."

In substance, coming out professionally brought none of the calamitous consequences I'd feared. On the contrary, in addition to the energy that became more available for productive use once it was no longer needed to maintain a protective closet (You can't blackmail an honest man!), I've enjoyed many serendipitous experiences that could not have been foreseen. I've found I could do a better job for my clients than either a straight or a homophobic homosexual therapist could do. How could I ever have hoped to help anyone learn it's fully okay to be gay, as long as it wasn't quite okay enough for me to be open about myself? Now I could be one of the living models for young gay people I wished I could have found in my own youth.

When I started my first gay men's therapy group, the decision to hold the meetings in my home rather than office reflected and enhanced the integration of my personal and professional selves. In my previous traditional practice, it would have been unthinkable to introduce clients (gay or straight) to my home, and particularly to my lover. Now, with an awareness of Paul's presence in the background, my clients could see how I lived as well as how I worked. We could now better help to humanize each other if I returned their trust in opening themselves to me by opening myself to them as well.

The decision to move my office from elite Beverly Hills to the gay neighborhood of West Hollywood held similar significance and serendipitous rewards. The "Couch Canyon" office, for example, had been carefully designed, in the psychoanalytic mode, to prevent the possibility of one "patient" encountering another. As in a French bedroom farce, with a set that includes plenty of closets, one client would exit by the backdoor while another waited in the anteroom, in accord with the presumably embarrassing nature of the proceedings. My West Hollywood suite, in the heart of the same beloved "Boys' Town" in which Paul and I make our home, is shared with three other gay male psychologists. No more back door! People meet people, sometimes at their worst and sometimes at their best. Camaraderie and sharing, rather than shame and fear, flourish in the waiting room, now the scene of comings, goings, developing friendships and raps on the relative merits of various gay community events posted on the bulletin board. My colleagues, clients and myself enjoy a new sense of community, intercommunication and mutual caring and helping, that provides a salutary setting for the growth of gay self-esteem and self-actualization we are all seeking.

As my professional *role* ceases to separate me from my personal gay identity, it ceases also to separate me from my clients. As an erstwhile member of the executive board of the Los Angeles Society of Clinical Psychologists, my fellow board members were officially *we* and our clients *they*, while in the unofficial turmoil of my then secret inner life I experienced the precise opposite. As a member of the Association of Gay Psychologists, in contrast, such distinctions vanish into absurdity. Where once the *we* and *they* were pitted against each other, there's now only *we*. Whereas my professional *role* perpetuated the sense of alienation that oppressed both me and my clients, my professional *skills* may serve us both with increasing effectiveness as we become more fully gay and human together. As one gay person engaged with another in a joint struggle for the freedom and dignity of *respect* rather than *respectability*, there is no room for stifling traditional formalities. The professional mystification, "blank screen" and "clinical detachment" of my analytic background, so convenient to the closeted homosexual therapist I was, are clearly exposed as self-deluding conceits to the gay-oriented therapist of the present. As I become less a part of the problem, the odds increase for becoming a more effective part of the solution.

The relationships I enjoy with my clients, as a fellow gay human being, provide a continuing forum for mutual growth. After being stymied by feeling too professional to be gay, and too gay to be professional, the experience of becoming a demystified, integrated gay professional is like entering a new universe, the exploration of which is limited only by the inherent limits of human living, loving and learning.

ROUND SIX—WORK IN PROGRESS

The preceding rounds have taken place in the arena of one gay person's continuing identity struggle. The "work in progress" involves every lesbian and gay man, preparing for or already practicing any profession, who seeks greater integration of personal and professional identity.

Self-disclosure *(coming out)* is the key to both personal integrity and social progress for gay people. It is by no means a magic key, nor is the process of using it to unlock oneself a simple one. The acute pain of risking disclosure is sharper than the chronic ache of concealment. The gay closet, however, like most paths of least resistance, is a *dead end* in which the chronic ache is apt to result in terminal despair. The sharper pangs of risking the uphill road of coming out, in contrast, have the power to move one toward a more wholesome atmosphere in which to grow stronger and happier, as well as more productive and successful. Happiness brings success more often than success brings happiness.

The main intent of the foregoing account is to illustrate the pain, the pride, the joy and the generous rewards of the arduous coming-out process for the gay professional, in the hope it may provide incentive and encouragement for others. In addition to the benefits for the individual, the socio-political importance of all gay self-disclosure needs emphasis, particularly the coming out of gay professionals. Prejudice can be defined as "being down on something you're not up on." Homophobia, perhaps the most pernicious of social prejudices, thrives on the ignorance, myths and stereotypes perpetuated by gays' general invisibility. Several recent polls* have determined that those who are personally acquainted with gay people are far more likely to support gay rights than those who think they have never known a homosexual. With approximately 20 million gay people in this country, we may assume approximately 40 million parents of gays. When we add siblings, grandparents, offspring, aunts, uncles, cousins, friends and colleagues of gay people, it becomes difficult to imagine how gay oppression could long endure if we should all come out of our closets. At present the vast majority of gay people feel unable to take that risk. They need our help. We need to help each other. As gay professionals, our status in society gives us the power, and with it the responsibilities of inspiration, assistance and leadership in one of the most difficult but far-reaching of all fights for human rights, freedom and dignity—gay liberation.

---

*National Gay Task Force Action Report, August/September 1978.

Job Security for Gays: Legal Aspects

Donald C. Knutson, LLD.

Over 60 years ago, the United States Supreme Court declared: "The right to work for a living . . . is of the very essence of the personal freedom and opportunity that it was the purpose of our Consitution to secure." With this decision the high court established that the right to work—the opportunity to achieve economic security—is "essential to the pursuit of life, liberty and happiness." Subsequent constitutional doctrine guaranteed that the government may not deny any class of persons the right to practice a lawful occupation without "compelling" and "constitutionally permissible" reasons.

Strong and unequivocal language. But we who are gay know all too well that employment discrimination against persons who are unable or unwilling to conceal their homosexuality is commonplace throughout our society. We have learned that the possibilities of promotion or the chances of a better job can vanish if we are labeled *homosexual.* For many of us, disclosure of our sexual preference could result in the loss of our job altogether. As a part of the sexual revolution, such discrimination has begun to come under open, serious, persistent attack.

Under the Kennedy administration, the federal government began to wage an impressive campaign to protect minority groups and women from discrimination in employment, in both the public and private sectors. In 1964, Congress enacted comprehensive legislation that protects against discrimination on the basis of age, color, race, religion, sex, physical handicap or national origin. The Equal Employment Opportunity Commission contributed extensive regulations designed to enforce this policy: "The principle of nondiscrimination requires that individuals be considered on the basis of individual capacities and not on the basis of any characteristics generally attributed to the class."

171

Many state and local legislative bodies have responded as well, with prohibitions against job discrimination by governmental agencies, by those contracting with or receiving aid from the government, and in many cases, by private employers.

"Sexual orientation" remains conspicuously absent from these federal and state nondiscrimination laws. However, judicial decisions and executive orders forbidding discrimination on that basis are beginning to appear. Proposals for such laws are presently before the Congress and several state legislatures. Many local governments and agencies have adopted ordinances and regulations which seek to protect the employment opportunities of gay persons. (It should be recognized that this trend is under severe attack. Some of the recent efforts to repeal these ordinances have been successful in Dade County, Florida; St. Paul, Minnesota; Wichita, Kansas; and Eugene, Oregon.) Private companies as well as professional organizations and unions have policies disclaiming and deploring discrimination against gay persons. The law is changing and important inroads are being made.

I cannot provide in these few pages a comprehensive appraisal of the current status of the law or an argument for its reform. I do mean to address some issues of immediate concern to gay persons and to provide answers, necessarily general, to those questions most often directed to me as an activist lawyer.

QUESTION: *What should I do if I believe that I was fired from my job or denied a promotion because of my sexual orientation?*

Before you do *anything*—protest or resign, answer or refuse to answer questions, deny or admit that you are gay, *anything*—seek the advice of an attorney. This may be more difficult than you think. The legal profession remains largely homophobic, sadly ill-informed on these issues and too often reluctant to take cases thought to be controversial.

If you cannot afford to hire a lawyer, there are groups to turn to for help: The American Civil Liberties Union; some Neighborhood Legal Services and Legal Aid agencies; a few public interest law firms, such as Gay Rights Advocates of San Francisco, the Houston Human Rights Foundation in Houston or the Lambda Legal Defense Fund in New York. Such organizations, however, are able to accept only "test" cases—those cases which can be used to establish a broad principle of law applicable to the rights of all gay persons. Free legal assistance may be available through your union or through other employee or professional organizations. Perhaps your local bar association referral service can find you a lawyer who will take the case without fee or at rates that you can afford.

If you are affluent and live in a large metropolitan area, it should be relatively easy to secure the services of a competent attorney, one knowledgeable about gay issues, who will aggressively pursue your rights. If you do not know of such a lawyer, call the American Civil Liberties Union or one of the gay rights organizations in your area. (See Appendix A for a representative list of such resources.)

A note of caution. Regardless of how you retain a lawyer, if she or he is not experienced in handling cases dealing with gay issues and discrimination, insist that a consulation be arranged with a lawyer who has had such experience. Even the most able and well-intentioned attorney can vastly improve your chances of success by drawing upon expertise that is increasingly available, at least in the big cities.

QUESTION: *What chance do I have of winning my case?*

Only after a careful review of the relevant facts can a lawyer determine whether or not you have a provable case. From the outset, it is necessary to have sufficient legal proof to convince a judge, jury or commission that you were discriminated against. To establish such a case requires evidence, not simply belief.

Up to the present time, such evidence had not been difficult to secure, since discrimination against us had occurred with impunity. Employers, on discovering the homosexuality of an employee, might simply have stated, "You're fired. We don't want any fags in our company" or "Dykes are not welcome in this office." Such discrimination is now practiced with more discretion and sophistication. Spurious reasons for dismissal are commonly given. In such cases, however, discrimination can be proven if you have documentation.

Assuming that yours is a provable case, the likelihood of success would then depend upon such factors as where you live or work, who your employer is, what type of business it is and what kind of work you do. Although the law is changing rapidly in this area, some general conclusions can be drawn.

If you are employed by the federal government, the likelihood of success is excellent. The leading case is *Norton* v. *Macy,* in which the court held that an otherwise qualified and competent civil servant could not be dismissed solely on the basis of "off-duty homosexual conduct." Mr. Norton, an employee of the National Aeronautics and Space Administration (NASA), was arrested for a traffic violation following an automobile rendezvous with another man. A NASA security chief was invited to listen in on subsequent police interrogations which suggested that Norton had invited the man into his apartment for a drink. Immediately thereafter, the NASA security chief interviewed Norton, who admitted having experienced homosexual desires in the past as well as having engaged in actual homosexual activity on two occasions. Consequently, NASA discharged him for "immoral, indecent, and disgraceful conduct." The court found that an employee's disqualification from federal employment was not permissible unless the government could prove that his or her conduct adversely affected the employee's ability to perform the job.

In the *Norton* case, the Civil Service Commission had defended its action—as well as its blanket disqualification of all gay persons—on the ground that the employment of known homosexuals would "bring the government service into public contempt." The court rejected this argument forcefully: "The notion that it would be an appropriate function of the federal bureaucracy to enforce the majority's conventional moral code of conduct in the private lives of its employees is at war with elementary concepts of liberty, privacy and diversity."

In 1975, after more than 15 years of litigation, the Civil Service Commission finally revoked its disqualification policy and adopted new regulations which now forbid a finding of unsuitability solely because the applicant "is a homosexual or has engaged in homosexual conduct." The new regulations require that there be some "rational connection between the individual's conduct and the efficiency of the service." In other words, the government must now demonstrate *with evidence* why the individual federal employee's homosexual activity made him or her unfit for the job in question.

The battle has not been won completely, however. The Commission retained a rule permitting disqualification of those engaged in what is described as "infamous or notoriously disgraceful" behavior. That policy, according to the Commission, is meant to apply only to "those few persons whose social behavior is so bizarre or so clearly aberrant that the conduct itself evidences depravity." It remains to be seen whether the federal bureaucracy will attempt to use this regulation to perpetuate its historical discrimination against gay persons, particularly against those who are open. Recent cases seem to hold that "flaunting" one's homosexuality—whatever that may mean—remains a permissible justification for disqualification.

In *Singer* v. *United States Civil Service Commission*, the court upheld the dismissal of a clerk-typist employed, ironically, by the Equal Employment Opportunities Commission. Mr. Singer had "openly admitted being 'gay' and indicated by his dress and demeanor that he intended to continue homosexuality as 'a way of life.' " He was the subject of news and television publicity, "active as an organizer, leader and member of the Board of Directors of the Seattle Gay Alliance." Together with his male lover, he had applied for a marriage license. The court reasoned that his dismissal was justified, since "openly and publicly flaunting his homosexual way of life" would bring discredit on the federal government, "impeding the efficiency of the service by lessening public confidence in the fitness of Government to conduct the public business."

Although it is too early to assess the impact of this decision on other courts, its implications are potentially dangerous not only to the employment opportunities of gay persons but to our First Amendment rights of free speech and association as well. The decision has been criticized severely by legal scholars and is in direct conflict with other cases holding that public advocacy of unconventional ideas does not justify employment discrimination. Yet the ruling cannot be overlooked by those seeking or holding federal positions. The disparity in reasoning between the *Norton* and *Singer* cases illustrates that in different geographic locations we may find different interpretations.

If you are employed by a public agency other than the federal government, or if your employer does substantial business with a governmental agency, the chances of prevailing in a discrimination suit are increasingly good. Many local governments have adopted laws forbidding these "public employers" to discriminate on the basis of sexual orientation. (See Appendix B.) Federal and state commissions are beginning to respond to demands that "sexual orientation" be included in their nondiscrimination policies. In a parallel example, the notion that individuals must be considered for employment opportunities according to their individual abilities, as opposed to "class" characteristics, was recently applied by the California Supreme Court to the bartending profession. The court concluded that women, as a class, could not be denied the opportunity to work as bartenders. The reasons given by the State to justify the ban—that women might "commit improprieties" or would be an "unwholesome influence" on young people if employed in that capacity— were rejected by the court as "constitutionally insufficient." The court's ruling has been extended to cases where the public employer seeks to justify dismissal on the basis of assumptions about stereotypical conduct of gay persons.

There are judicial decisions from a few states, as well as from federal courts, holding that employment opportunities may not be denied gay persons unless the employer can prove some reasonable negative connection between the individual's sexual conduct and his or her occupational capabilities. The California Supreme Court has adopted this approach, recognizing that "It is difficult to see how the public welfare is furthered by preventing a barber from cutting hair because his personal behavior is at variance with the generally accepted views of society."

Judicial decisions, as well as executive policies, are coming to adopt the position that government employment cannot be denied any person because of factors unconnected with the responsibilities of that employment. The notion is still popularly held, however, that the "immorality" of homosexuality should be sufficient reason in itself for dismissal or refusal to employ.

If you are employed in a private business that has no government contracts or involvements, the chances for legal protection from discrimination are presently very slim. For the most part, the constitutional provisions forbidding discrimination apply only to "government" action, that is, to action undertaken by a public agency or by an employer who does substantial government business. Discrimination, for whatever reason, by private employers having no government involvement cannot be challenged in court with any substantial prospect of success unless there are already local ordinances or regulations forbidding such discrimination. (See Appendix C.)

A recent case, again from California, has raised the claim that the equal protection clause of the Constitution should be interpreted to require those states that provide protection for racial and ethnic minorities and women to extend that protection to gay persons as well. There are many large corporate employers who have made public commitments to hire and retain personnel on the basis of their capabilities, not their sexual orientation. (See Appendix D.)

The aggressive pursuit of our claims in the courts as well as before legislative bodies and executive boards is the most effective way to achieve protection. Although the chance of immediate success may not be great under present law, this should not deter those who are resourceful, willing and courageous enough to undertake the costs—social, economic and psychological—of seeking reform of these laws.

QUESTION: *I intend to enter a profession that requires a state license to practice. Will I have problems because I am gay?*

All states have laws that require a finding of "good moral character" as a condition for receiving a license to engage in certain occupations and professions. Almost all states restrict medicine, law and teaching in this way, while many extend the requirement to a broader range of occupations from accountant to midwife to x-ray technician. Historically, the administration of these laws has severely limited the employment opportunities of gay persons. Licensing agencies have often deemed our lifestyles irrefutable proof of immoral conduct. Furthermore, the courts have traditionally been reluctant to interfere with these determinations on the theory that a state must have the power to require conventional standards of morality as a qualification for the professions.

Some recent judicial decisions recognize, however, that terms such as *immoral conduct* or *moral turpitude* cover so wide a range as to embrace an almost unlimited area of conduct, giving licensing agencies the power to dismiss any applicant or class of applicants whose personal and private lives incur their disapproval without proof of any adverse effect on professional competence. Coupled with the realization that "today's morals may be tomorrow's ancient and absurd customs," this awareness has led some courts to reject the traditional approach.

The California Supreme Court, for example, in a case holding that private homosexual conduct is not, in itself, sufficient justification for the revocation of a professional license, observed: "A particular sexual orientation might be dangerous to one profession and irrelevant to another. Necrophilism and necrosadism might be objectionable in a funeral director or embalmer, yet neither or these unusual tastes would seem to warrant disciplinary action against a geologist or shorthand reporter."

A similar view was expressed by the Florida Supreme Court in a recent decision concerning the right of gay persons to practice law. In order to be admitted to the bar in Florida, one must satisfy the state-imposed requirement of "good moral character." Robert Eimers, a graduate of Hastings College of Law and a member of the Pennsylvania bar, passed all parts of his Florida bar examination. At a hearing, the bar examiners asked about his sexual orientation, and Eimers admitted his homosexual preference. He was not questioned about what sexual acts he may have engaged in or in which he planned to engage. The examiners deadlocked over whether to admit Eimers and informed the Supreme Court of Florida that after months of "torturous debate" they were unable to decide whether homosexuality violated the good moral character standard required of all candidates for admission. The court held that homosexual status is not sufficient for exclusion from the bar saying that "in determining fitness for admission to the bar, state courts must now meet the standard imposed by the due process clause found in the Fourteenth Amendment."

The Court did, however, draw a peculiar distinction between the "status" of homosexuality and the actual commission of homosexual acts. In this case, Eimer responded truthfully to questions regarding his sexual orientation. He was not asked to comment about his involvement in specific sexual activities. The court argued that unless the commission of prior illegal acts was shown, a homosexual preference would not affect the ability of an individual "to uphold the standards of the state bar." The Court required that all qualifications demanded of applicants have a rational connection with the capacity to practice law.

School teachers continue to face especially difficult problems with licensing, often due to the reliance by some courts on unproven assumptions that, for example, gay teachers would attempt to inject their views regarding sexual morality into the classroom or would be unable to act effectively as proper role models for students. A prominent illustration of this judicial attitude was expressed in the case of *Gaylord* v. *Tacoma School District.* James Gaylord, a high school teacher, was discharged because he was a "known homosexual." Gaylord had been a teacher at the same school in the Tacoma, Washington, School District for 12 years and had consistently received favorable evaluations. His homosexuality became known when a former student told the vice-principal that he suspected that Gaylord was homosexual. Upon questioning by the vice-principal, Gaylord responded that he had been gay for 20 years. He was discharged.

The Washington Supreme Court framed the issue by asking, "Was Gaylord guilty of immorality?" It answered its questions in the affirmative, relying on psychological treatises and the New Catholic Encyclopedia. Although the court stated that proof that such "immorality" adversely affected Gaylord's ability to teach was required, it concluded that the school had been damaged and that Gaylord could no longer be an effective teacher because of the Court's assumption that "If Gaylord had not been discharged after he became known as a homosexual, the result would be fear, confusion, suspicion, parental concern and pressure on the administration by students, parents, and other teachers."

Although there was no evidence that Gaylord had committed any criminal acts, the court reasoned that it was proper to *infer* from his status as a homosexual that Gaylord had in fact committed acts of unlawful lewdness and sodomy.

Not all courts will adopt this approach, I believe. Critical of a policy which attempts to exclude gay persons from the teaching profession, some school boards and organized teachers' groups have begun to speak out. (See Appendix E.) The prestigious American Association of University Professors, for example, recently adopted a policy "to use its procedures and to take measures, including censure, against colleges and universities practicing discrimination on the basis of sexual or affectional preference." The Yale Law School faculty joined the University of Southern California Law Center and other law schools in forbidding discrimination against gay students, staff and faculty.

The courts are beginning to respond, sensitive to criticism that they have been blind to the contemporary reality of sexual behavior. Representing a minority view at present, these courts require proof—in the form of legal evidence, rather than unproven assumptions—that the behavior of the individual teacher, rather than that of a stereotype, warrants denial of her or his teaching credential. In the view of such courts, there must be a reasonable basis for concluding that the individual cannot be relied upon to fulfill the obligations of the profession before certification can be denied or a license revoked. The law is moving in this direction.

QUESTION: *I have a less-than-honorable military discharge. This makes it difficult for me to find a civilian job. Can anything be done?*

There is hopeless confusion in the recent court decisions dealing with reinstatement of persons discharged by the military establishment under regulations which state that "Knowing participation in a homosexual act or strong tendencies toward such acts constitute a sufficient basis for discharge."

In the celebrated *Matlovich* case, for example, the court held that "there is no constitutional right to engage in homosexual actions," and that therefore the military is free to continue what the court described as its "knee jerk" reaction of blanket disqualification. Sergeant Matlovich had an exemplary military career for nearly 12 years. He had received a Bronze Star, a Purple Heart and several other medals for meritorious service. Throughout his career he had consistently received the highest possible ratings from his supervisors and was continually recommended for accelerated promotion. At the age of 30, Matlovich told his commanding officer that he was gay. During the ensuing court martial, it was established that all of his sexual conduct had been in private with consenting adults away from his military base. Nevertheless the court upheld his discharge.

The case of *Saal* v. *Middendorf*, represents the contrary view. Ms. Saal was denied extension of her Navy enlistment contract on the ground that she had had homosexual involvements with another enlisted woman. Despite an outstanding record of service, she was discharged under Navy regulations requiring the "prompt separation" and discharge of all homosexuals. The court reasoned that the Constitution required the Navy to base its judgment on an individual's fitness for service on the merits of each case, not on a policy of mandatory exclusion of any class of persons. Since Navy regulations resulted in a blanket expulsion of all gay persons, the court concluded that there was no rational connection between the Navy's objectives and the removal of persons judged unfit for military service. Under this ruling, the military must now provide some procedure whereby the individual's ability to serve is evaluated in light of "all relevant factors."

The appellate courts have yet to decide this disagreement which may eventually find its way to the U.S. Supreme Court. Hopefully, as Judge Gesell observed in the *Matlovich* case: "The time has arrived or may be imminent when the Armed Forces need to reappraise the problem which homosexuality unquestionably presents in the military context. . . . In the light of increasing public awareness and the more open acceptance of what is in many respects essentially a matter of private sexual conduct, it would appear that the Armed Forces might well be advised to move toward a more discriminatory and informed approach."

Considerable success has been achieved in securing honorable discharges and in upgrading less-than-honorable discharges that had been given under the exclusionary regulations. There has been surprisingly little resistance by the military to such efforts, especially in cases where the discharge was based on private, consensual, adult sexual conduct. Several veterans self-help groups offer expert (and free) legal assistance to those who seek it. (See Appendix F.)

QUESTION: *Should I accept a job or promotion that requires a security clearance?*

Until very recently, the Defense Department's policy has been one of automatic denial of security clearance when evidence of homosexuality or "homosexual tendencies" has surfaced from the required investigation. The courts routinely upheld this policy on the now discredited ground of "the susceptibility to blackmail of homosexuals" or the equally indefensible notion that homosexuality is evidence of a "personality disorder."

That policy is beginning to change. Hearing examiners in two recent cases ordered reinstatement of security clearances to gay men. The decisions were based on the view that clearance cannot lawfully be denied in the absence of proof that the individual applicant is susceptible to blackmail, is mentally unstable or is otherwise unqualified to protect classified information.

The Defense Department's failure to appeal these decisions is a positive sign. Yet it cannot be safely assumed that its policy has been altered nationwide. The courts remain divided on the question of whether a person may be deprived of a security clearance solely on the basis of that person's homosexual orientation.

Any of us who contemplates seeking a security clearance must be aware that the investigator is likely to demand responses to such objectionable and demeaning questions as: "Have you ever engaged in acts of oral or anal copulation with another member of your own sex?" "Approximately how many acts have you engaged in?" "With how many different persons have you engaged in such acts?" "What were the circumstances leading to such acts? Be specific." The courts again are hopelessly divided on the issue of whether or not refusal to respond to this line of questioning is, in itself, justification for revocation of a security clearance.

The leading case, *Gayer* v. *Schlesinger*, requires that there be some connection between the question asked and the ability of the applicant to protect classified information. In *Gayer*, the court held that homosexuality may in some cases be relevant to job efficiency as well as to the ability to protect classified information. Thus, it reasoned, questions regarding sexual activities, sexual "perversions" and prior criminal involvements of a sexual nature must be permitted. Since Richard Gayer had initially refused to answer such questions, the court instructed that if he again refused to respond, the suspension of his security clearance would be justified.

Other courts have taken the view that the contitutional right to privacy extends to these matters, holding that private and personal sexual conduct is irrelevant to suitability for clearance. It is clear that you have the right to seek the advice of a lawyer before deciding whether or not to respond to such inquiries. Take advantage of that right.

QUESTION: *Should I come out of the closet on my Job?*

This is an intensely personal question, one that should be approached with sobriety and gravity, and one that I would not presume to answer for anyone but myself.

It is undeniable that the low visibility of the gay community—explained by the ability of so many of us to conceal our sexual orientation if we choose—has been an asset as well as a devastating liability. On the one hand, it has enabled many of us to pursue and achieve occupational ambitions that would have been otherwise impossible. Justice William O. Douglas once observed: "It is common knowledge that homosexuals have risen high in our public service—both in Congress and in the Executive Branch—and have served with distinction." We know that gay persons are found in all professions and occupations, in every social stratum and at every economic level. That is a diversity not enjoyed by more visible minority groups.

On the other hand, this ability to remain largely invisible has permitted, even contributed to discrimination against us. Our government obviously would find it impossible to ignore demands for the civil rights of a recognizable and organized movement of more than 20 million of its citizens.

Yet most gay persons are unwilling or unable to surface until our civil liberties are firmly established and it is safe to do so. It is a vicious circle. Our civil liberties have not been established. It is not safe for all. In spite of the progress made by the gay liberation movement, the open and active gay community remains but the tip of the iceberg. That fact not only permits society to continue to indulge in fantasy with respect to who and what we are, but it also denies gay people, young and old, the ability to understand that it is all right to be gay, that many accomplished and worthy people are gay, that we are a group as diverse and varied as any other.

In the last analysis, a rational response to the question of coming out on the job must depend on the answer to yet another question: What price am I willing to pay for the experience of regaining my dignity as a human being, of reclaiming my personal integrity, of shedding the burden of deceit and hypocrisy?

APPENDIX A

Gay Rights Organizations

Atlanta

Atlanta Lesbian Feminist Alliance
P.O. Box 7684
Atlanta, Georgia 30309
(404) 872-5071

Gay Information Service
P.O. Box 7922
Atlanta, Georgia 30309
(404) 874-4400

Boston

Homophile Union of Boston
419 Boylston Street
Boston, Massachusetts 02116
(617) 536-6197

Chicago

Chicago Gay Alliance
P.O. Box 909
Chicago, Illinois 60609
(312) 664-4708

Denver

Gay Coalition of Denver
P.O. Box 18501
Denver, Colorado 80218
(303) 831 8838

Houston

Houston Human Rights
   Defense Foundation
1310 McDuffie #28A
Houston, Texas 77019
(713) 526-2668

Los Angeles

Gay Community Services Center
   (LA-GCSC)
1213 North Highland Avenue
Hollywood, California
(213) 464-7485

American Civil Liberties Union
Gay Rights Chapter
633 South Chatto Place
Los Angeles, California 90005
(213) 487-1720

Milwaukee

Gay People's Union
   1568 North Farwell
Milwaukee, Wisconsin 53202
(414) 271-5273

Minneapolis

Minnesota Committee for
   Gay Rights
Box 4226 Anthony Falls Station
Minneapolis, Minnesota 55414
(612) 721-3738

New York

American Civil Liberties Union
22 40th Street
New York, New York 10016
(212) 741-5800

Lambda Legal Defense Fund
22 East 40th Street
New York, New York 10016
(212) 532-8197

National Gay Task Force
80 Fifth Avenue
New York, New York 10011
(212) 741-10011

Philadelphia

Gay Activists Alliance
P.O. Box 15748
Middle City Station
Philadelphia, Pennsylvania 19103
(215) 387-2813

Portland
  The Portland Town Council
  320 S.W. Tark #506
  Portland, Oregon 97204

San Francisco
  American Civil Liberties Union
  Gay Rights Chapter
  814 Mission Street
  Suite 301
  San Francisco, California 94103
  (415) 777-4545

  Gay Legal Referral Service
  The Pride Foundation
  330 Grove Street
  San Francisco, California
  (415) 621-3900

  Gay Rights Advocates
  540 Castro Street
  San Francisco, California 94114
  (415) 863-3622

Seattle
  Seattle Gay Alliance
  P.O. Box 1170
  Seattle, Washington 98111
  (206) 323-6969

Washington, D.C.
  Mattachine Society of
    Washington, D.C.
  5020 Cathedral Avenue N.W.
  Washington, D.C. 20016
  (202) 363-3881

  Gay Activists Alliance
  P.O. Box 2554
  Washington, D.C. 20013
  (202) 462-8729

APPENDIX B

Ordinances Forbidding Sexual Orientation Discrimination
by the Municipal Government

Municipality	Date Enacted
Berkeley, California	11/73
Cupertino, California	2/75
Los Angeles, California	5/76
Mountain View, California	3/75
Palo Alto, California	8/74
Santa Barbara, California	8/75
Sunnyvale, California	12/74
Atlanta, Georgia	1972
Boston, Massachusetts	4/76
Detroit, Michigan	11/73
Chapel Hill, North Carolina	9/75
Ithaca, New York	9/74
New York, New York	2/72
Ottawa, Ontario	4/76
Toronto, Ontario	11/73
Portland, Oregon	12/74
Austin, Texas	7/75
Pullman, Washington	4/76

APPENDIX C

Ordinances Forbidding Sexual Orientation Discrimination
by Private Employers

Municipality	Date Enacted
Tucson, Arizona	1/77
San Francisco, California	4/78
Aspen, Colorado	12/77
Washington, D.C.	11/73
Champaign, Illinois	7/77
Urbana, Illinois	11/75
Bloomington, Indiana	11/75
Iowa City, Iowa	5/77
Amherst, Massachusetts	5/76
Ann Arbor, Michigan	5/73
East Lansing, Michigan	5/73
Minneapolis, Minnesota	3/74
Alfred, New York	5/74
Seattle, Washington	11/73
Madison, Wisconsin	3/75

APPENDIX D*

Some Companies Publicly Committed to Nondiscrimination
on the Basis of Sexual Orientation

American Airlines
American Broadcasting Company
American Telephone and Telegraph
Avon Products
Bank of America
Citicorp
Columbia Broadcasting Company
Eastern Airlines
Honeywell

International Business Machines
MacDonald's
Procter and Gamble

*Copies of statements are on file with the
National Gay Task Force
Room 506
80 5th Avenue
New York, New York 10011

APPENDIX E

Education Groups Opposed to Discrimination Against Gays

American Federation of Teachers
1012 - 14th Street N.W.
Washington, D.C. 20005

AFT "protests any personnel actions taken against any teacher merely because he or she practices homosexual behavior in private life." (1970)

National Education Association
1201 - 16th Street N.W.
Washington, D.C. 20036

NEA "believes that personnel policies and practices must guarantee that no person be employed, retained, paid, dismissed, or demoted because of . . . sexual orientation." (1974)

The District of Columbia Board of Education "recognizes the right of each individual to freely choose a lifestyle, as guaranteed under the Constitution and Bill of Rights. The Board further recognizes that sexual orientation, in and of itself, does not relate to ability in job performance or service.

Therefore, it is resolved that henceforth it shall be the policy of all departments and services of the education system under the jurisdiction and control of the District of Columbia Board of Education to promote a policy of nondiscrimination in hiring, employment, promotion, tenure, retirement and/or job classification

practices, within its jurisdiction and control, relative to the sex or personal sexual orientation of any individual(s) regardless of past, present, and/or future status of such individual(s).

The San Francisco Board of Education resolution "move (d) that the nondiscrimination policy of the district be amended to provide that there be no discrimination on the grounds of sexual orientation." (#56-17 A-1)

APPENDIX F

Veterans Groups that Offer Free Legal Assistance

Alabama
Frank Angarola
Veterans Service Assoication
P.O. Box 6196
University, Alabama 35486
(205) 348-5513

California
San Diego Pro-Vets
2541 'B' Street
San Diego, California 92102
(714) 233-5196
(will also make referrals)

Swords to Plowshares
Veterans Rights Organization, Inc.
944 Market Street
San Francisco, California 94120
(415) 391-6984
(will also make referrals)

Tony Williams
Military and Veterans Counseling
   Center
514 West Adams Boulevard
Los Angeles, California 90007
(213) 748-4662

Colorado
Rocky Mountain Military Project
1764 Gilpin Street
Denver, Colorado 80218
(303) 321-3717
(will also make referrals)

Connecticut
HECUS

Cortez Stockes
328 Park Avenue
Bridgeport, Connecticut 06604
(203) 334-9348

Delaware
Community Legal Aid Society
Bill Anderson
Linnis Cook
204 West 7th Street
Wilmington, Delaware 19801
(302) 655-7351

District of Columbia
Military Rights Project
   (LMDC/ACLU)
1346 Connecticut Avenue,
   N.W. #604
Washington, D.C. 20036
(202) 659-1138
(consultation only)

Florida
AFSC
3005 Bird Avenue
Coconut Grove
Miami, Florida 33133
(305) 443-9836

Georgia
CCCO Southern Regional Office
848 Peachtree Street, NE
Atlanta, Georgia 30308
(404) 881-6666

Hawaii
  AFSC
  Ian Lynd
  2426 Oahu
  Honolulu, Hawaii 96822
  (808) 988-6266

Illinois
  CCCO-Midwest Office
  5615 S. Woodlawn Avenue
  Chicago, Illinois 60637
  (312) 363-2587
  (referrals only: M–F 10–5 p.m.)

Indiana
  Military Discharge Review Project
  Metropolitan Manpower
     Commission
  Richard Bollen
  2101 N. College Avenue
  Indianapolis, Indiana 46205
  (317) 925-9231

Kentucky
  Lexington Discharge Upgrading
     Project
  120 State Street
  Lexington, Kentucky 40503
  (606) 277-0663

Louisiana
  Lou Smith
  Community Advancement, Inc.
  Veterans Project
  2147 Government Road
  Baton Rouge, Louisiana 70806
  (504) 387-0465

Maine
  Maine Veterans and Military
     ʼRights Project
  Bob Howe
  Maine Civil Liberties Union
  193 Middle Street
  Portland, Maine 04111
· (207) 774-5444

Maryland
  AFSC
  319 East 25th Street
  Baltimore, Maryland 21218
  (301) 366-7200

Massachusetts
  Legal In-Service Project
  355 Boylston Street
  Boston, Massachusetts 02116
  (617) 262-1431

  Committee on Military Justice
  Room 303, Austin Hall
  Harvard Law School
  Cambridge, Massachusetts 02138
  (617) 495-4820

Michigan
  Clarence Brown
  Mayors Committee for
     Human Resources
  Center for the Education of
     Returning Veterans
  5031 Grandy Avenue
  Detroit, Michigan 48211
  (313) 224-6262

Minnesota
  Gene T. Kelly
  University of Minnesota
  Discharge Review Service
  1633 Eustis
  St. Paul, Minnesota 55108
  (612) 376-5085

Missouri
  Military Law Project
  Washington University School
     of Law
  Lindell and Skinker Boulevards
  St. Louis, Missouri 63130
  (314) 863-0100, ext. 4902
  (consultation only)

New Jersey
  VETS Program
  Rutgers—The State University
  53 Washington Drive
  Newark, New Jersey 07102
  (201) 648-5817

New York
  Military Counseling Project
  15 Rutherford Place
  New York, New York 10003
  (212) 533-2350
  (after 1 p.m. only)

North Carolina
  Quaker House
  223 Hillside Avenue
  P.O. Box 1586
  Fayetteville, North Carolina 28301
  (919) 485-3213

Ohio
  Bob Bonthius
  ACLU, Room 825
  2108 Payne Avenue
  Cleveland, Ohio 44114
  (216) 781-6276

  Central Ohio Military and Veterans
    Project
  255 W. 5th Avenue
  P.O. Box 10116
  Columbus, Ohio 43201
  (614) 299-6921

Oregon
  Portland Draft and Military
    Counseling Center
  633 S. W. Montgomery
  Portland, Oregon 97201
  (503) 224-9307
  MWF 12–7 p.m.

Pennsylvania
  CCCO
  2016 Walnut Street
  Philadelphia, Pennsylvania 19103
  (215) 568-7971
  (consultation only)

Rhode Island
  Rhode Island Veterans
    Action Center
  742 Broad Street
  Providence, Rhode Island 02907
  (401) 941-1331

South Dakota
  Dan Block
  Veterans Affairs Office
  Agustana College
  Sioux Falls, South Dakota 57102
  (605) 336-4124
  (will also make referrals)

Tennessee
  Delton Pickering
  Veterans Advocacy Program

  Wesley Foundation
  3625 Midland Avenue
  Memphis, Tennessee 38011
  (901) 323-4790

Texas
  American Civil Liberties Union
  905 Richmond
  Houston, Texas 77006
  (713) 524-5925

  American GI Forum
  Veterans Outreach Program
  1713 Castroville Road
  San Antonio, Texas 78237
  (512) 434-0677

Utah
  Charles T. Williams
  VETS Project
  #28 East 2100 South Street
  Salt Lake City, Utah 84110
  (801) 328-7924

Vermont
David Ross
  VVAW/WSO
  15 Clymer Street
  Burlington, Vermont 05401
  (802) 862-8175

Virginia
  Clifton McCall
  Bob Morrison
  VETS Project
  904 Granby Street
  Norfolk, Virginia 23510
  (804) 622-1361

Washington
Harold Chesnin
  Washington State Discharge
    Upgrading Project
  3230 Rainier Avenue, South
  Seattle, Washington 98144
  (206) 464-5931
  (will also make referrals)

Wisconsin
  Madison Discharge Review Project
  823 South Park Street
  Madison, Wisconsin 53715
  (608) 255-8388

Gay Issues in Financial Planning

Ronald J. Jacobson *

You are gay and you have a lover. You may not have given much thought to your joint financial future, assuming perhaps that society has prevented you from taking advantage of the opportunities available to nongay couples. This is not true. There are numerous things you can and should do to plan now for the future.

As a gay couple, you have to use the system creatively to achieve the results that nongay couples reach almost automatically. This chapter will deal briefly with federal income tax, principles of property owner-ship, retirement planning and estate planning. Each is an important area requiring special planning for gay people, and of course, each applies to you whether or not you are currently in a couple relationship.

FEDERAL INCOME TAX

Federal income tax is so complicated that if you want to be creative you almost have to consult with an accountant or attorney. Short of that, however, the Internal Revenue Service publishes many helpful pamph-lets that summarize various aspects of the tax laws. A list of these pamphlets is contained in IRS Publication 522—A Guide to Tax Publica-tions, available at any Internal Revenue Service office.

Any of these pamphlets could be useful, but several might be of special interest to gay people because they contain information suited to many typical gay living situations. Publications 535—Tax Information on Business Expenses; 503—Child Care and Disabled Dependent Care;

---

* With the assistance of Jonathan Wright, Esq., member, California State Bar.

504—Information for Divorced or Separated Individuals; 448—A Guide to Federal Estate and Gift Taxation; 501—Your Exemptions and Exemptions for Dependents; 587—Business Use of Your Home; 590—Tax Information on Partnership Income and Losses; 583—Recordkeeping for a Small Business; 533—Information on Self-Employment Tax; and 463—Travel, Entertainment and Gift Expenses.

Among the areas that you should look into are deductions for dependents and business deductions. Briefly, if one person qualifies as a dependent of the other, the dependent is worth a $750 deduction from the other person's taxable income. The dependent must live in the same household with the person claiming the deduction, and the claimant must contribute over half of the dependent's total support for the year. Take a look at IRS publication 501, mentioned above, because there are also other requirements you must meet.

Another way for a gay couple to lower their combined income tax is to form a business partnership. This will only work in a few situations, but it's worth looking into. Again, since federal income tax is so complex, you should consult an accountant or attorney to be certain you have chosen the best plan for yourself.

PRINCIPLES OF PROPERTY OWNERSHIP

If you are a gay couple, you may want to have control over each other's bank accounts and safe deposit boxes. This can be done very easily. You can open a bank account in "joint tenancy." This requires one or two signatures (at your preference) for withdrawal or to write checks. Legally a joint tenancy means that during your joint lifetimes you each have equal control, and upon the death of one, the survivor would automatically own the accounts—without the need for a will or probate. This is discussed in greater detail further on.

The principles of joint tenancy apply to other forms of property, such as real estate or a new grand piano. In addition to equal control of the property, though, you both may want to receive the tax advantages from owning certain types of property (for example, deducting from your taxable income the interest payments on the grand piano or the condominium). This can be done by holding the property as joint tenants or by forming a business partnership and holding the property in the name of the business. You should probably consult an attorney or an accountant about a partnership, but you can arrange a joint tenancy on your own. Simply request that the title papers or receipts or whatever other evidences of ownership you receive say "A and B as joint tenants." Note that the tax benefits to each of you will be in proportion to the payment each makes on the property. In other words, A cannot get half of the deductions if B makes all of the installment payments.

If you both want access to a bank safe deposit box, rent the box as "corenters." There is no joint tenancy for safe deposit boxes because the property inside the box is owned separately from the safe deposit box itself. The most you can accomplish with a safe deposit box is to be sure that each of you has equal access to the contents of the box.

An alternate way of having control over each other's property (that is, if it remains in one person's name) is to give each other "power of attorney." Power of attorney is the right that A gives to B to legally sign A's name in place of A. Most stationery stores have general power of attorney forms, which are fine for most situations. Some banks have their own forms, though, and do not like to accept general powers of attorney. So, for bank transactions, use the bank's forms. A power of attorney is no longer legally valid when the person giving it dies or is legally incompetent.

If you wish to keep your property separate, you should take title as "tenants in common." Each of you will then have a one-half interest which will *not* go to the other automatically when you die. Instead it will be a part of your estate. (See Principles of Estate Planning below.)

If one of you has been involved in a heterosexual marriage and is still legally married, watch out. In states in which there are community property laws (such as California, Texas, Washington and Louisiana, among others) the husband and wife each owns half of the property and the money earned during the marriage—even if only one works. These rules continue until there is a legal separation. It is, therefore, important to be sure that you are legally separated. Consult an attorney.

PRINCIPLES OF RETIREMENT PLANNING

Contemporary culture is truly youth oriented. Everything from fashions to food seems to cater to those with young, healthy bodies and an unlimited future. As a result, younger people, gay and nongay, lack awareness of the need to plan today for retirement tomorrow. There is such a need, however, since the average person retiring now at age 65 can expect to live another 15 years. This figure will undoubtedly increase with better medical care. It certainly is a substantially long and an important part of your life. Remember, there are a number of things that can be done now no matter what your age.

First of all, retirement systems in the United States deserve a few words. Traditionally, workers have based their retirement on Social Security payments, private pension plan benefits and personal savings.

Social Security

Social Security taxes are paid equally by you as a worker covered by Social Security and by your employer. The taxes are withheld from wages, matched by your employer and credited to your Social Security account.

In order to qualify for Social Security benefits, you must accumulate the minimum work-time credit, measured in number of calendar quarters of covered employment. Normally ten years are required (40 quarters). In addition, you must be at least 62 years old, or 60 if you are a widow or widower.

In order to figure out your benefits under the current law consult the brochure Estimating Your Social Security Checks, obtainable free from any Social Security office. It is a good idea to check with the Social Security Administration in Baltimore, Maryland 21235, every three years to make sure that its records of your earnings agree with yours. (Check your W-2 forms or tax returns.) You only have three years, three months and 15 days to correct an error or it will become permanent.

Recent legislation, effective January 1979, will have a substantial impact on the Social Security system. It will not change it enough, however, to provide you with any real "security" for your retirement. Remember: *Social Security was not designed to provide you with enough money to live comfortably. It is strictly to supplement your income from other sources.*

Private Pension Plans

Many employers maintain one or more pension or profit-sharing plans that can be an important source of retirement income for you. Be sure to inquire about such plans where you work and whenever you get a new job with a different employer.

Congress in 1974 passed the Employee Retirement Income Security Act (ERISA), or as it is sometimes called, "The Pension Reform Act." This complicated law is your Bill of Rights as an employee with regard to your company's employee benefit plans. ERISA requires your employer to furnish you with a statement of your benefits and a summary description of each employee benefit plan in which you participate. Study these provisions carefully because subtle differences between plans may have a great impact on your job decisions. You may, for example, decide to quit after working nine years. If your plan requires ten years service, you won't receive a pension when you retire. Had you realized this at the time, you might have decided to work another year.

There are many types of employee benefit plans. A popular one is the *pension plan* under which you receive certain benefits when you retire, usually a certain percentage of your salary at retirement. Normally the percentage increases the longer you work for the company. Most pension plans require you to work for a set number of years before your benefits become "vested." *Vesting* is the continuing process of accumulating permanent rights to pension benefits. Once vested, a benefit may not be taken away even if you are fired or quit. Pension plans vary as to vesting periods, but generally you must be at least 50% vested after ten years of credited service and 100% vested after 15 years. In addition, some plans require that you work up to three years before participating in the plan. Once you are a participant, your prior years of service will normally be counted for vesting purposes.

ERISA established the Pension Benefit Guarantee Corporation (PBGC), a federally supported insurance company to provide insurance coverage for benefits from certain types of pension plans in case they terminate or are improperly funded.

Another type of employee benefit plan is profit sharing. These plans differ from pension plans in that they do not promise a defined benefit but are geared to the company's profits or to performance of the company stock. They are designed to act as an incentive to work harder for the company. The company contributes a certain percentage of its profits to the plan and, typically, your share is allocated to an account in your name. These funds may be invested in the common stock of your employer or in some other investment medium. Sometimes you can choose which type of investment. The value of your account will vary depending on investment performance and company profits. In most profit sharing plans you receive the balance of your account when you retire or terminate employment. Profit sharing plans are not covered by PBGC insurance and the rules for participation and vesting are the same as for pension plans. Consult your plan documents and benefit statements for information.

There is another broad category of employee benefit plans known as *employee welfare plans.* These are less important for retirement purposes, but may help you while you work at the company. Before taking on a new job, be sure to ask about medical plans, vacation plans, prepaid legal services plans or any number of related fringe benefits. Chances are that part of your compensation is going to pay for them and it's to your benefit to know about them and to take advantage of them. Some medical plans, for example, allow retired employees to participate even though they no longer work at the company—a great opportunity because health insurance is difficult to get after retirement.

If you work for a federal, state or local government, you will be a participant of the governmental employee's pension plan (no government earns a "profit," so there are no profit sharing plans). Congress exempted these plans from the strict rules of ERISA, so the requirements for participation and vesting may be different. Consult your benefit statements and plan documents for information.

Individual Retirement Accounts

If you are not covered by a government pension plan or a private tax-qualified employee benefit plan, you may be eligible to start your own retirement plan, by setting aside up to $1500 a year from your earnings in an individual retirement savings arrangement. You get an income tax deduction for the amount you contribute and the earnings on the contributions will not be taxed until you withdraw at retirement. There are several types of these plans: The Individual Retirement Account (IRA) offered by many banks and savings and loan associations; individual retirement bonds and individual retirement annuities from some insurance companies. There are complicated rules for setting up these plans, so be sure to check them out before you plunge in. There also are substantial tax penalities if you contribute too much, not withdraw enough when you should or withdraw too much when you shouldn't. The Pension Reform Act requires each institution offering one of these services to give you a complete disclosure statement in plain English. If you still have questions, ask.

Keogh Plans

If you own your own business as a sole proprietor or partner, you may want to set up a plan for the business under the rules established by the so-called *Keogh Plans*. Ask your bank or savings and loan for information.

Investment and Savings

As a final backup for your retirement years, plan early to save as much as you can so that you'll have extra money to do the things you want to do to enjoy a satisfying gay lifestyle. This sounds old-fashioned, but it's good advice. If you manage to accumulate more than you need to live on, then, plan how to invest the funds, even if you have only a modest amount.

Savings Accounts

The most basic investment is an insured savings account. These accounts are normally considered the foundation for other types of investment, because they do not require large sums of capital and they are safe.

Even if you do nothing more than save, you should plan your savings programs carefully. There is a confusing variety of interest rates, term deposits, maturities and the like. Study them carefully before deciding what is best for your financial situation. In addition, every financial institution computes interest differently and some may be more to your advantage than others. Be sure to check out savings arrangements with your credit union if your are eligible.

Securities

You may be interested in diversifying your investments by buying one or more types of securities, even if only a few U.S. Government Series E Savings Bonds. Although space does not permit a more detailed discussion of all the different types of securities, here are two basic types.

Common Stocks. Stocks are shares of ownership in a corporation. When you buy stock you become an owner of a part of a business. If the business is profitable, it will normally pay dividends to you. Stocks vary in value, of course, and may result in gains or losses when you sell them.

Bonds. Technically a bond is evidence of a "loan" you have made to a government or company. They provide income because interest is paid on the amount of money loaned and they "mature" at a certain date when the "loan" becomes due. Bonds are called *fixed-rate investments* because their rate of return is determined at the time they're issued. They tend to be more stable than stocks, but because they are less risky they won't offer the dramatic increases in value that stocks can. Some governmental bonds provide tax-exempt income.

Life Insurance

Many gay people discount the need for life insurance. Not only is it an important part of estate planning, as we will discuss later, but it can also be helpful in providing money after retirement. "Whole life" policies, for example, can be converted into an annuity to pay you a certain sum of money regularly.

Real Estate

A very popular investment at the moment is real estate. For gay people, owning your own home can be an effective means of beating inflation while providing tax advantages. You may want to buy a second home for vacations where you may want to live after retirement. If you're near retirement, before selling your home, check to see if you qualify for exclusions on capital gains taxes. If you wait until 65 to sell, there may be certain tax advantages. Consult IRS publication #523—Tax Information on Selling Your Home.

CHECKLIST FOR RETIREMENT

In summary, here are the practical steps you can take:

To Prepare for Retirement

1. File for a statement of your Social Security account once every three years. Forms are available from the Post Office, your local Social Security office or the Social Security Administration, Baltimore, Maryland 21235.

2. Study your pension and other employee benefit plans carefully. Take them into consideration when making job-related decisions.

3. If eligible, consider establishing your own Individual Retirement Account savings program or Keogh Plan.

4. Analyze your assets. Consider the liquidity and income generating capacity of each one, especially as you near retirement.

5. Review your liabilities, debts, mortgages, etc. Make sure you'll have enough income to pay them; perhaps pay some off while you are still working.

At Age 62

1. Determine whether you're eligible for a property tax rebate on your home. (In California file an application with the local office of the State Franchise Tax Board.)

2. Check for other benefits, like free banking services.

3. If you are considering early retirement do as follows:

One year before retirement, check to see if you can extend your coverage under your employer's group health insurance plan. If not, begin to look for another plan. Be sure the plan you choose covers extended illness and convalescent care. If you are a member of a trade or professional organization, ask about a group health insurance plan, since it will almost always carry the lowest rates.

Three to six months before retirement, check with the personnel department where you work to begin filling out all the necessary forms for pension benefits and continued health insurance coverage.

File for Social Security benefits two to three months before you retire. You must file for benefits in person at a local Social Security office and bring the following: (a) your Social Security card; (b) a copy of your last W-2 form or previous year's income tax return; (c) certified copy of your birth certificate or baptismal record. (There are documents you can substitute if you don't have either of these. Ask at the Social Security office.)

If you collect Social Security, you'll get Medicare automatically. If not, you'll have to apply for it independently, no earlier than three months before your 65th birthday and no later than three months after it. Check out the Medicare option that covers additional services for a small monthly fee; it may be worth it.

Check with your life insurance agent to decide when or whether to convert your policy's cash value into annuities.

PRINCIPLES OF ESTATE PLANNING

As you near retirement you will undoubtedly begin to think about what you would like to happen to your property after you die. This process, called estate planning, is something that should be started even earlier than retirement planning, since death may come at any time.

It is a common misconception that gay people have no need for estate planning. Generally, the theory goes, they have few if any dependents, do not have lasting relationships and cannot take advantage of many of the tax-savings arrangements available to married couples. This, however, is usually inaccurate. You undoubtedly have some property that you wish to leave to your lover or to others. You might want to have some of it go to one or more charities. To accomplish either of these ends, you need to think about estate planning.

Definitions

In order to discuss the planning of your estate and some of the basic concepts associated with it, you should know the meanings of a few simple terms. The first term is *estate*. Basically, your estate consists of all the assets you hold at your death, including life insurance proceeds, trusts (unless irrevocable) and others. Your estate is probably bigger than you think.

The second term is *probate*. Probate is the legal process by which the property in your estate is placed under the jurisdiction of a probate court, your debts and taxes are paid, and your property is disbursed to the beneficiaries you have either named in your will or who are identified under the particular laws of your state. Probate can be complicated and time consuming, but it will result in your property being transferred to the beneficiaries you choose.

The third term you should be familiar with is *will*. A will is a legal document which must be signed by you in accordance with the particular law of your state and witnessed by the appropriate number of witnesses, also determined by the law of your state. Your will should name a person to handle your estate (executor) and should name those people or charities who will receive your property (beneficiaries). If you die without a will your property will pass to your heirs-at-law under the laws of intestacy (without a will) of your particular state. If you are not legally married, in most cases your children, if any, or your parents would receive the bulk of the estate. Obviously, if you are a couple, your lover would not normally be named under the laws of intestacy. If you want to leave your property to each other, both of you definitely need wills. The wills should be drafted by an attorney, because your family may want to get your property and contest the will. The gay person who is concerned about leaving an estate (total or in part) to a lover should never use a preprinted will form. They're just too dangerous!

Taxes

The federal government assesses a federal estate tax on the property you own at death. Most states also assess an estate or inheritance tax; this should also be considered. Normally, you will not have to pay any federal estate tax if your estate does not exceed the following limits: during 1979—$147,000; during 1980—$161,000; after December 31, 1980—$175,000.

There are a few tax-saving techniques that can be used to minimize the amount of federal estate tax and state inheritance (if any) which your estate will have to pay. Since the marital deduction is not available for gay couples, charitable deduction is the primary tax-saving technique for you. Basically, if you leave a portion of your property to charity then no estate tax will be assessed on that gift. Thus, by lowering your taxable estate by the amount of the charitable deductions, you reduce the overall level of estate tax that will have to be paid.

Avoiding Probate

There are other ways, of course, to leave your property to your lover. Some of these have been discussed above, but the most common is joint tenancy. By placing your assets in joint tenancy during life you will insure that the surviving joint tenant (your lover) will receive them at your death. Holding assets in joint tenancy provides for little or no tax planning, but if you have only a modest amount of property this might be the best solution.

Placing your assets in joint tenancy results in giving your lover, as joint tenant, some control over your property. If you are not quite sure about doing this, consider the alternative of leaving part of your property through a will. And, of course, placing your assets in joint tenancy does not provide for the contingent beneficiary who will receive the property if your lover does not survive you or if you both die in a common accident. You might also name your lover in an "informal trust" bank account (i.e., "Mary Jones, Trustee for Virginia Johnson"). This has the same effect as joint tenancy at death, but it does not allow the lover to have any control over the account during your lifetime. You, as trustee, may withdraw the proceeds held in the account at any time. The arrangement has the same disadvantages as a joint tenancy, however.

Another way to provide for your lover or other beneficiaries is through life insurance, discussed above under Retirement Planning. Life insurance can provide not only a method of saving for retirement but also a vehicle for leaving cash to your beneficiaries to pay the debts and expenses remaining at your death, including federal and state death taxes. If you have a sizeable portion of your estate in real estate or other assets difficult to sell, you should definitely consider purchasing life insurance while you are young enough to do so, so that your lover will not have a difficult time selling the properties to raise cash for these expenses. Life insurance proceeds are included in your estate for tax purposes, but they do not pass through probate. If your lover or other beneficiaries die before you, however, you have the same problems as with informal trust accounts and joint tenancy arrangements.

But You Still Need a Will

It is important for you to have a will even if all of your property is held in joint tenancy with your lover. You can have an attorney draft a will for a modest price, usually starting around $50. Unless you have minor children to provide for in a trust or other complicated provisions, your total estate plan should not amount to much more than the minimum figure.

You may be motivated to plan your estate because you want to leave your property to your lover, friends or charities. Even if this is not the case you should realize that without a will or other arrangement, your property will either go to your heirs-at-law under the laws of intestacy or it may be forfeited to the state. And your heirs-at-law, of course, may not necessarily be those whom you would put in your will. Certainly, forfeiture to the state is not an attractive alternative either. Even if you don't have close friends or family to whom you wish to leave your property, you should consider having a simple will drafted to provide for a gift to your favorite gay charity rather than allow your estate to be confiscated by the state as unclaimed property.

Using Your Gay Voting Power

R. Adam DeBaugh

THE GAY CONSTITUENCY

The initial task facing the gay community in organizing for political influence is to identify the gay constituency. Who is the gay community? How do we reach them? Crucial questions for constituency education and especially important for the gay political effort, since the gay constituency is not readily visible.

By *gay constituency* I mean all people who have something to gain by the passage of gay civil rights legislation, the repeal of sodomy laws and other sexually related legislation. I believe very strongly that gay people have an important stake in women's issues, in marriage laws and in any law that attempts to limit personal freedom of sexual, relational and affectional lifestyles. Thus, the gay constituencey I refer to includes all men and women who identify themselves either publicly or in their own minds as gay, lesbian or homosexual. It also includes people who may be heterosexually married or otherwise publicly identified or assumed to be heterosexual, but who engage occasionally in sexual behavior of a homosexual nature which is prohibited by law. It also includes most heterosexuals as well, although they may not understand this, since most states that still have sexual conduct laws also prohibit all but the most traditional heterosexual couplings. And it includes all other people who share the hope for the end of discrimination and who ask that the government neither continue nor permit the unwarranted persecution of people based on their sexual orientation or practices.

As the gay community has become better organized, our potential political power has grown as well. Most minority groups that have organized for their liberation have quickly begun to develop not only politi-

199

cal awareness, but also a knowledge of how to use the political system for their ultimate benefit. The gay community is no exception.

The first big step any group needs to take when organizing for political influence is to educate and organize its constituency. For the gay community, this poses unique problems.

Most minority groups are easily identified. Blacks, native Americans, Hispanic Americans, Orientals, women and other groups are highly visible in our society. But homosexuality cuts across these and all other subgroups. Gay people are, in essence, an invisible minority, and this fact makes our oppression unique. The weapons needed to fight our oppression are also unique.

Gay men and lesbians often feel the best way to fight gay oppression is to hide their gayness. Yet this head-in-the-sand approach to life is just not realistic. As long as laws exist affecting what people do in the privacy of their bedrooms, we can be prosecuted for our sex acts. Any demagog who thinks he or she can further an otherwise lackluster political career by cracking down on "perverts" can start the process. Any mayor, sheriff, chief of police, district attorney or city council can decide to enforce the law.

The inescapable conclusion is that gays *must* work in all areas starting with the education of each other. If we are discussing organizing for political power, we should first define politics. Politics is the way Americans select the people who make up their government. It boils down to a fairly simple formula: people + money + communications = power. The *people* component is made up of voters, workers and warm bodies: voters to get out and vote for the candidates we support; workers to campaign for those candidates; and warm bodies to appear at political meetings, rallies, demonstrations and speeches. *Money* is a major tool in political work, especially in campaigns. Gay organizations can back up their efforts to influence legislators and other politicians by contributing financially to the campaigns of people who support gay rights. *Communication* is very important for organizing a constituency. Gays need to show they can communicate to large numbers of people who will in turn respond by, for instance, contributing money to a campaign, volunteering to work for a candidate, writing letters to a Congressperson or just voting. Communication means alerting the gay community to the good things gay *supporters* do and to the bad things gay *opponents* do— it is as simple as that. Gays also need to be able to follow up on promises made by politicians. If that city councilperson who promised to support gay rights gets into office and fails to do anything, gays should be able to inform the gay community so that pressure can be applied.

There are at least 22 million gay people in the United States. That is about 10% of the American population. A city of one million people would then have 100,000 gay men and lesbians. But in most areas, the vast majority of our gay brothers and sisters are invisible. Adding together the members of gay organizations, the people who patronize gay bars and other businesses, the subscribers to gay publications, and the people who attend gay religious services and functions would never yield anywhere near the number of gay people a given city is statistically supposed to have.

In order to begin to identify the gay constituency, you need to start where gay people are. Gay organizations are, of course, the first source of active and involved gay people. Most areas also have gay bars. Many have gay baths, book stores and movie houses. More and more cities now also have gay religious groups like Metropolitan Community Church, Dignity, Integrity, gay temples, and chapters of gay caucuses of other religious denominations. There are often medical and health clinics that serve the gay population, hot lines or switchboards, and doctors and lawyers who have a large gay clientele. Specialized social clubs are ideal places to contact gay people. Often there are also private, little known discussion groups to contact. Finally, every gay person involved in even the smallest way with gay life knows other gays, many of whom are not involved in any other way. We mustn't forget to include as constituents the people who are not involved in any organization, who never go to bars or other gay businesses, and who never come in contact with gay publications or speakers.

Now that we have a list of gay organizations, businesses, clubs, discussion groups, bridge clubs, coffee klatches and parties, what are we going to do with it?

ORGANIZING FOR POLITICAL INFLUENCE

Constituency education implies that there is an organization working to develop the political presence of the gay community. This organization should develop a program of action. We will discuss some suggested areas of action later in this chapter. After a relatively simple statement of general purpose is drawn up, and after requirements and cost (if any) of membership are decided upon and regular (or the next) meeting dates are planned, and once the organization has something in the way of real programs to offer, then a brochure should be produced for distribution at all places where gay people are likely to get a copy. This means leafleting the bars, baths, bookstores, and movie houses. It means making sure every member of every other organization gets a copy. It means, perhaps, posting signs on bulletin boards around town. It certainly means news releases and stories in gay-oriented newspapers, magazines and newsletters in your area. It may mean advertisements in campus or regular newspapers and magazines in locales that have few other gay information outlets. It also means getting the word out to all of your friends and acquaintances. This process doesn't stop after one big effort; it should be continual if you want your organization to grow and if you want to inform more and more people.

What kinds of programs are appropriate and important for an organization devoted to organizing for political influence? Let's consider six types of programs: voter registration and voting, public education, polling candidates, endorsing candidates, fund raising and lobbying.

REGISTER AND VOTE

If we are truly to organize for political influence, the only place to start is with voter registration. Unless our supporters are registered and voting on election day we will never have the political base necessary for real political power.

Registering and voting are two of our most important civic responsibilities. Our system of representative government only works if the people take these responsibilities seriously. More importantly, we need to register and vote for a selfish reason: political survival. Unless the citizens of this country care enough about good and truly representative government, we won't have a good and representative government. It begins with us, the voters.

The first step, then, for any gay political organization is to make sure all of its members are registered to vote. The second step is more involved: making sure as many people as possible are registed to vote—gay women and men and others who support the quest for basic human rights. This can be done in a number of ways, depending on what kind of voter registration system your community has.

Some areas have postcard registration. Organizations can obtain voter registration postcards from the registrar of voters and go out and register our own voters. Many groups have had great success in doing this in gay bars and other gay businesses. Once filled out, the forms are taken to the registrar. This serves two purposes. First, it assures that the forms *will* be filed rather than stuck in someone's pocket and forgotten. Second, a gay political organization bringing large numbers of voter registrations to the registrar will make an impact on local politics as word gets around that gay people and their friends are registering. That means *power*.

In cities that don't have postcard registration, the registrar of voters will explain the registration process to any caller. Your group might want to organize a voter registration day when you gather a lot of people together and go, en masse, to the registrar. Some cities have even had success in getting a gay establishment (for instance, an MCC church, a gay community center, a bar,) designated as a voter registration location by the local registrar. Mobile registrars will often agree to set up registration facilities at your building on a given day. Advance notice will bring a lot of people to register at this kind of event.

During the registration process it may be possible for your organization to develop a mailing list. As people register, ask if they want to be on your mailing list in order to keep informed about issues of common concern. Be sure, however, to protect the anonymity of the people on your list and assure people that their names will not be made public. This mailing list can be the core of an effective political organizing network.

Once people are registered, it is important to make sure that they vote. Letters and posters urging people to vote can be followed up by phone calls on election day. Your organization could organize car pools to help people get to the polls. It will be especially important to get out the vote if the race pits an opponent of gay rights against one of our friends.

PUBLIC EDUCATION

Public education is central to any gay political organization's work. We can break this area down into a number of different tasks.

Know your representatives. It is important to be able to tell people who their elected representatives are. Many good and responsible Americans are ignorant about the pople they elect to serve them. Keep up-to-date lists of the names, office addresses, and phone numbers of all your elected representatives: city government, that is mayor and city council; county government; state government, members of the state assembly and senate; and federal government, members of the House of Representatives and U.S. Senate, and the President. Urge your people to write and visit these representatives.

Know where your representatives stand. Spread the word about your elected representatives' positions on gay rights and other issues of interest and concern to your community. (We will discuss later in this chapter some techniques for finding out where politicans stand.) It is important to let our constituency know who our friends are, as well as our enemies.

Educate your representatives. Not only should we educate our constituency about our representatives, but we should make a real effort to educate our representatives about us. Communicate with city, state and national elected officials. Provide them with information about the gay community. One of the biggest obstacles we face is the massive ignorance about gays that prevails in the nongay community. We have a major responsibility to provide accurate information about the gay community to our representatives.

Educate the media. The same educational priority is needed for members of the media. The electronic and print media need information about the gay community if they are to report accurately about it. It is important to develop a good working relationship with members of the press and to provide them with information that will help them do their job well.

Educate nongays. The process of public education must expand to reach all people. Ignorance about gay people is a prime cause of gay oppression. If people understood who we really are, not the stereotypes they have been fed, but who gay men and lesbians *really* are, then homophobic attitudes would begin to change. Public education is a crucial role for the gay rights organization.

POLLING CANDIDATES

We talked earlier about letting our constituents know the stands candidates have taken on gay-related issues. Many gay organizations have had remarkable success in polling political candidates on their views. The first step is to put together a list of questions to ask each candidate. Make them specific; it isn't enough to ask a candidate if he or she supports gay rights. Ask whether a congressional candidate, for instance, will co-sponsor a national gay civil rights bill. Ask whether a city council candidate will support a civil rights bill in your city. Ask if a candidate for the state legislature will support the repeal of sodomy laws (if they still exist in your state) and if they will support gay civil rights legislation on the state level. Ask candidates if they will support public financing for VD clinics, gay help lines and other gay-related services.

After the list of questions has been drawn up, get the names and addresses of all candidates who have announced for the election (obtainable from your elections board). Then send the questionnaire with a cover letter to *all* of the candidates. Explain that their responses will be published widely in the gay community and supportive nongay community. Let them know that you represent a large bloc of votes.

A week or so after the questionnaires go out, *call* candidates to urge them to respond. Within a few days of the deadline for response, call those candidates who have not responded and urge them to respond. You may not hear from some candidates, but it is important to give them every chance to answer your questions. When all the responses are in, publish them. Make sure you list all candidates, even those who refused to answer your questions. This protects you from charges of bias. "No Answer" *is* an answer, after all, and hostile answers are clear demonstrations of the way the candidate feels.

Then be sure the word reaches as many people as possible. If there is a gay publication in town, make sure the results of the poll get published, well enough in advance of the election so that as many people as possible see it. Distribute the poll results in the bars, bookstores, religious groups, wherever gay people gather. Ask local gay organizations to include a copy in their mailings. Have members of your organization give copies to friends and neighbors. Gathering this kind of information is useless unless large numbers of gays and supportive nongays find out the results. Dissemination of the information is as important as gathering it.

Nonprofit, tax-exempt organizations can educate the public about political candidates, so long as they do not endorse specific candidates. If the organization (and this includes religious organizations) simply reports to the people the positions of *all* the candidates, they are well within their rights under the Internal Revenue Code. Even those who do not respond should be listed; simply indicate "no answer." Let the statements stand on their own and refrain from endorsing candidates. You can and should urge people to vote in the election, but you shouldn't tell people who to vote for.

In addition to the formal poll of candidates, raise relevant gay issues at candidates' public appearances. Everywhere a politician appears, he or she should be confronted with valid questions about gay rights from concerned voters. Question them at public meetings as well as in private. The more they hear about gay concerns from a wide variety of people, the more they will support us.

Your organization may want to invite political candidates to speak before your group. Such candidate forums have been used effectively by a number of gay groups. Get as many people as possible at such forums to hear the candidates; candidates are going to be impressed by large numbers of voters.

ENDORSE CANDIDATES

If your group is specifically a political organization, you may endorse candidates running for public office. Once again, no religious organization or other nonprofit, tax-exempt organization may endorse political candidates. But if your group is a gay Democratic or Republican club, a gay political organization, you can and should endorse candidates.

Endorsement should be based on the candidates' responses to questionnaires, on personal interviews and perhaps on speeches made before your group. Don't be afraid *not* to endorse someone in a specific race. Don't fall into the trap of thinking that any candidate who supports gay rights is the best person for the job. Gay rights are important but should not be the only issue on which to judge a candidate. By the same token, a person is not necessarily the best one for a political office simply because he or she is gay. Sexual orientation alone is not reason enough to support a person for public office.

Endorsing a candidate, if it is to have maximum impact, should involve three components: votes, money and people. First, spread the word. Let as many gay people and supportive nongays know about the endorsement as possible. News of the endorsement should reach every gay person in your community, one way or another. That means that leaflets should be made up with your organization's list of endorsements and circulated in all the places gay people congregate. Newspapers, both gay and nongay, should get the word. As many people as is humanly possible should find out about the endorsement.

Second, a campaign runs on money. A political organization that endorses a candidate and doesn't give a monetary contribution is missing the boat. It doesn't have to be a large contribution (be careful to stay within the election contribution laws of your state). A discussion about fund raising comes later in this chapter.

The last aspect of political endorsement is providing volunteers for the campaign. Envelope lickers and stuffers, canvassers, leafletters and other campaign workers are usually desperately needed by candidates. Supplying the candidate you endorse with volunteer campaign workers shows the candidate your commitment to materially help in the campaign, and also gives you a chance to reach the community. On election day, volunteers are always needed to drive people to the polls, to staff telephone banks and to act as poll workers.

With this kind of assistance to candidates, our impact on their term in public office will be measurably increased. If you are successful at getting out the gay vote and raising money and providing volunteers, candidates will come to you for endorsement.

FUND RAISING

Raising money is an important function for any organization. A political group that expects to endorse candidates needs money for a campaign chest, that is, money to give to candidates, as well as funds for printing and advertising and other expenses.

There are a lot of ways to raise money and it would be futile to present an exhaustive list here. Your people should get together to brainstorm and find ways to raise funds that involve a minimum of work, that are fun and can raise the most money.

Cities with an active theater should explore the possibility of theater parties. All that is needed is the money to buy a bloc of tickets to a play, concert, show or other event that you are sure a lot of people want to see. This initial capital can be borrowed from people in the community. Then add a few dollars to the per-ticket cost and sell the tickets to the community. Gay organizations should be encouraged to assist in the sale of tickets. After the initial outlay is met, all additional income is profit. With that profit another bloc of tickets can be bought for the next fund raising event.

Anything that people do together can be turned into a fund raiser— boat rides, tours, picnics, parties, dances, games, movie parties, speeches, and so on. Individuals who are reluctant to get involved publicly may agree to have small fund raising parties at their homes for an invited list of friends. Any party can be a fund raising event; simply ask for a contribution at the door.

LOBBYING

Ideally, elected officials represent the concerns of their constituents. If we are not in communication with our representatives about our concerns, however, they cannot be expected to know what positions to take on issues that are important to us.

In my work as director of the Washington Field Office of the Universal Fellowship of Metropolitan Community Churches, I have a lot of contact with members of Congress. Unfortunately, most members of Congress have never heard from a gay person. This means that most members of Congress have never gotten a letter or a call or a visit from someone who told them that they are gay or that they want the representative to support gay rights legislation. If we are not telling our politicians about what we want them to do for us, we have failed in our responsibility as citizens.

Writing letters is a major way of letting our elected representatives know how we feel about the issues confronting them once they reach political office. Organize letter writing campaigns. Let people know the names and addresses of their representatives. Provide model letters for people to use. Have letter writing parties, where you provide the paper, envelopes, stamps, addresses and ideas and get people to write a letter to their Congressperson, state representative or city councilperson. If you are getting people to write to members of the U.S. House of Representatives or Senate, have them send copies to the Congressional File, UFMCC

Washington Office, Suite 210, 110 Maryland Ave., N.E., Washington, D.C. 20002. State gay rights organizations usually keep files of letters to state representatives as well.

Lobbying is very simply defined: attempting to influence legislation. Every time we write a letter to a representative, we are lobbying. But there are other ways to lobby as well. Telegrams and mailgrams are useful when there is a matter of urgency, for instance, when a vote is imminent. Telephone calls are often helpful as well and if the staff knows you are calling long distance and your representative is in the office, it is sometimes possible to get to talk to the representative directly. Talking to staff is a close second. The staff is there as adjuncts of the representative and they should be used as such by constituents.

A very effective lobbying technique is the personal visit. This doesn't always mean a trip to Washington, D.C., or to your state capital. Each member of Congress and each state representative has district offices, often very close to where you are. Since the district offices are customarily staffed year round and the representative usually has regular office hours there, it is not difficult to see your representative right at home.

Remember that letters, calls and visits to elected representatives are not the sole responsibility of community leaders. Anyone has the right to participate in this basic political act. And lobbying is everyone's responsibility. A brochure on writing to Congress is available from the Washington Office of UFMCC.

Finally, I wish to point out that constituency education for the purpose of building political power is really nothing more than people *getting together* to help each other attain common goals. In that getting together we must remember to agree to disagree with love and tolerance for each other. We are going to disagree about tactics, plans and programs, but we have to recognize our common goal. Disagree, by all means, but if disagreement becomes divisive, we have given up our power to our enemies.

We are a very diverse community. We come from all conceivable backgrounds—economic, religious, political, educational, racial, ethnic and cultural. Our diversity is our strength. As we develop awareness that our role in the political arena is a part of our struggle for equality, we are engaging in constituency education. It all begins right where we are, with ourselves.

The Positively Gay Discussion Guide

Changing attitudes toward one's self or others when those attitudes have been held a long time and are deeply ingrained in one's thinking is a very difficult thing to accomplish. Social psychologists tell us that one of the best approaches to attitude change is through social facilitation—learning in the context of an experience *shared* with others. Based on that knowledge we suggest use of group discussion of the contents of this book to enhance the probability that real attitude change, with regard to the objectives below, will occur.

OBJECTIVES OF THIS DISCUSSION PROGRAM

For Gays

To better understand the options and opportunities for growth open to gay people, and to explore ways of making use of these possibilities in their lives.

For Nongays

To become better informed about issues of concern to lesbians and gay men in their everyday lives, and to increase understanding of how these issues influence the thoughts, feelings and actions of gay people.

WHO MIGHT USE THIS DISCUSSION PROGRAM

Gay

It might be used by:
(1) any two people who've read the book and want to go more deeply into the significance of its contents for themselves;
(2) a gay person with her/his family to help them understand better what the lives of gay people are about;
(3) a gay organization, such as a community service center, a student union, a social or political club or a religious group, to structure personal growth groups.

Nongay

It might be used by:

(1) a group of parents or other relatives of gays who want to inform themselves about gay life;

(2) a church or other community service group to conduct gay/straight dialog;

(3) a college or university, for human sexuality courses or graduate curricula in the helping professions;

(4) a mental health or social service agency for in-service training;

(5) a law enforcement agency for human relations training;

(6) an organization conducting continuing education courses for physicians, lawyers or other professionals in allied fields.

SCHEDULING THE SESSIONS

It is suggested that the program be divided into ten sessions, each dealing with one area of special interest:

Session 1—Developing a positive gay identity (Berzon chapter)

Session 2—The new gay world (De Crescenzo and Fifield, Leighton, Lotman chapters)

Session 3—Growth for gay couples (Berzon, Toder chapters)

Session 4—Improving family relationships (Berzon, Fairchild chapters)

Session 5—Resolving religious issues (Johnson, Brick, McNaught chapters)

Session 6—Concerns of gay parents (Abbitt and Bennett, Clark chapters)

Session 7—Adjustments to aging in gay life (Kimmel, Martin and Lyon chapters)

Session 8—Gay issues in the world of work (Knutson, Rochlin chapters)

Session 9—Sound financial planning for gay people (Jacobson chapter)

Session 10—Organizing for political influence (De Baugh chapters)

A variety of formats is possible. For instance:

(1) *Weekly two-hour sessions for ten weeks.*

(2) *A weekend workshop*, when there are enough people for multiple groups. Possible schedule:

Saturday morning, 10:00–12:00—Developing a positive gay identity (all groups).

Saturday afternoon, 1:30 – 3:30—The new gay world (all groups).

Saturday afternoon, 4:00–6:00—Improving family relationships (all groups).

Sunday morning, 10:00–12:00—choice of one: Gay issues in the world of work; Concerns of gay parents.

Sunday afternoon, 1:30–3:30—choice of one: Sound financial planning for gay people; Resolving religious issues; Organizing for political influence.

Sunday afternoon, 4:00–6:00—choice of one: Growth for gay couples; Adjustments to aging in gay life.

(3) A *one-day workshop* for multiple small groups, in which participants would select one of three sessions in each time period, for instance:

Saturday morning, 10:00–12:00—Identity and gay world; Work; Financial.

Saturday afternoon, 1:30–3:30—Family; Aging; Parents.

Saturday afternooon, 4:00–6:00—Couples; Political; Religious.

SIZE OF THE DISCUSSION GROUP

The best size for a discussion group of this kind is probably 8 to 12 members, though the program can also be used with smaller or larger groups.

Suggestions for Structuring the Sessions

If there is an instructor, trainer or leader, he or she should ask that chapter material related to each session be read by the members before the group meets. If there is no designated leader, a volunteer from the group could act as coordinator, or that role might be rotated among the members.

The following questions (or similar ones) might be used to give form to the discussion:

(1) What did you learn from the material you read that you didn't know before?

(2) What was it most helpful to read, whether you knew it before or not?

(3) What surprised you most in what you read?

(4) If you were trying to educate someone about gay life, what in the material you read would you particularly want them to know?

(5) What in your own personal life can you relate to the material you've read?

To encourage participation by everyone in the group you might:

(1) Go around the group for each question, having the members answer each one for themselves.

(2) Or, go around the group having each person choose one of the questions to answer.

If you use the above suggestions, the initial, structured interaction should be followed by open discussion in which opportunity should be provided for participants to talk about any of the material covered in the session and how they feel about it.

It is likely that whatever needs motivated group members to participate in the first place will determine the directions the discussion takes at this point. Those needs should be cooperated with but care should be taken to provide opportunity for *all* persons involved to be heard from.

It is hoped that this book, and others like it, will encourage and facilitate discussion of these issues in as many forums as possible, public and private. The conspiracy of silence attending the concerns of gay people has been broken. It is crucially important that we talk, and keep talking. There must never be such a conspiracy again.

CONTRIBUTORS

Diane Abbitt, J.D., is a mother, feminist activist, law school graduate, member of the Continuing Committee of the International Women's Year, co-founder of the Lesbian Rights Task Force of Los Angeles N.O.W., Co-Chair of New Alliance for Gay Equality (NEW AGE), and member of the California Task Force on Medical Assurance.

Bobbie Bennett, J.D., is a mother, feminist activist, law school graduate, co-founder of the Lesbian Rights Task Force of Los Angeles N.O.W., Board Member of the National Gay Task Force, member of the Discrimination Based on Sexual Preference Committee of the Los Angeles County Commission on the Status of Women. She was a California delegate to the International Women's Year.

Betty Berzon, Ph.D., a gay therapist in private practice in Los Angeles, specializes in working with lesbians and gay men and their families. She writes, lectures, teaches and consults on homosexuality and gay-related issues. A Research Associate at the Western Behavioral Sciences Institute in La Jolla, California for nine years, she is author of numerous published articles on human relations training and small group process, and is co-editor of the book, *New Perspectives on Encounter Groups*, published in 1972. At UCLA she designed and conducted the 1972 program, "The Homosexual in America" and the 1977 program, "Homosexuality: New Cultural Perspectives." She has served on the Board of Directors of the Gay Community Services Center in Los Angeles and the Whitman-Radclyffe Foundation. Active in the gay movement since 1971 she is currently national president of the Gay Academic Union.

Barrett L. Brick is Chairperson of the Community Relations Committee of Congregation Beth Simchat Torah, New York's gay synagogue. He is a graduate of the Columbia University School of Law where he was on the Editorial Board of the *Columbia Human Rights Law Review* and was President of the Institute of Human Rights. He has been active in the gay movement since 1974.

Don Clark, Ph.D., is a writer, teacher and clinical psychologist in private practice in San Francisco and Menlo Park, California. His books include *Loving Someone Gay*, 1977; *Permission to Grow*, 1969; and *Humanistic Teaching*, 1971. He specializes in working with gay men and training gay-oriented therapists. He is the father of two children.

Adam DeBaugh is the social action director of the Universal Fellowship of Metropolitan Churches. Based in Washington, D.C., since 1971, he has served as an Administrative Assistant to a U.S. Congressmember and as Director of the Center for the Study of Power and Peace. His column, "We the Gay People," originates in *The Blade* and is syndicated in a number of gay newspapers.

Teresa De Crescenzo, M.S.W., is a clinical social worker practicing in Los Angeles. She wrote the column "Womensbeat" for the gay newspaper, *NewsWest*. She is vice-president of the Board of Directors, Gay Community Services Center, Los Angeles, and is national secretary of the Gay Academic Union. She was a California delegate to the International Women's Year.

Betty Fairchild lives in Denver, Colorado. In 1970 she learned that one of her children is gay. For many years she has worked actively with Parents of Gays groups and has counseled and corresponded with hundreds of lesbians and gay men and their parents. She is co-author of a book for parents, *Now That You Know*, Harcourt, Brace, Jovanovich, 1979.

213

Lillene Fifield, M.S.W., is a lesbian feminist activist, researcher, author and psychotherapist in private practice in Los Angeles. She specializes in working with lesbians. She was a California delegate to the International Women's Year. In 1978 she was selected as Los Angeles Gay Community Woman of the Year.

Evelyn C. Hooker, Ph.D., is a world-renowned clinical psychologist whose pioneering research in the 1950s demonstrated that being gay does not mean one is mentally ill. In the 1960s, as Chairperson of the prestigious National Institute of Mental Health Task Force on Homosexuality, she guided formulation of some of the major principles underlying the gay rights movement of the 1970s. On the UCLA faculty for over 35 years, she is now Clinical Professor in the Department of Psychiatry, UCLA School of Medicine.

Ronald J. Jacobson is a graduate of the UCLA Law School where he was Associate Editor of the *UCLA Law Review*. From 1974 to 1977 he practiced law in the legal department of the Bank of America specializing in motion picture financing. He is now in private practice in Los Angeles.

Rev. William Regan Johnson is co-author, with Dr. Sally Gearheart, of *Loving Women/Loving Men: Gay Liberation and the Church*, Glide, 1974. His ordination to the ministry of the United Church of Christ in June 1972 marked the first time an affirmed gay person was ordained in the Christian Church. He lives in New York City.

Douglas C. Kimmel, Ph.D., is Associate Professor of Psychology at City University of New York. In 1977 he chaired the Association of Gay Psychologists. He is a member of the National Association of Gay Gerontologists. His publications include *Adulthood and Aging: An Interdisciplinary, Developmental View*, Wiley, 1974.

Donald C. Knutson is Professor of Law at the University of Southern California and Executive Director of Gay Rights Advocates, Inc., a public interest law firm in San Francisco. He is a member of the Board of Directors of the Lambda Legal Defense and Education Fund. His book. *Homosexuality and the Law* will be published by Haworth Press in 1979.

Robert Leighton has spent his 18-year professional life in the publishing industry as an editor, writer, publisher and graphic designer. During that time he has been associated with Scholastic Magazines, E.P. Dutton, Dell Publishing and World Publishing in New York. After moving to California ten years ago, he was managing editor of Holloway House Publishing Company, where he developed a line of ethnic books. He also developed the Books for Better Living series for American Art Associates. For the past four years he has been active in gay journalism, most recently as managing editor of *News West*. His involvement in the gay movement began in 1972.

Loretta Lotman is an author currently pursuing a television writing career in Los Angeles. She has been published in *The Village Voice, Gay Community News, In Touch, Lesbian Voices, SoHo Weekly News* and *Quest*. Her plays have been performed in New York and Los Angeles, on radio, television and on the stage.

Phyllis Lyon is one of the founders of the Daughters of Bilitis (1955) and was the first editor of *The Ladder* (1956–1960). She is co-author of *Lesbian/Woman* (1972) and has been published extensively in religious, gay, women's and other popular national magazines. She serves as a commissioner on the San Francisco Human Rights Commission.

Del Martin is a founder of the Daughters of Bilitis, co-author of *Lesbian/Woman*, and author of *Battered Wives* (1976). She was the first "up front" lesbian on N.O.W.'s National Board of Directors and is presently coordinator of N.O.W.'s National Task Force on Battered Women/Household Violence. She serves as a commissioner on San Francisco's Commission on the Status of Women.

Brian McNaught is a Boston-based freelance writer, editor and lecturer. A graduate of Marquette University's College of Journalism, he is the recipient of the 1976 Journalism Award from the Catholic Press Association for Best Maga-zine Article of the Year. More recently he was named one of the "Outstanding Young Men in America." His column appears in a variety of gay publications.

Martin Rochlin, Ph.D., was the first openly gay clinical psychologist in Los Angeles, where he is now in private practice specializing in gay-oriented therapy. Formerly on the Executive Board of the L.A. Society of Clinical Psychologists and the Board of Directors of the L.A. Gay Community Services Center, he is a lecturer and consultant to universities and mental health centers.

Nancy Toder, Ph.D., is a clinical psychologist in private practice in Los Angeles specializing in therapy with lesbians. She has been active in the radical lesbian and women's movements since 1971. She consults to universities and mental health centers training therapists and counselors to work more effectively (and less destructively) with lesbian clients.

READING AND OTHER MATERIALS

Nonfiction Books

- Abbott, Sidney, and Love, Barbara. SAPPHO WAS A RIGHT-ON WOMAN. Stein & Day, 1972.

  Readable, pertinent discussion of gay women: how it really is; revealing account of lesbians and the Women's Movement a few years ago; much on "becoming an independent and whole person," of interest to straight women, too.

- Clarke, Lige, and Nichols, Jack. I HAVE MORE FUN WITH YOU THAN ANYBODY. St. Martin's, 1972.

  An engaging yet serious account of two young men's relationship and experiences. Includes good times together, problems met and solved, family reactions, activity in gay liberation, and much personal philosophy. Good initial reading.

- Gearhard, Sally, and Johnson, William R. (eds.). LOVING WOMEN/LOVING MEN: GAY LIBERATION AND THE CHURCH. Glide Publications, 1974.

  Offers a helpful perspective to those who are troubled by Biblical references "against" homosexuality. Also, excellent overview of the conflict between organized religion and gays, with various views on the subject.

- Hammarskjold, Dag. MARKINGS. Alfred A. Knopf, 1968.

- Jay, Karla, and Young, Allen (eds.). OUT OF THE CLOSETS: VOICES OF GAY LIBERATION. Douglas-Links Books, 1972.

  Collection of writings of a few years ago. Excellent for range of attitudes and concepts shown.

- Martin, Del, and Lyon, Phyllis. LESBIAN/WOMAN. Glide Publications, 1972.

  Highly recommended by gay women. A forthright, warm, understanding presentation by two women who have been on the scene for a number of years and who helped establish a national lesbian organization. Full of verve, humor.

- McNeill, John J., S.J. THE CHURCH AND THE HOMOSEXUAL. Sheed Andrews and McMeel, Inc., 1976.

  A Jesuit priest and scholar's intensive study and analysis of the subject, in terms of theology, Biblical study, ethics and morality. A powerful presentation, and a *must* for those who seek understanding.

- Nicolson, Nigel. PORTRAIT OF A MARRIAGE. Bantam Books, 1973.

  An intimate and sensitive portrayal of the author's parents—in particular, his mother, Vita Sackville-West.

- Perry, Troy, and Lucas, Charles L. THE LORD IS MY SHEPHERD AND HE KNOWS I'M GAY. Bantam Books, 1973.

  The founder of the now-international Metropolitan Community Church relates simply and readably how his homosexuality and his personal Christian commitment led through troubled times to acceptance and action.

- Pittenger, Norman. MAKING SEXUALITY HUMAN. United Church Press, 1969.

- Scanzoni, Letha, and Mollenkott, Virginia Ramey. *Is the Homosexual My Neighbor?* Harper and Row, 1978.

- Silverstein, Charles. A FAMILY MATTER: A PARENT'S GUIDE TO HOMOSEXUALITY. McGraw-Hill, 1977.

- Simpson, Ruth. FROM THE CLOSET TO THE COURTS. Richard Seaver Book/The Viking Press, 1976.

  The author, incorporating her personal experiences as an active feminist, analyzes the impact on lesbians of various societal institutions. Very readable.

- Tobin, Kay, and Wicker, Randy. THE GAY CRUSADERS. Paperback Library, 1972. Out of print, but may still be in bookstores/libraries. Reprinted by Arno publishers in 1975 series.

  Biographical sketches of key people in the gay movement, delineating their family ties and relationships; excels in showing the diversity of backgrounds from which gay people emerge.

- Tournier, Paul. THE MEANING OF PERSONS. Harper and Row, 1957.

- Tripp, C.A. THE HOMOSEXUAL MATRIX. McGraw Hill, 1975.

  Offers a broad perspective on homosexuality (and heterosexuality). Gives new insights and viewpoints and expands the reader's overall understanding of this sexual orientation, all in quite readable terms. Considered a "major achievement" by distinguished reviewers.

- Weltge, Ralph W. (ed.). THE SAME SEX: AN APPRAISAL OF HOMOSEXUALITY. Pilgrim/United Church Press, 1969.

  Several professional people, including some gay activists, give personal views on homosexuality, in terms of religious beliefs, ethics and morality, and society today.

- Weinberg, George. SOCIETY AND THE HEALTHY HOMOSEXUAL. Anchor Books, 1973.

  Contemporary, positive presentation of common (inaccurate) stereotypes and myths, refuting "popular" psychiatric views and therapies. Excellent chapter on "telling parents" directed to both gay child and parent. This book is definitely a *must*, especially as initial reading.

- Young, Wayland. EROS DENIED: SEX IN WESTERN SOCIETY. Grove Press, 1964.

Fiction

- Hobson, Laura Z. CONSENTING ADULT. Doubleday & Company, Inc., 1975.

  A troubled young man reveals to his mother that he is homosexual. An exceptionally fine novel of resulting family conflicts and their eventual resolution. A *must* for all parents of gay children and for gay women and men—and a *should* for everyone else!

- Warren, Patricia Nell. THE FRONT RUNNER. William Morrow & Company, 1974.

  A sensitive novel frankly and understandingly portraying the love between a mature man and his young protege. Dignified, touching and persuasive.

Pamphlets

- "20 Questions About Homosexuality." Gay Activists Alliance, P.O. Box 2, Village Station, NYC 10014. Clear, direct answers to all the questions everyone asks.

- "Parents of Gays, Washington, D.C." (Available from Lambda Rising, 2012 S St., N.W., Washington, D.C. 20009 ; send $1 + 35 cents p/h.)

  Describes early activities and achievements of one such parents group, and discusses the common feelings and variety of responses of parents of gay children; offers a positive approach to homosexuality, plus helpful hints for both parent and gay child.

Audio Cassette

- COUNSELLING PARENTS OF GAYS by Rev. Paul R. Shanley, 1975. (Available for $7.95 from Ampro, Inc., 101 Tremont, Boston, MA 02108.)

  Father Shanley addresses parents of gay men in particular, but his message is helpful to all. Gives information about homosexuality, points out the myths/stereotypes, discusses homophobic attitudes, and shows how and why a parent can and must be supportive of the gay child. A reassuring perspective on the subject.

Additional Material

  There are now many excellent books, articles, magazines, films, audiovisuals and gay publications, too many to list all of them here. For comprehensive reference, see:

- A GAY BIBLIOGRAPHY, prepared by the Task Force on Gay Liberation, Social Responsibilities Roundtable, American Library Assoication. Single copy—25 cents. Send to: Barbara Gittings, Coordinator, Box 2382, Philadelphia, PA 19103.

This periodically updated publication includes nonfiction books, bibliographies, directories, articles, pamphlets, periodicals, audiovisuals and special collections.

And Don't Miss These

- Brown, Howard. FAMILIAR FACES, HIDDEN LIVES. Harcourt Brace Jovanovich, 1976.

   An exceptionally moving account of a variety of peoples lives, including his own, by one of the first doctors to publicly acknowledge his homosexuality.

- Clark, Don. LOVING SOMEONE GAY. Celestial Arts, 1977.

   A knowledgeable and matter-of-fact guidebook for anyone who cares about "someone gay"—that is, another gay person, parents, spouses, friends or children of gay people.

- Hutchinson, Bill. NOW WHAT? Center for Dialog of Dade County, Inc. 2175 NW 26th St., Miami FL 33142. ($3.50)

   "A practical and personal guide to the subject of homosexuality written especially for the parent who knows or assumes a son or daughter is gay" (from the flyleaf). An easy-to-read, readily understood, comprehensive treatment of the topic.

BOOKS OF RELATED INTEREST

LOVING SOMEONE GAY by Don Clark, PhD, is a sympathetic and perceptive guide for gays and their families and friends. Clark, an experienced clinical psychologist, removes much of the mystery that surrounds gay people and gay identity in a voice uniquely qualified to speak to the gay, the straight and the professional world. A Lambda Book Club selection. 204 pages, soft cover, $4.95

WHERE WILL I BE TOMORROW? by Walter Rinder combines prose and poetry with the author's own outstanding photography to tell the story of the love of a man for another man. A Lambda Book Club selection. 144 pages, soft cover, $4.95

HOW TO BE SOMEBODY: Open The Door To Personal Growth by Yetta Bernhard develops a working idea that anyone can use to be somebody. From the goals you will set for yourself to the "goofs" you will make and how to handle them...it is all here in clear and precise language. 96 pages, soft cover, $3.95

POSITIVE SELFISHNESS: A Practical Guide to Self-Esteem by Frieda Porat, PhD, with Margery Quackenbush tells you how to get to know yourself, accept yourself and affirm yourself. You are a unique individual and it is imperative that you learn to recognize your own qualities and abilities and then build on them. 180 pages, soft cover, $4.95

In **MAKING CONTACT** noted therapist Virginia Satir draws on her experience, observation and rich understanding of human potential to show how to better use the basic tools for making contact with others. She helps you make changes in your perception, your action and your life. 96 pages, soft cover, $3.95

Available at your local book or department store or directly from the publisher. To order by mail, send check or money order to:

Celestial Arts
231 Adrian Road
Millbrae, Ca 94030

Please add $1.00 for postage and handling. California residents add 6% tax.